Steel Design Manual

Authors:

R.L.BROCKENBROUGH
*Senior Research Engineer, Applied Research Laboaratory,
United States Steel Corporation*

B. G. JOHNSTON
Professor of Structural Engineering, University of Michigan

United States Steel Corporation
ADUSS 27-3400-01
July 1968
Printed in U.S.A.

It should be noted that, although the information in this Manual is based on the best available knowledge, publication of the material contained herein is not intended as a warranty on the part of United States Steel—or that of any person named herein—that the information is suitable for any general or particular use or of freedom from infringement of any patent or patents. Nothing herein contained shall be construed as granting a license, express or implied, under any patents. Further, any use of this material can only be made with the understanding that United States Steel Corporation makes no warranty of any kind respecting such use and the user assumes all liability arising therefrom.

USS, COR-TEN, TRI-TEN, MAN-TEN, EX-TEN, CON-PAC, CHAR-PAC and T-1 are Trademarks of United States Steel.

Preface

Most engineers, because of their educational training and their experience, are familiar with the geometrical considerations in design. These considerations involve the three dimensions of space— length, width, and height. However, these dimensions are intimately related to, and dependent on, the types and grades of materials used.

In the past, the designer was limited primarily to the use of structural carbon steel and, consequently, the subject of design was essentially one of geometrical considerations. With the development of the many new steel grades, the designer must now concern himself not only with the geometrical considerations, but also with the equally important selection of the most satisfactory and economical type and grade of material required to perform the desired function.

With the increased number of steels available today, the scope of this "material selection" in designing with steel is almost unlimited. The "Family of Steels" available for engineering use that are discussed herein range in strength, as measured by yield point or yield strength, from 30,000 psi to 100,000 psi. Each of these steels was developed to fill a particular need, such as improved strength, better toughness, corrosion resistance, ease of fabrication and other attributes.

The design of structures and mechanical components that effectively and efficiently utilize the properties of the "Family of Steels" requires an understanding of the principles that govern the behavior of members and fabricated assemblies made of the steels when subjected to different loading conditions and environments. To foster the efficient utilization of steels of different strength levels, U. S. Steel published in 1954 the "Design Manual for High-Strength Steels" by H. M. Priest and J. A. Gilligan. The Manual has been used widely by practicing engineers, structural, equipment and product designers; and as a text and reference in engineering and design courses in a large number of colleges and universities.

Since that Manual was published many advances have been made in the quality and properties of steel products and in the knowledge of the behavior of steel structures and mechanical components when subjected to load. The present Manual recognizes these advancements. It is intended to provide a concise explanation of the structural behavior of the different types of structural members and to supply useful data for the design of such members.

Information in this Manual is general in that its application is not confined to any particular industry. Engineers and designers concerned with machinery, construction, mining, automotive, transportation and agricultural equipment, and building and highway structures will find design information in this Manual on the structural components that make up their equipment or structures. Because of the wide variety of loadings and environments to which different items of equipment and structures are subjected in service, no publication of this type can hope to evaluate the effects of all such variables on each component. However, the information in this Manual, together with designers' and engineers' experience and information in a particular field and their knowledge of performance criteria should result in more efficient and economic designs.

The authors wish to acknowledge the contribution of the many people who helped prepare this Manual. Particular acknowledgment is due to the late F. H. Dill and to J. A. Gilligan, G. Haaijer, J. B. Scalzi and C. G. Schilling, all of United States Steel, who reviewed the manuscript and offered many valuable suggestions.

The Manual contains a number of references to provisions of specifications of AISC, AASHO, AREA and AISI. These references and the discussion of their provisions are not intended to be interpretations of those specifications. Engineers and designers concerned with the design of a structure that is covered by existing specifications and/or codes are obliged to make direct reference to the latest editions and/or revisions of the particular specification or code that is applicable to the structure.

Table of Contents

Nomenclature

A   area of concrete in composite beams

A_c cross-sectional area

A_e area of elastic portion of column cross-section

A_f area of compression flange

A_s area of stiffener; also area of steel beam

A_{st} total area of stiffeners

A_t total area

A_w area of web

C   compressive force in concrete slab of composite beam

C'   compressive force in steel member of composite beam

C_1 or C_b coefficient for moment gradient in lateral buckling

C_2 coefficient for position of load in lateral buckling

C_c column slenderness ratio dividing elastic and inelastic buckling

C_m coefficient applied to bending term in interaction formula for beam-columns

C_v ratio of elastic web buckling stress to shear yield stress

C_w warping constant

D   area coefficient for girder stiffeners

E   modulus of elasticity

E_T tangent modulus of cross section of actual column

E_{st} initial strain-hardening modulus

E_t tangent modulus of material free of residual stresses

F   stiffener compressive force; also, applied tensile force on bolts

F_a allowable axial stress

F_b allowable bending stress

F_b' reduced allowable bending stress

F_e, F_e' Euler stress divided by factor of safety

F_t allowable tensile stress for bolts

F_t' allowable tensile stress for bolts under combined tension and shear

F_v allowable shear stress for bolts

F_v' allowable shear stress for bolts under combined shear and tension

FS   factor of safety for static stress

FSF   factor of safety for fatigue stress

G   shearing modulus of elasticity or shear modulus; also, relative stiffness at end of column

I   moment of inertia

I_1, I_2 maximum and minimum moment of inertia about principal axes

I_b moment of inertia of bottom flange about y axis

I_c moment of inertia of column

I_e moment of inertia of elastic portion of column cross-section

I_g moment of inertia of girder

I_p polar moment of inertia

I_s moment of inertia of stiffener

I_t moment of inertia of top flange about y axis

I_{tr} moment of inertia of transformed section for composite beams

I_x moment of inertia with respect to x axis

I_y moment of inertia with respect to y axis

I_{xy} product of inertia

J torsional constant

K effective length factor

L length

L_c length of column

L_g length of girder

M bending moment

M_1 moment caused by loads perpendicular to major axis; also, smaller bending moment in beam columns

M_2 moment caused by loads perpendicular to minor axis; also, larger bending moment in beam columns

M_d dead load moment

M_l live load moment

M_o maximum initial moment in beam columns

M_p plastic moment

M_u ultimate moment

M_x moment caused by loads perpendicular to x axis

M_y bending moment that causes first yielding; also moment caused by loads perpendicular to y axis

M_{yf} moment that causes initial yielding in flange of hybrid beam

M_{yw} moment that causes initial yielding in web of hybrid beam

N safety factor; also, number of load cycles

P, P' load

P_e Euler load of column

P_H horizontal load

P_u ultimate load

P_x vertical load

P_y axial load that causes yielding

Q statical moment of cross-sectional area for calculating shear stress

R stress ratio for cyclic loading; also, radius

S section modulus; also, stress in cyclic loading

S_b section modulus with respect to bottom of beam

S_o limiting maximum stress in cyclic loading

S_s section modulus of steel beam

S_t section modulus with respect to top of beam

S_x section modulus with respect to x axis

T   torsional moment; also, tensile force in composite beam; also, proof load of bolts; also membrane tension

V   shear force

V_h total horizontal shear

V_p plastic shear force

W, W'   total load

Y   ratio of web yield stress to stiffener yield stress

Z   plastic section modulus

a   plate length or stiffener spacing; also depth of compressive region in concrete slab of composite beam; also, torsional flange bending constant

b   plate width; also, effective width of concrete slab

b_b width of bottom flange

b_e effective plate width

b_f flange width

b'   plate width between stiffeners

b_t width of top flange

c   distance from centroid to outer fiber; also, depth of channel lips

d   beam depth; also, distance between center of beam flanges; also, diameter of roller

e   eccentricity

e_1, e_2 end eccentricity

e'   effective eccentricity

e_{st} value of strain at which strain hardening begins

f   stress

f_1, f_2, f_3 principal stresses; also, f_1 and f_2 are used to indicate maximum and minimum applied edge stress for plates in compression and bending

f_a axial stress

f_b bending stress

f_c buckling stress for columns; also, compressive stress in plates or tubes; also, bending stress in concrete; also, theoretical elastic lateral buckling stress

f'_c actual buckling stress for plates in the inelastic range; also, ultimate compressive strength of concrete

f_{cr} elastic buckling stress for plates and tubes in compression

f'_{cr} inelastic buckling stress for plates

f_{crb} elastic buckling stress for plates in bending

f'_{crb} inelastic buckling stress for plates in bending

f_{crl} buckling stress for plates in compression and bending

f'_{crs} inelastic buckling stress for plates in shear

f_{crs} elastic buckling stress for plates or tubes in shear

f_{eq} equivalent tensile stress

f_m maximum stress in column

f_r residual stress

f_s bending stress in steel of composite beam; also, shear stress

f_u tensile strength; also, average stress at ultimate load

f_{us} ultimate shear stress

f_v shear stress

f_y yield stress (yield point or yield strength, whichever is applicable)

f_y' average column stress at initial yielding

f_{yf} yield stress of flange of hybrid beam

f_{ys} yield stress in shear

f_{yw} yield stress of web of hybrid beam

g gage of rivets or bolts (transverse spacing)

h height of beam web

h_b web height from neutral axis to bottom of shape

h_t web height from neutal axis to top of shape

k_1 plate buckling coefficient for plates in compression and bending; also, ratio of W'/P'

k_{bd} numerical factor for bending deflection of beam

k_c dimensionless plate buckling coefficient

k_e correction coefficient for eccentric load in beam columns

k_m equivalent load factor for beam columns

k_s plate buckling coefficient for plates in shear

k_{sd} numerical factor for shear deflection of beam

k_w plate buckling coefficient modified for interaction of adjacent long plates in compression

k_ψ correction coefficient for deflection in beam columns

m a distance perpendicular to the major axis; also, slope of limiting design curve for cyclic loading

n ratio of modulus of elasticity of steel to that of concrete; also, a distance perpendicular to the minor axis; also, number of fasteners in vertical gage line

p factor used for calculating moment in laterally loaded plates

q uniform unit lateral loading on plates

r radius of gyration

s pitch of rivets or bolts (longitudinal spacing)

t thickness

t_c thickness of concrete slab

t_f thickness of flange

t_w thickness of web

u   Poisson's ratio

v' ultimate shear force per unit length for girder stiffeners

v_h shear force per unit length in composite beams

w   load per unit length; also, channel length for shear connectors

W', W_e deflection of a laterally loaded plate

w_1 longitudinal deflection

w_o midspan deflection for laterally loaded plate

w_{oo} initial deflection for laterally loaded plate

x   distance perpendicular to y axis

y   lateral deflection of column; also, distance perpendicular to x axis

$\bar{y}$ distance from x axis to centroid of area

y_o initial lateral deflection of column

y_0, y_1, y_2 distance between compressive and tensile resultants of composite beam

Δ elongation or deflection; also change in magnitude

Δ_x deflection perpendicular to x axis

Δ_y deflection perpendicular to y axis

α factor used for calculating moment in laterally loaded plates

ε strain

γ ratio of moment of inertia of stiffener to that of plate; also, numerical factor for calculating torsional shear stress

θ the angle between an axis through a rectangular element and a reference axis

θ_t unit angle of twist

θ_p the angle between the principal axis and a reference axis

λ dimensionless slenderness parameter for columns

λ_p dimensionless slenderness parameter for plates

ϕ dimensionless parameter for buckling of stiffened plates

ψ numerical factor for calculating J for rectangular bar; also, deflection coefficient for beam columns

δ numerical factor for torsion at juncture of web and flange

CHAPTER 1

The Structural Steels and
Their Mechanical Properties

1.1 Introduction

As used in this Manual, the term "structural steels" includes all steels that, because of their economy, strength, ductility, and other properties, are suitable for load carrying members in a wide variety of fabrications and engineering structures. Although they are not technically structural steels, certain steels commonly used in pressure vessels and other critical structures are discussed in this chapter to give an appreciation of the broad spectrum of steels and steel properties that are available.

Presently, a large number of structural steels having yield stress values* ranging from 30,000 to 100,000 psi are available as plates, rolled shapes, tubes, and bars. Steel plates and shapes intended for use in bridges, buildings, transportation equipment, and similar applications are generally furnished in "Structural Quality." "In addition, plate steels are also available in "Pressure Vessel Quality" for use in fired or unfired pressure vessels. Generally, a greater number of mechanical-property tests, and additional steel making practices are required as the steel plate quality increases from Structural Quality to Pressure Vessel Quality." Reference 1 gives additional information on steel qualities.

---

*The term "yield stress" is used in this Manual as a generic term to denote either the yield point (for those steels that have a yield point) or the yield strength (for those steels that do not have a yield point). However, the specific terms, yield point and yield strength, are used where they are uniquely applicable.

1

A summary of the mechanical properties of some of the most frequently used structural steels is given in Table 1.1. The steels are referred to by their ASTM[2]* designation and/or by their brand name. As shown in the table, these steels may be grouped into four general classifications in which the ranges of specified minimum yield stress are approximately:

1. Carbon steels — 30,000 to 40,000 psi.

2. High-strength low-alloy steels — 40,000 to 70,000 psi.

3. Heat-treated high-strength carbon steels —
   46,000 to 80,000 psi.

4. Heat-treated constructional alloy steels —
   90,000 and 100,000 psi.

Typical stress-strain curves for several structural steels having specified minimum tensile properties are shown in Figures 1.1 and 1.2 and will be discussed in Section 1.6.

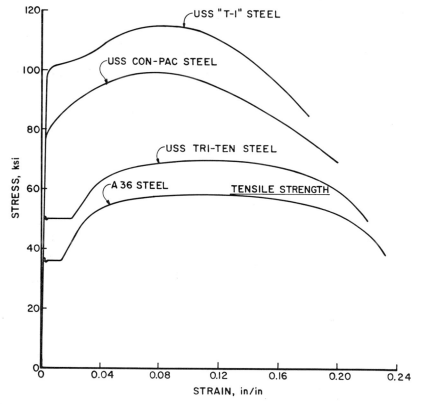

FIGURE 1.1   TYPICAL STRESS-STRAIN CURVES FOR STRUCTURAL STEELS HAVING SPECIFIED MINIMUM TENSILE PROPERTIES

---

*See References.

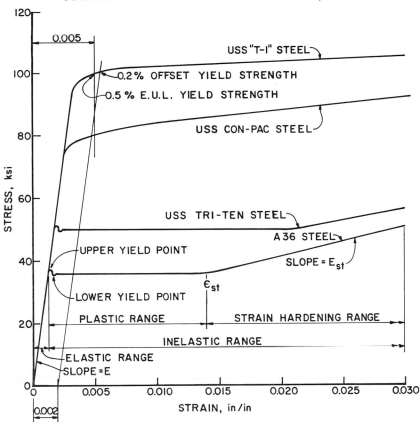

FIGURE 1.2 TYPICAL INITIAL STRESS-STRAIN
CURVES FOR STRUCTURAL STEELS HAVING
SPECIFIED MINIMUM TENSILE PROPERTIES

In addition to a large range of strengths, these steels provide a wide range of other useful material properties such as corrosion resistance, abrasion resistance, and toughness. The prices of the various steels also differ considerably, but in general, the "yield stress-to-price ratio" (yield stress divided by average net mill price per pound) is favorably higher for the higher-strength steels. For a large number of applications, the relative economy increases as the yield stress-to-price ratio increases. Therefore, to aid in the selection of the most suitable steel for each application, a description of the structural steels and their material properties is given in this chapter.

For special applications where the structural steels do not provide the desired properties, many other special purpose steels are available. Additional technical information, as well as specific price data, for all of these steels is available from U. S. Steel.

1.2 Structural Carbon Steels

Carbon steels are generally used where unit stresses are low and rigidity is the main criterion. The criteria for a carbon steel[1] are (1) that the maximum content specified for any of the following elements does not exceed the percentages noted: manganese—1.65 percent, silicon—0.60 percent, and copper—0.60 percent, and (2) that no minimum content is specified for other elements added to obtain a desired alloying effect.

The first carbon steel listed in Table 1.1—A36—is a weldable steel* available as plates, bars, and structural shapes. The other carbon steels listed in Table 1.1 are available only as plates. Although each is available in two or more strength levels, only one strength level is listed in the table for A283 and A285 plates.

A283 plates are furnished as structural quality steel in four strength levels — designated as Grades A, B, C, and D—having specified minimum yield points of 24,000, 27,000, 30,000 and 33,000 psi. This plate steel is of structural quality and has been used primarily for oil and water storage vessels. A 573 steel, which is available in two strength levels, is a structural quality steel intended for service at atmospheric temperatures where improved notch toughness is important. The other plate steels—A285, A515, and A516—are all furnished in pressure vessel quality only and are intended for welded construction in more critical applications such as pressure vessels. A515 and A516, the newest of the plate steel specifications, have replaced the earlier A201 and A212 specifications. Both A515 and A516 are furnished in four strength levels—designated as Grades 55, 60, 65, and 70 (denoting their tensile strength)—having specified minimum yield points of 30,000, 32,000, 35,000, and 38,000 psi. A515 steel is for "intermediate and higher temperature service," whereas A516 is for "atmospheric and lower temperature service."

1.3 High-Strength Low-Alloy Steels

Structural steels that have specified minimum yield points above about 40,000 psi and that achieve their strength in the hot-rolled condition rather than through heat treatment are designated high-strength low-alloy steels. USS COR-TEN high-strength low-alloy steel, which is available in nearly all rolled steel products—plates, structural shapes, bars, sheets, and strip—combines high strength and weldability with superior atmospheric corrosion resistance. As a result of the superior atmospheric corrosion resistance, COR-TEN steel provides a longer paint life than other structural steels. In addition, in many architectural and other applications involving members exposed to the atmosphere, COR-TEN steel can be used bare, uncoated, because it forms a tight oxide which substantially reduces further corrosion.

---

*Throughout this Manual, the use of the terms "weldable" or "weldability" presupposes that the welding procedures and techniques employed are in accordance with the approved methods for the steel. Specific welding information for each of the steels is available from U. S. Steel.

Three compositions are used for making COR-TEN steel designated A, B and C. COR-TEN A, which has a Cr-Si-Cu-Ni-P composition, and a resistance to atmospheric corrosion 5 to 8 times that of carbon steel,* is used in thicknesses through ½ inch for general applications. In Figure 1.3, a corrosion curve for this composition is compared with a similar curve for other steels exposed to an industrial atmosphere. COR-TEN A steel provides a specified minimum yield point of 50,000 psi in thicknesses to ½ inch inclusive. In thicknesses over ½ inch, COR-TEN A is used only for special applications, and special precautions must be taken when welding these greater thicknesses. COR-TEN A steel can be produced to the requirements of ASTM A242, A374 and A375.

COR-TEN B steel which has a Mn-Cr-Cu-V composition, and a resistance to atmospheric corrosion 4 times that of carbon steel, is used in thicknesses over ½ inch for general applications. This composition of COR-TEN steel provides a minimum yield point of 50,000 psi in plate and bar thicknesses to 4 inches inclusive and in all structural shapes except for wide flange shapes weighing more than 550 pounds per foot, and a slightly reduced yield point in thicker and heavier sections and shapes. COR-TEN B steel can be produced to the requirements of ASTM A242 and A588 Grade A. COR-TEN C steel, which also has a Mn-Cr-Cu-V composition, and a resistance at atmospheric corrosion 4 times that of carbon steel, provides 60,000 psi minimum yield point in plate and bars to 1 inch thick inclusive, and in ASTM Group I structurals.

USS TRI-TEN high-strength low-alloy steel, is available in most steel products, and has been used for the structural members of bridges, buildings, trailers, and equipment. Plates, structural shapes, and bars have a specified minimum yield point of 50,000 psi in thicknesses to ¾ inch inclusive and slightly reduced yield points for greater thicknesses. Sheets, strip, and certain thin plates (plates ⅜-inch-thick and less furnished for severe cold forming applications) have a specified minimum yield point of 45,000 psi. TRI-TEN steel provides a resistance to atmospheric corrosion twice that of carbon steel. TRI-TEN steel can be produced to the requirements of ASTM A441.

USS MAN-TEN (A440)** is available in plates, bars and structurals, and provides high strength at a price slightly less than that of TRI-TEN steel. This steel is intended primarily for riveted and bolted structures and has a resistance to atmospheric corrosion two times that of carbon steel. MAN-TEN (A440) steel, which can be produced to the requirements of ASTM A440, provides a specified minimum yield point of 50,000 psi in thicknesses to ¾ inch inclusive and a reduced yield point in thicker sections.

---

*Relative corrosion resistance ratings are based on the slopes of curves of corrosion versus time. All references made to the corrosion resistance of carbon steel refer to carbon steel without copper.

**Because of its chemical composition, this steel cannot be defined as "high-strength low-alloy" steel. However, because of the mechanical properties, it is listed in this section of the manual and is referred to as "high-strength steel."

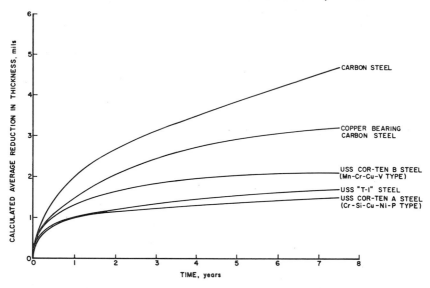

CALCULATED AVERAGE REDUCTION IN THICKNESS, mils

TIME, years

CARBON STEEL

COPPER BEARING CARBON STEEL

USS COR-TEN B STEEL (Mn-Cr-Cu-V TYPE)

USS "T-I" STEEL
USS COR-TEN A STEEL (Cr-Si-Cu-Ni-P TYPE)

FIGURE I.3 CORROSION CURVES FOR FOR SEVERAL STEELS IN AN INDUSTRIAL ATMOSPHERE

USS EX-TEN high-strength low-alloy steels are generally available in four different strength levels: EX-TEN 42, EX-TEN 50, EX-TEN 60, and EX-TEN 70.* The number following EX-TEN indicates the specified minimum yield point in psi.** Each of these steels is weldable and provides high strength at minimum cost. The resistance to atmospheric corrosion for EX-TEN steels is the same as that of carbon steels, but may be doubled by specifying 0.20 percent minimum copper content. These steels are available in most hot-rolled products within certain thickness limitations, depending on strength levels. The EX-TEN steels can be produced to the requirements of ASTM A572.

1.4 Heat-Treated High-Strength Carbon Steels

This group is comprised of carbon steels that have been heat-treated to obtain more desirable mechanical properties. USS CHAR-PAC steel is a weldable plate steel furnished in pressure vessel quality that provides excellent notch toughness and high strength for pressure vessels, tanks at low temperatures, and other critical applications. This steel is furnished to pressure quality in either the normalized condition or the quenched and tempered condition. In thicknesses not exceeding 1¼ inches, normalized CHAR-PAC steel provides a minimum yield point of 50,000 psi, whereas quenched and tempered CHAR-PAC steel provides a minimum yield strength of 60,000 psi. CHAR-PAC steel with a slightly reduced yield stress is available in thicknesses over 1¼ to 2 inches

---

*Other strength levels available but not generally used include EX-TEN 45, EX-TEN 55, and EX-TEN 65.

**Grades 42, 45, and 50 are intended for welded bridge construction but should be limited to a maximum thickness of 1½ inch. Grades 42 through 65 are intended for welded building construction but should be limited to the maximum thickness listed in ASTM A572.

inclusive. CHAR-PAC steel, normalized, has a specified minimum Charpy-V notch toughness of 15 foot-pounds at −75F in longitudinally oriented test specimens.* In the Quenched and Tempered condition, CHAR-PAC steel has a specified minimum Charpy V-notch toughness of 15 foot-pounds at −90F. CHAR-PAC steel can be produced to the requirements of ASTM A537.

USS CON-PAC steel is a weldable plate steel which provides a strength level between that of the high-strength low-alloy steels and the heat-treated construction alloy steels. This steel is furnished in the quenched and tempered condition and has a specified minimum yield strength of 80,000 psi in thicknesses to ¾ inch inclusive and 70,000 psi in thicknesses over ¾ through 1½ inches.

1.5 Heat-Treated Constructional Alloy Steels

Heat-treated steels that contain alloying elements and are suitable for structural applications are called heat-treated constructional alloy steels. Three constructional alloy steels having yield strengths of 90,000 and 100,000 psi are available.

USS "T-1" constructional alloy steel, a quenched and tempered steel that is available in plates, bars, tubes, and in many rolled structural shapes, combines high strength with other desirable properties. "T-1" steel has a specified minimum yield strength of 100,000 psi in thicknesses from ⅜₆ inch through 2½ inches and 90,000 psi in thicknesses over 2½ inches through 6 inches. "T-1" steel is weldable, provides excellent notch toughness at low temperatures, and has a resistance to atmospheric corrosion 4 times that of carbon steel. An atmospheric corrosion curve for this steel is included in Figure 1.3. "T-1" steel can be produced to the requirements of ASTM A514 Grade F and A 517 Grade F steels. Specification A514 covers structural quality plates while A517 covers pressure vessel quality plates. In thicknesses of ⅞₆ inch through 2½ inches, pressure vessel quality "T-1" steel has a Charpy V-notch toughness (longitudinal value—average of 3 specimens per ASTM procedure) of 20 foot pounds at −50 F.

USS "T-1" type A constructional alloy steel is a lower priced steel that provides a 100,000-psi yield strength in thicknesses from ⅜₆ inch through 1¼ inches. It has a resistance to atmospheric corrosion 2 times that of carbon steel, and has other properties that are similar to those of "T-1" steel. "T-1" type A can be produced to the requirements of ASTM A514 Grade B and A517 Grade B steels.

USS "T-1" type B constructional alloy steel provides a specified minimum yield strength of 100,000 psi in thicknesses from ⅜₆ inch through 2 inches and is particularly economical in thicknesses over 1¼ inches through 2 inches. It has a resistance to atmospheric corrosion which is 2 times that of carbon steel, and has other properties which are generally similar to those of "T-1" steel. "T-1" type B steel can be produced to the requirements of ASTM A514 Grade H, and A517 Grade H.

---

*Longitudinally oriented test specimens have their principal axis parallel to the direction of final hot rolling of the steel. See Section 1.11.3 for a description of this test.

An important additional property of these three constructional alloy steels is their ability to resist abrasion. Although the abrasion-resistance characteristics of a metal may differ considerably—depending upon the type of abrasion to which the metal is subjected—for many types of abrasion the hardness of the metal is an index of relative abrasion resistance. It is generally agreed that hardness is directly related to tensile strength. Thus, with a specified minimum tensile strength nearly twice that of structural carbon steel, the constructional alloy steels in many applications would be expected to have nearly twice the resistance to abrasion provided by carbon steel. For applications where even greater resistance to abrasion is required, "T-1", "T-1" type A, and "T-1" type B steel plates can be furnished to a specified minimum Brinell hardness of either 321 or 360, but all other minimum mechanical properties for the steels are waived. Typical values of the other mechanical properties are given in Table 1.2 for the "T-1" steels treated to specified minimum hardness values. Because of their lower ductility, caution must be exercised when these specially hardened constructional alloy steels are used for structural applications.

1.6 Behavior at Room Temperature

1.6.1 *Tension and Compression*

Typical engineering type tensile stress-strain curves for several structural steels having specified minimum tensile properties are shown in Figure 1.1. The initial portion of each of the curves is shown to a magnified horizontal scale in Figure 1.2. These are called engineering type curves because the stress plotted was calculated by dividing the load on the specimen by its original cross-sectional area, and the strain was calculated by dividing the elongation of a gage length of the specimen by the original gage length.

As indicated by the initial straight segment of each curve, stress is directly proportional to strain during the first portion of a tension test. The ratio of stress to strain, which is the slope of the straight line in this elastic range, is the modulus of elasticity, or Young's modulus, and is approximately equal to 29×10^6 psi for each of the structural steels.

As illustrated in Figure 1.2, immediately after the stress-strain curve for two of the steels—A36 carbon steel and TRI-TEN high-strength low-alloy steel—departs from linearity, the stress reaches a peak, dips slightly, and during a considerable amount of additional strain remains constant at a stress slightly above the minimum stress in the dip. The peak value of stress is the yield point as defined by ASTM, and the range of constant or nearly constant stress and increasing strain is the "plastic range." For these steels the plastic range is followed by a strain-hardening range in which stress again increases with strain. The plastic range and the strain hardening range may be considered as parts of the "inelastic range." The stress-strain curve for CHAR-PAC heat treated (normalized) steel is generally similar to that shown for TRI-TEN steel.

The rate at which stress increases with strain in the strain hardening range is the strain-hardening modulus, and is given by the slope of the curve. Both the initial strain-hardening modulus, E_{st}, and the value of strain at which strain hardening begins, ε_{st}, are important in plastic design. Average values that have been determined for two of the steels are:

Steel	E_{st}, psi	ε_{st}, in./in.
ASTM A36	900,000	0.014
ASTM A441	700,000	0.021

Similarly, the stress-strain curves for "T-1" constructional alloy steel and for CON-PAC heat-treated (quenched and tempered) carbon steel exhibit an elastic range and an inelastic range. For these two steels, the transition between the elastic and inelastic portions may be somewhat different from that for the other structural steels; that is, these two steels generally exhibit a more gradual transition rather than a distinct yield point as described above. For such materials, the stress at which the material exhibits a specified limiting deviation, expressed in terms of strain, from perfectly elastic behavior is defined as the yield strength and has essentially the same significance in design as yield point. As permitted in ASTM specification A370, the yield strength is usually specified by the 0.5 percent extension-under-load (E.U.L.) definition. As indicated in Figure 1.2, this definition gives values that are closely equivalent to those attained under the 0.2 percent offset definition for steels at this strength level. The curves show that these steels are elastic under stresses approaching their yield strengths. Unlike the other structural steels, these steels do not usually show a distinct plastic range or a large amount of strain hardening. For all the steels, the maximum stress indicated on the stress-strain curve (Fig. 1.1) is the tensile strength of the steel.

Resilience and toughness are measures of the energy-absorbing capacity of a material, and for uniaxial stress can be determined from the engineering stress-strain curves. Resilience (or modulus of resilience) is the amount of elastic energy that can be absorbed by a unit volume of a material loaded in tension, and is equal to the area under the stress-strain diagram up to the yield point. Toughness (or modulus of toughness) is the total amount of energy, both elastic and inelastic, that can be absorbed by a unit volume of a material loaded in tension, and is equal to the area under the stress-strain curve up to the rupture point.* Values of these properties calculated from the curves shown in Figure 1.1 are:

Steel	Resilience, in. pounds/in.³	Toughness. in. pounds/in.³
ASTM A36	22	12,000
USS TRI-TEN	43	15,000
USS CON-PAC	110	18,000
USS "T-1"	170	19,000

---

*Notch toughness, a related property discussed in Section 1.10.3 is measured by the impact energy necessary to fracture a notched specimen.

Ductility, an index of the ability of a material to deform in the inelastic range, is usually measured in a tension test by the elongation over a given gage length or by the reduction of the cross-sectional area. The elongation is equal to the difference between the initial gage length and the gage length after fracture, and is usually expressed as a percentage of the initial gage length. Similarly, the reduction of area is equal to the difference between initial and least cross-sectional area after fracture, and is usually expressed as a percentage of the initial cross-sectional area. Both measurements are strongly influenced by specimen geometry. For example, the elongation over a 2-inch gage length determined from two different size standard ASTM tension specimens of the same material may differ significantly. Reduction of area for round specimens is not significantly affected by the specimen diameter, but values determined from round specimens are not directly comparable to values determined from specimens of rectangular cross-section.

Ductility is important because it allows redistribution of high local stresses. Such stresses are frequently encountered in engineering structures near holes and other abrupt geometrical changes. However, there is no generally accepted criterion for the minimum amount of ductility required for engineering structures. Therefore, the determination of whether the ductility of a steel is adequate for engineering structures can best be made by service experience. Successful service experience with the structural steels discussed herein has demonstrated that each has adequate ductility for the types of structures in which it is ordinarily used.

The ratio of transverse to longitudinal (axial) strain under load is known as Poisson's ratio. For each of the structural steels, Poisson's ratio is approximately 0.30 in the elastic range and 0.50 in the plastic range.

For the structural steels, the yield stress, modulus of elasticity, and Poisson's ratio in compression are approximately equal to those in tension. The specimen does not usually fracture in a compression test, but its height is decreased and it expands laterally as the load is applied.

1.6.2 *Shear*

Stress-strain curves for specimens loaded in shear are generally similar in appearance to tension curves. The slope of the initial straight line portion of the shear stress-strain diagram is the shearing modulus of elasticity, shear modulus, or modulus of rigidity. According to the theory of elasticity, the shear modulus, G, is related to Poisson's ratio, μ, and the modulus of elasticity, E, by the equation

$$G = \frac{E}{2(1 + \mu)} \tag{1.1}$$

A minimum value of G for the structural steel is about 11×10^6 psi. The yield stress in shear is approximately equal to its theoretical value of $1/\sqrt{3}$ times the yield stress in tension. Results of shear tests indicate that the ultimate shear strength ranges from 2/3 to 3/4 of the tensile strength.

1.6.3 *Yielding Under Combined Stresses*

Under combined stress, that is, stresses acting simultaneously at a point in more than one principal direction, yielding in ductile metals such as the structural steels may occur at a stress that is not equal to the uniaxial (stress in one direction only) yield stress. As explained in most text books on strength of materials, the stresses at any point in a loaded structure can be resolved into three principal stresses — tensile or compressive stresses that act in principal directions on three mutually perpendicular planes of zero shear. In structural steels, yielding will occur when the principal stresses, f_1, f_2, and f_3, satisfy the relationship

$$f_y{}^2 = \frac{1}{2}[(f_1 - f_2)^2 + (f_2 - f_3)^2 + (f_3 - f_1)^2] \qquad (1.2)$$

where f_y is the yield stress determined from the uniaxial tensile test. This relationship is usually referred to as the "Hencky-Von Mises" or "distortion-energy" yield criterion. For most applications involving plates, the principal stress perpendicular to the surface of the plate is zero and the relationship reduces to

$$f_y{}^2 = f_1{}^2 + f_2{}^2 - f_1 f_2$$

In Figure 1.4, Equation 1.3 is presented as a nondimensional interaction curve for biaxial stresses. The curve shows that when f_1 equals f_2, yielding will occur when f_1 and f_2 simultaneously reach f_y. If f_1 and f_2 are not equal but are of the same sign, yielding will not occur until the larger stress reaches a value slightly greater than f_y. If f_1 and f_2 are opposite sign, yielding will occur before either stress reaches f_y.

1.7 Behavior at Elevated Temperatures

1.7.1 *Mechanical Properties*

The behavior of structural steels when subjected to short-time loading at elevated temperatures is similar to the behavior at room temperature, but the shape of the stress-strain curve and the values of the properties discussed previously change as the temperature is increased. The stress-strain curve generally becomes more rounded at elevated temperatures, and, as shown in Figures 1.5 and 1.6, yield strength and tensile strength are generally reduced. Similarly, the modulus of elasticity, which, as noted previously, is approximately the same for all structural steels, decreases significantly with increasing temperature as shown in Figure 1.7. The variation in the shear modulus with temperature is similar to that shown for the modulus of elasticity, but Poisson's ratio does not vary over this temperature range. The ductility of the structural steels, as indicated by elongation and reduction-of-area values, decreases

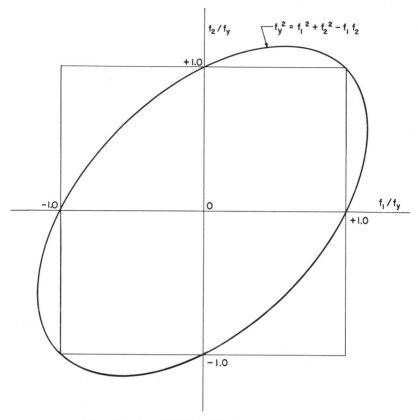

**FIGURE I.4 INTERACTION CURVE FOR
YIELDING UNDER BIAXIAL STRESSES**

with increasing temperature until a minimum value is reached
(about 0.6 of the room-temperature value for A36 steel) and,
thereafter, increases to a value much greater than the room-temperature value. The exact effect depends upon the type and thickness of steel. The decrease in ductility is caused by strain aging
and is most pronounced in the temperature range of 300 to 700 F.
Strain aging also accounts for the increase in tensile strength in
this temperature range shown for two of the steels in Figure 1.6.
An explanation of strain aging phenomena is given in Section 1.9.1.

1.7.2 *Creep*

The behavior of structural steels under long-time loading depends
significantly upon temperature. When a load that is smaller than
the ultimate load is applied to a specimen at room temperature,
the specimen deforms relatively rapidly to an equilibrium point,
and thereafter, the deformation remains constant with respect to
time. When a load is applied to a specimen at an elevated temperature, the specimen likewise deforms rapidly at first but then

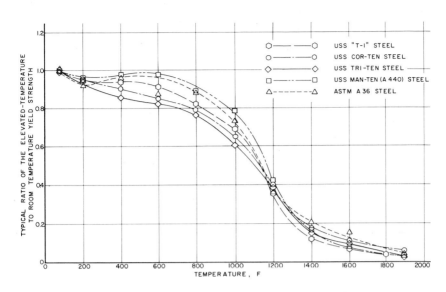

FIGURE 1.5 EFFECT OF TEMPERATURE ON THE RATIO BETWEEN
ELEVATED-TEMPERATURE AND ROOM-TEMPERATURE YIELD STRENGTHS

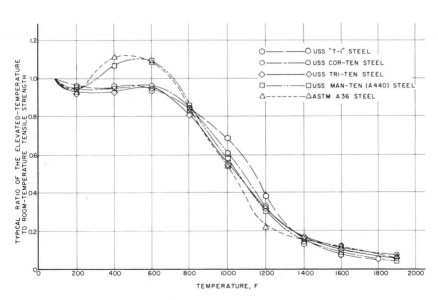

FIGURE 1.6 EFFECT OF TEMPERATURE ON THE RATIO BETWEEN
ELEVATED-TEMPERATURE AND ROOM-TEMPERATURE TENSILE STRENGTHS

continues to deform, or creep, at a much slower rate. A schematic creep curve for a steel subjected to a constant tensile load and at a constant elevated temperature is given in Figure 1.8. The initial elongation occurs almost instantaneously and is followed by three stages in which elongation increases at a decreasing rate, Stage 1, increases at a nearly constant rate, Stage 2, and increases at an increasing rate, Stage 3. The failure, or creep-rupture, load is less than the load that would cause failure at that particular temperature in a short-time loading test.

The compression creep curve for a structural steel would be similar to the tension creep curve, except that there would be no region in which deformation increases at an increasing rate such as in the third stage of tension creep curves, and there would be no fracture point. However, creep may contribute to buckling failures of compression members. A discussion of this phenomenon, referred to as creep buckling, is outside the scope of this manual

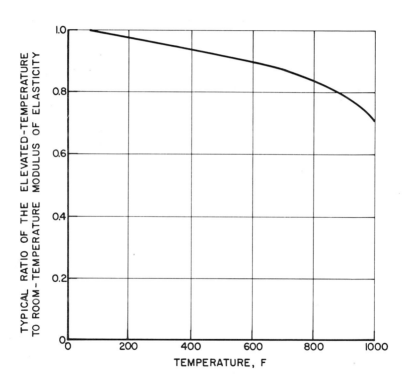

FIGURE 1.7   EFFECT OF TEMPERATURE ON THE RATIO BETWEEN ELEVATED-TEMPERATURE AND ROOM-TEMPERATURE MODULUS OF ELASTICITY FOR STRUCTURAL STEELS

but references are available on the subject.[3] Creep may also occur in shear.

Table 1.3 indicates typical creep and rupture data for a carbon steel and a constructional alloy steel. The table denotes, (1) the stress that will cause a given amount of creep in a given time at a particular temperature, and (2) the stress that will cause rupture in a given time at a particular temperature. For special elevated-temperature applications where the structural steels do not provide

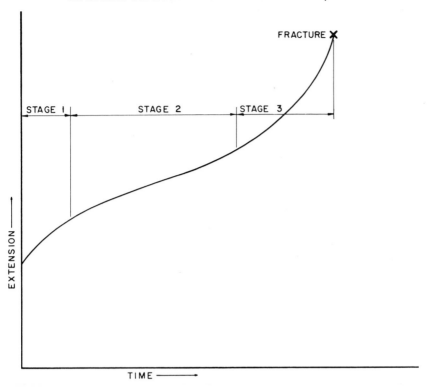

FIGURE I.8 SCHEMATIC CREEP CURVE

adequate properties, a large number of alloy and stainless steels with excellent high-temperature properties are available.[4]

1.7.3 *Other Effects of High Temperatures*

Although this manual is primarily concerned with structural design, a few other effects of high temperatures will be mentioned briefly here because they may control the selection of a steel for a particular application. There are a considerable number of metal-lurgical phenomena that may affect the mechanical properties of steel at high temperatures, such as precipitation hardening or aging, temper embrittlement, and carbide instability.[4] For the structural steels these phenomena are not usually important for most applications involving temperatures below approximately 1000 F. However, it should be noted that the "T-1" steels are not recommended for applications where the metal temperature exceeds 800 F.

Oxidation, a type of corrosion that causes scaling of steels subjected to the atmosphere, is particularly important at elevated temperatures. The resistance of steels to oxidation depends on their composition. For the structural steels, atmospheric oxidation is negligible at temperatures below approximately 1000 F but increases rapidly at higher temperatures.

1.8 Effects of Strain Rate

The mechanical properties referred to thus far have been those measured by testing at relatively slow strain rates, that is, at rates not exceeding the rate corresponding to the maximum stress rate of 100,000 psi per minute allowed by ASTM. The properties determined at these relatively slow rates are used in the design of most ordinary structures. The effect of much faster strain rates, such as those which would be encountered in severe shock loadings, on mechanical properties is discussed in the following paragraphs.

Most mechanical-property determinations made at rapid strain rates have been performed by either rapid tension tests, or by tension or compressive impact tests.[5]* The rapid tension test is generally made in a tension-testing machine which has been modified for rapid motion, but which loads the specimen at a relatively uniform rate. In tension or compressive impact tests, the specimen is placed in a special jig and either continuously strained or strained by successive blows. The behavior observed in rapid tension tests is generally similar to that observed in tension impact tests. It has been established also that the dynamic tensile and dynamic compressive behavior of metals are very similar. Therefore, the results of tension impact tests will be used to illustrate the general behavior of a steel loaded at a high strain rate.

In Figure 1.9, curves "a" and "b" were obtained by repeated impact, the faster strain rate occurring for curve "a." Curve "c"

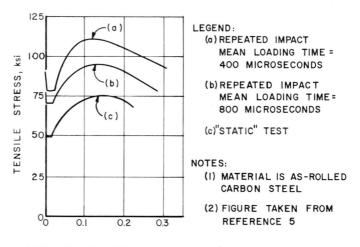

FIGURE 1.9 DYNAMIC AND "STATIC" STRESS-STRAIN CURVES

---

*Extremely high strain rates have also been obtained by explosive loading tests. Such tests will not be discussed here, but the effects on mechanical properties of the extremely high strain rates show the same general trends as discussed herein.

shows the conventional slow-rate tension test, referred to here as a "static" test. Both the yield point and tensile strength of the dynamically shocked specimen are substantially higher than the corresponding values observed in the static test. The greatest increases occurred for the bar that was strained at the greatest rate.

The general trends regarding tensile strength and yield point discussed above have been confirmed for the structural steels by rapid tension tests conducted on specimens of ASTM A515, COR-TEN, TRI-TEN, and "T-1" steels. The tests, conducted at three strain rates and at three temperatures to evaluate the interrelated effect of these variables on the strength of the steels, were performed on a tension-testing machine of special design that produced a rapid and relatively constant strain rate. The results of the tests are shown in Figure 1.10. The values shown for the slowest and the intermediate strain rate on the room temperature curves reflect the usual room temperature yield stress and tensile strength, respectively.* The curves show that the tensile strength and 0.2-percent-offset yield strength of all the steels increased as the strain rate increased at −50 F and at room temperature. The greatest increase in tensile strength was approximately 15 percent for "T-1" steel, whereas the greatest increase in yield strength noted

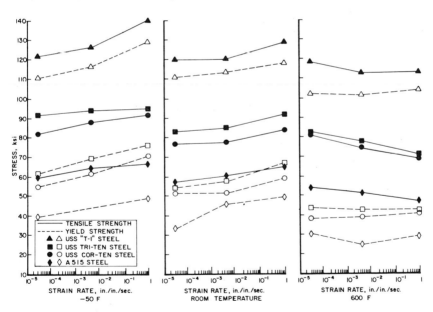

FIGURE 1.10 EFFECT OF STRAIN RATE ON THE YIELD AND TENSILE
STRENGTHS OF STRUCTURAL STEELS AT INDICATED TEMPERATURES

---

*In determining yield stress, ASTM specification E8 allows a maximum stress rate of 100,000 psi/min. For an E of 29 x 10[6] psi, this stress rate is approximately equivalent to 5.75 x 10[-5] in./in./sec. In determining tensile strength, ASTM specification E8 allows a maximum strain rate of 0.5 in./in./min. or 8.33 x 10[-3] in./in./sec.

was about 48 percent for A201 steel. However, at 600 F, increasing the strain rate had a relatively small influence on the yield strength, but caused a slight decrease in the tensile strength of most of the steels. The ductility of the steels, as measured by elongation or reduction in area, was not affected much by strain rate. Other tests have shown that the modulus of elasticity and Poisson's ratio do not vary significantly with the strain rate.

1.9 Effects of Cold Work

1.9.1 *Strength and Ductility*

In the fabrication of metal structures, flat plates and straight beams are often formed at room temperatures into desired shapes. These cold-forming operations obviously cause inelastic deformation, since the steel retains its formed shape. To illustrate the general effects of such deformation on strength and ductility, the elemental behavior of a carbon steel tension specimen subjected to plastic deformation and subsequent reloadings will be considered. However, it should be noted that the behavior of actual cold-formed structural members often may be much more complex.

As illustrated in Figure 1.11, if a steel specimen is unloaded after being stressed into either the plastic or strain hardening range, the unloading curve will follow a path parallel to the elastic portion of the stress-strain curve and, thus, a residual strain or permanent set will remain after the load is removed. If the specimen is promptly reloaded, it will follow the unloading curve to the stress-strain curve of the virgin (unstrained) material. If the amount of plastic deformation is less than that required for the onset of strain-hardening, the yield strength of the plastically deformed steel will be approximately the same as that of the virgin material. However, if the amount of plastic deformation is sufficient to cause strain hardening, the yield stress of the steel will be increased. In either instance, the tensile strength will remain the same but the ductility measured from the point of reloading will be decreased. As indicated in Figure 1.11, the decrease in ductility is approximately equal to the amount of inelastic prestrain.

A steel specimen that has been strained into the strain hardening range, unloaded, and allowed to age for several days at room temperature (or for a much shorter time at a moderately elevated temperature) will tend to follow the path indicated in Figure 1-12 during reloading.[6] This phenomenon, known as strain aging, has the effect of increasing yield and tensile strength while decreasing ductility.[7]

The effects of cold work on the strength and ductility of the structural steels can be eliminated largely by thermal stress relief or annealing. However, such treatment is not always possible and, fortunately, is not often necessary.

1.9.2 *Bauschinger Effect*

If a specimen that has been plastically strained in tension is unloaded and subsequently strained in compression, the stress-

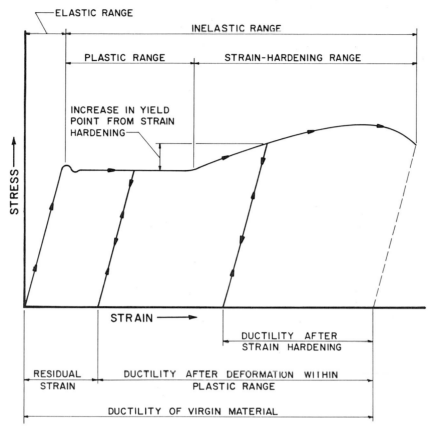

NOTE: DIAGRAM IS SCHEMATIC AND NOT TO SCALE

FIGURE I.II EFFECTS OF STRAIN HARDENING

strain curve for the compression loading deviates from linearity at stresses well below the yield point of the virgin material, but, if strained sufficiently, will eventually reach a stress equal to the yield point of the virgin material. The same effect is observed if the specimen is first strained in compression and then strained in tension. This phenomenon of reduced modulus of elasticity (slope of the stress-strain curve) is known as the Bauschinger effect and may be of interest where buckling or deflections are important.

An illustration of the Bauschinger effect in A36 steel is given in Figure 1.13. As shown in the figure, if a tension loading is applied after the specimen has been loaded, first in tension and then in compression, the stress-strain curve will again deviate from a linear relationship at stresses well below the virgin yield point, but will return to the point of maximum stress and strain for the first tension

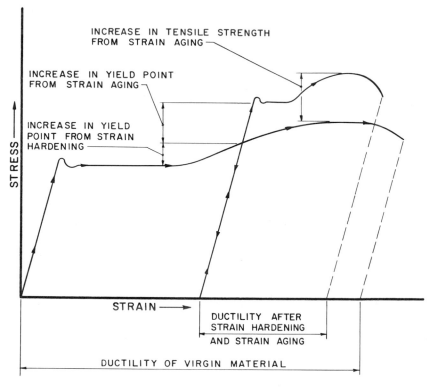

INCREASE IN TENSILE STRENGTH FROM STRAIN AGING

INCREASE IN YIELD POINT FROM STRAIN AGING

INCREASE IN YIELD POINT FROM STRAIN HARDENING

STRESS

STRAIN

DUCTILITY AFTER STRAIN HARDENING AND STRAIN AGING

DUCTILITY OF VIRGIN MATERIAL

NOTE: DIAGRAM IS SCHEMATIC AND NOT TO SCALE

FIGURE I.I2 EFFECTS OF STRAIN AGING

loading cycle. Tests have shown that the stress-strain curve for subsequent cycles of alternate tension and compression loading will tend to follow the same path as the curve for the first cycle provided that the maximum strains are not increased beyond those in the first cycle and that the effects of aging between cycles are eliminated.

The Bauschinger effect may also occur in specimens strained in one direction and subsequently loaded in a perpendicular direction or in specimens loaded by biaxial or triaxial stresses. The amount of deviation from a linear relationship caused by the Bauschinger effect varies with the amount of prestrain. Tests on carbon-steel sheets have shown that, sometimes, aging tends to restore the original shape of the stress-strain curve.[7]

1.10 Effects of Repeated Stress

1.10.1 *General Considerations*

A structural member subjected to repeated or cyclic stresses may eventually fail even though the maximum applied stress is less than

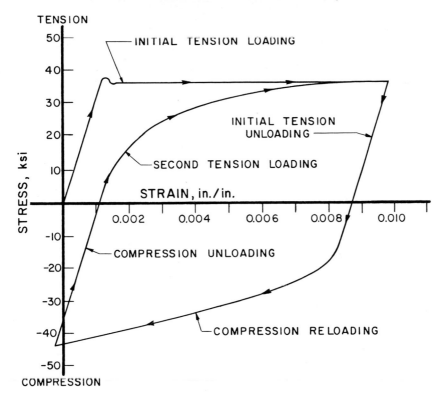

FIGURE 1.13   THE BAUSCHINGER EFFECT IN A36 STEEL

the yield stress. This phenomenon is known as fatigue. The fatigue behavior as determined from tests on polished specimens is discussed here; the fatigue behavior of structural members, which may be quite different because of the effects of surface conditions and stress raisers, is discussed in Chapter 10. Although the data below are for one steel only, the behavior discussed is typical for all of the structural steels.

1.10.2 *Determination of Fatigue Strength*

Resistance to failure under repeated stress can be evaluated by testing a series of specimens in the rotating beam test, the flexure test, or the axial load test. For the rotating beam test, a polished, round specimen with a reduced cross section is supported as a beam and subjected to a bending moment while being rotated so that fibers of the specimen are subjected alternately to compression and tension stresses of equal magnitude. For the flexure test, a specimen is bent back and forth as a beam instead of rotated and, for the axial load test, the specimen is subjected to an alternating axial stress. In the flexure and the axial load tests, the specimen may be polished or may be a rectangular specimen cut from a plate so that the mill surface is left intact. In the rotating beam test, the stress ratio R, which is the algebraic ratio of minimum to maximum stress, is −1. In the other two tests, the effect of various stress ratios may be investigated. In addition, there is a stress gradient over the cross section of the flexure or rotating beam specimen, whereas the stress is uniformly distributed over the cross section of the axially stressed specimen.

In each of the tests, the specimen is subjected to alternating stresses that vary between fixed limits of maximum and minimum stress until failure occurs. This procedure is repeated for other specimens at the same stress ratio but at different maximum stress values. The results of the tests are plotted to form an "S-N" diagram, where S represents the maximum stress in the cycle and N represents the number of cycles required to produce failure. An S-N diagram for polished specimens of "T-1" steel obtained from a series of rotating beam tests is shown in Figure 1.14. At any point on the curve, the stress value is the "fatigue strength"—the value of maximum stress that will cause failure at a given number of stress cycles and at a given stress ratio—and the number of cycles is the "fatigue life"—the number of stress cycles that will cause failure at a given maximum stress and stress ratio.

As shown in Figure 1.14, the fatigue strength of a structural steel decreases as the number of cycles increases until a "fatigue limit" is reached. If the maximum stress does not exceed the fatigue limit, an unlimited number of stress cycles can be applied at that stress ratio without causing failure. Tests on a large number of steels having tensile strengths up to 200,000 psi indicate that the fatigue limit of polished rotating beam specimens is about ½ the tensile strength. The fatigue limit of polished rotating beam specimens is about the same as that for axially loaded polished specimens, although the fatigue strength at a low number of cycles is different.

1.10.3 *Influence of Stress Ratio*

The influence of the stress ratio on fatigue strength is illustrated by the S-N curves for axially loaded polished specimens of "T-1" steel shown in Figure 1.15. Stress ratios of 0, −½, and −1 correspond to the following respective loading conditions: zero to tension, half compression to full tension, and complete reversal of stress between equal compression and tension stresses. The curves show that the fatigue strength decreases significantly as the stress ratio decreases.

These S-N curves can be used to construct a fatigue chart shown in Figure 1.16 for the polished "T-1" steel specimens. Each curved line in the chart represents the locus of all combinations of maximum and minimum stress at which failure will occur in the indicated number of cycles. Rays can be drawn from the origin in an obvious manner to represent various stress ratios. Such charts are convenient for determining fatigue strength at a stress ratio different from those at which the tests were conducted.

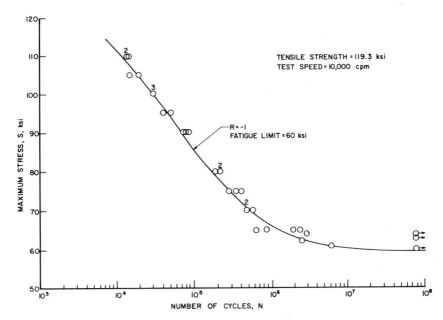

FIGURE 1.14 S-N DIAGRAM FOR POLISHED SPECIMENS OF "T-1"
STEEL OBTAINED FROM ROTATING-BEAM FATIGUE TESTS

1.11 Brittle Fracture Considerations in Structural Design

1.11.1 *General Considerations*

As the temperature decreases, an increase is generally noted in
the yield stress, tensile strength, modulus of elasticity, and fatigue
strength of the structural steels. In contrast, the ductility of these
steels, as measured by reduction in area or by elongation, decreases
with decreasing temperatures. Furthermore, there is a temperature
below which a structural steel subjected to tensile stresses may
fracture by cleavage,* with little or no plastic deformation, rather
than by shear,* which is usually preceded by a considerable amount
of plastic deformation or yielding.

Fracture that occurs by cleavage at a nominal tensile stress below
the yield stress is commonly referred to as brittle fracture. Generally, a brittle fracture can occur in a structural steel when there
is a sufficiently adverse combination of tensile stress, temperature,
and geometrical discontinuity (notch) present. Other design and
fabrication factors may also have an important influence. Because
of the interrelation of these effects, the exact combination of stress,
temperature, notch and other conditions that will cause brittle fracture in a given structure cannot be calculated. Consequently, designing against brittle fracture consists of (1) avoiding conditions

---

*Shear and cleavage are used in the metallurgical sense (macroscopically) to
denote different fracture mechanisms. Reference 8 as well as most elementary
textbooks on metallurgy, discusses these mechanisms.

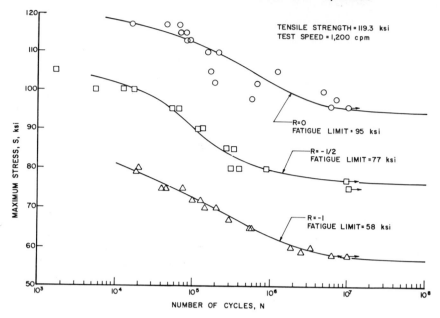

FIGURE 1.15 S-N DIAGRAMS FOR POLISHED SPECIMENS OF
"T-1" STEEL OBTAINED FROM AXIAL-LOAD FATIGUE TESTS

that tend to cause brittle fracture, and (2) selecting a steel appropriate for the application. A discussion of these factors is given in
the following sections. References 8, 9, and 10 cover the subject
in much more detail.

1.11.2 *Conditions Causing Brittle Fracture*

It has been established that plastic deformation can occur only
in the presence of shear stresses. Shear stresses are always present
in a uniaxial or in biaxial state-of-stress. However, in a triaxial
state-of-stress, the maximum shear stress approaches zero as the
principal stresses approach a common value, and thus, under equal
triaxial tensile stresses failure occurs by cleavage rather than by
shear. Consequently, triaxial tensile stresses tend to cause brittle
fracture and should be avoided. As discussed below, a triaxial state-
of-stress can result from a uniaxial loading when notches or geometrical discontinuities are present.

If a transversely notched bar is subjected to a longitudinal tensile force, the stress concentration effect of the notch causes high
longitudinal tensile stresses at the apex of the notch and lower
longitudinal stresses in adjacent material. The lateral contraction
in the width and thickness direction of the highly stressed material
at the apex of the notch is restrained by the smaller lateral contraction of the lower stressed material. Thus, in addition to the longitudinal tensile stresses, tensile stresses are created in the width and
thickness directions so that a triaxial state-of-stress is present near

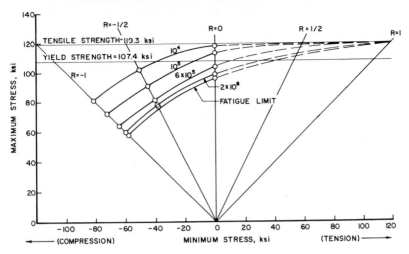

FIGURE I.16 FATIGUE CHART FOR AXIALLY LOADED POLISHED SPECIMENS OF "T-I" STEEL

the apex of the notch. The effect of a geometrical discontinuity in a structure is generally similar to, although not necessarily as severe as, the effect of the notch in the bar. Examples of geometrical discontinuities sometimes found in structures include poor design details—such as abrupt changes in cross section, attachment welds on tension flanges, and square-cornered "cut-outs"—and fabrication flaws—such as weld cracks, undercuts, arc strikes, and scars from chipping hammers.

Increased strain rates tend to increase the possibility of brittle behavior. Thus, structures that are loaded at fast rates are more susceptible to brittle fracture. However, a rapid strain rate or impact load is not a required condition for a brittle fracture.

Cold work, and the strain aging that normally follows, generally increases the likelihood of brittle fracture. This behavior is usually attributed to the previously mentioned reduction in ductility. The effect of cold work that occurs in cold forming operations can be minimized by selecting a generous forming radius and, thus, limiting the amount of strain. The amount of strain that can be tolerated depends on both the steel and the application. A more severe but quite localized type of cold work is that which occurs at the edges of punched holes or at sheared edges. This effect can be essentially eliminated for holes by drilling instead of punching or by reaming after punching and, for sheared edges, by machining or grinding. Severe hammer blows may also produce enough cold work to reduce the toughness of the steel.

When tensile residual stresses are present, such as those resulting from welding, they add to any applied tensile stress and thus, the actual tensile stress in the member will be greater than the applied stress. Consequently, the likelihood of brittle fracture in a structure that contains high residual stresses is generally minimized by a stress-relief treatment. Of course, such treatment is not always necessary but depends upon the specific application considered. Avoiding high restraint when welding also serves to minimize residual stresses.

Welding may also contribute to the problem of brittle fracture by introducing notches and flaws into a structure and by causing an unfavorable change in microstructure. However, by properly designing welds and by using good welding practice, such detrimental effects can be minimized. The proper electrode must be selected so that the weld metal will be as resistant to brittle fracture as the base metal.

1.11.3 *Charpy V-Notch Test*

Some steels will sustain more adverse temperature, notch, and loading conditions without fracture than will other steels. Numerous tests have been developed to evaluate the susceptibility of steels to brittle fracture, that is, to assign a numerical value indicating the relative susceptibility of each steel to brittle fracture. Although, presently, each of these tests can establish only the relative susceptibility to brittle fracture under the particular conditions in the test, some tests provide a meaningful guide to the relative performance of steels in structures subjected to severe temperature and stress conditions. The most commonly used of these rating tests, the Charpy V-notch test, is described below, and the interpretation of results is discussed briefly. Reference 8 and 9 give detailed discussions of many other rating tests.

The Charpy V-notch test specifically evaluates notch toughness — the resistance to fracture in the presence of a notch — and is widely used as a guide to the performance of steels in structures susceptible to brittle fracture. In this test, a small rectangular bar with a specified size V-shaped notch at its mid-length is simply supported at its ends as a beam and fractured by a blow from a swinging pendulum. The amount of energy required to fracture the specimen, which can be calculated from the height to which the pendulum raises after breaking the specimen, or the appearance of the fracture surface is determined for a range of temperatures. The appearance of the fracture surface is usually expressed as the percentage of the surface that appears to have fractured by shear as indicated by a fibrous appearance. A shiny or crystalline appearance is associated with a cleavage fracture.

These data are used to plot curves such as those shown in Figure 1.17, of energy or percentage of shear fracture as a function of temperature. For the structural steels, the energy and percentage of shear fracture decrease from relatively high values to relatively low values over a region of decreasing temperature. The temperature near the bottom of the energy-temperature curve, at which a selected low value of energy is absorbed, often 15 foot pounds, is called the ductility transition temperature* The temperature at which the percentage of shear fracture decreases to 50 percent is often called the fracture-appearance transition temperature or sometimes just fracture transition temperature. Both transition temperatures provide a rating of the brittle-fracture resistance of various steels: the lower the transition temperature, the better the resistance to brittle-fracture.

For many of the structural steels, Table 1.4 gives ductility transition temperatures corresponding to 15 ft-lb of energy for longitudinal specimens in the Charpy V-notch test. The values listed are for 1-inch-thick plates; other thicknesses may have different

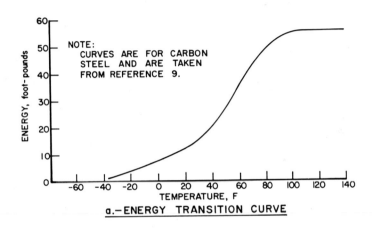

a.–ENERGY TRANSITION CURVE

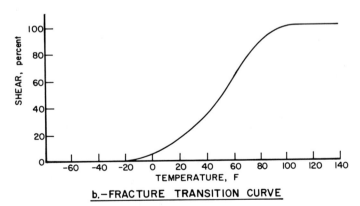

b.–FRACTURE TRANSITION CURVE

FIGURE 1.17–TRANSITION CURVES OBTAINED FROM CHARPY V-NOTCH IMPACT TESTS

---

*When "transition temperature" is used in this manual, it refers to the ductility transition temperature.

transition temperatures. As indicated in the table, CHAR-PAC, CON-PAC, and the "T-1" steels, which are used in critical applications such as pressure vessels or penstocks, are sold to specified transition temperatures. All other values listed in the table are typical or average values rather than specified values and, consequently, are important mainly in showing the relative brittle-fracture resistance of the steels.

Table 1.4 illustrates the considerable range in transition temperatures among the structural steels — from 30 F for A36 structural carbon steel to −90 F for CHAR-PAC quenched and tempered carbon steel. For low-temperature applications where the steels discussed herein may not provide adequate notch toughness, a large number of stainless and alloy steels with greater notch toughness (lower transition temperature) are available.[11]

1.11.4 *Selecting a Steel*

The best guide in selecting a steel that is appropriate for a given application is experience with existing and past structures. The A36 steel, which may have almost the lowest brittle-fracture resistance of any present structural steel, has been successfully used in a great number of applications, such as buildings, transmission towers, transportation equipment, and bridges, even at the lowest atmospheric temperatures encountered in the continental United States. Therefore, it appears that any of the structural steels, when designed and fabricated in an appropriate manner, could be used for similar applications with little likelihood of brittle fracture. Consequently, brittle fracture is not usually considered in such structures unless unusual temperature, notch, and stress conditions are present. Nevertheless, it is always desirable to avoid or minimize the previously mentioned adverse conditions that increase the susceptibility to brittle fracture.

Definite requirements of notch toughness have been determined for steels used in some applications such as ships, pressure vessels, and cryogenic applications. For example, a study of ship failures due to brittle fracture showed that the plates in which failure initiated absorbed no more than 12 ft-lb of energy in the Charpy V-notch test conducted at the temperature at which the ship fractured. Consequently, on the basis of this knowledge, various agencies responsible for the satisfactory performance of ships have specified steels that will provide adequate notch toughness.

A requirement that steels must absorb 15 ft-lb of energy (Charpy V-notch test) at the lowest expected operating temperature is used in some applications where notch toughness is considered very important. It should be emphasized, however, that a large number of structures have performed successfully, even though the steels used did not meet a 15 ft-lb requirement at the lowest operating temperature. Therefore, this requirement should not be applied indiscriminately to all structures.

References (Chapter 1)

1. American Iron and Steel Institute, **Steel Products Manual.**

2. American Society for Testing and Materials, "ASTM Standards, Part 4."

3. I. Finnie and W. R. Heller, **Creep of Engineering Materials,** McGraw Hill Book Company, New York City, 1959.

4. "Steels for Elevated Temperature Service," U. S. Steel Corporation, 1965.

5. W. Goldsmith, **Impact,** Edward Arnold, Ltd., London, 1960.

6. G. E. Dieter, Jr., **Mechanical Metallurgy,** McGraw-Hill Book Company, New York City, 1961.

7. A. Chajes, S. J. Britvec, and G. Winter, "Effects of Cold-Straining on Structural Sheet Steels," **Journal of the Structural Division,** Proceedings, ASCE, **89,** No. ST2, April 1963.

8. E. R. Parker, **Brittle Behavior of Engineering Structures,** John Wiley & Son, New York City, 1957.

9. **Control of Steel Construction to Avoid Brittle Failure,** Welding Research Council, 1957.

10. M. W. Lightner and R. W. Vanderbeck, "Factors Involved in Brittle Fracture," **Regional Technical Meetings,** American Iron and Steel Institute, 1956.

11. USS Low Temperature and Cryogenic Steels—Materials Manual, U. S. Steel Corporation, 1966.

Table 1.1
Specified Mechanical Properties of Structural Steels[1,2]

Steel — Brand Name	ASTM Designation	Plate Thickness Range, Inches	Web Thickness Range or ASTM Group for Structural Shapes	Yield Point or Yield Strength, psi	Tensile Strength, psi	Elongation[a], percent — In 8 Inches	In 2 Inches
Carbon Steels							
	A36	to 8, incl.	All	36,000	58,000 to 80,000	20	23
	A283 Grade C	to 2, incl.	Not applicable	30,000	55,000 to 65,000	23	27
	A285 Grade C[b]	to 2, incl.	Not applicable	30,000	55,000 to 65,000	22/23	26/27
	A515 or A516 Grade 55[b]	to 12, incl.	Not applicable	30,000	55,000 to 65,000	23	27
	A515 or A516 Grade 60[b]	to 8, incl.	Not applicable	32,000	60,000 to 72,000	21	25
	A515 or A516 Grade 65[b]	to 8, incl.	Not applicable	35,000	65,000 to 77,000	19	23
	A515 or A516 Grade 70[b]	to 8, incl.	Not applicable	38,000	70,000 to 85,000	17	21
	A573 Grade 65	to 1½, incl.	Not applicable	35,000	65,000 to 77,000	20	
	A573 Grade 70	to 12, incl.	Not applicable	38,000	70,000 to 85,000	18	21
High-Strength Low-Alloy Steels							
USS COR-TEN A (Cr-Si-Cu-Ni-P type)	A242, A374 and A375	to ½, incl.	d	50,000	70,000	19	22
		over ½ to 1½, incl.	d	47,000	67,000	19	
		over 1½ to 3, incl.	d	43,000	63,000		24
USS COR-TEN B (Mn-Cr-Cu-V type)	A242 and A588 Grade A	to 4, incl.	Groups 1, 2, 3, and 4	50,000	70,000	19	21
		over 4 to 5, incl.	Group 5	46,000	67,000		
USS COR-TEN C (Mn-Cr-Cu-V type)		to 1, incl.	Group I	60,000	80,000	16	21
USS TRI-TEN	A441	to ¾, incl.	Group 1 and 2	50,000	70,000	18	
		over ¾ to 1½, incl.	Group 3	46,000	67,000	19	24
		over 1½ to 4, incl.	Group 4 (to 426 lb/ft)	42,000	63,000	16	24
		over 4 to 8, incl.		40,000	60,000		

(Continued)

Table 1.1 (Continued)
Specified Mechanical Properties of Structural Steels[1,2]

Steel Brand Name	ASTM Designation	Plate Thickness Range, Inches	Web Thickness Range or ASTM Group for Structural Shapes	Yield Point or Yield Strength, psi	Tensile Strength, psi	Elongation,[a] percent In 8 Inches	In 2 Inches
High-Strength Low-Alloy Steels (Continued)							
USS MAN-TEN (A440)	A440	to ¾, incl.	Group 1	50,000	70,000	18	24
		over ¾ to 1½, incl.	Group 2	46,000	67,000	19	24
		over 1½ to 4, incl.	Group 3	42,000	63,000	19	
USS EX-TEN 42	A572	to 8, incl.	Groups 1, 2, 3, and 4 (to 426 lb/ft)	42,000	60,000	20	
USS EX-TEN 50	A572	to 1½, incl.	Groups 1, 2, 3, and 4 (to 426 lb/ft)	50,000	65,000	18	
USS EX-TEN 60	A572	to 1½. incl.	Groups 1, 2, 3, and 4 (to 426 lb/ft)	60,000	75,000	16	
USS EX-TEN 70	A572		to ⅜, incl.	70,000	85,000	14	
Heat-Treated High-Strength Carbon Steels							
USS CHAR-PAC[b] (normalized)	A537	to 1¼, incl.	Not applicable	50,000	70,000 to 90,000	18	22
		over 1¼ to 2, incl.		46,000	65,000 to 85,000	18	
USS CHAR-PAC[b] (quenched and tempered)	A537	to 1¼, incl.	Not applicable	60,000	80,000 to 100,000		22
		over 1¼ to 2, incl.		56,000	75,000 to 95,000		22
USS CON-PAC		to ¾, incl.	Not applicable	80,000	100,000		18
		over ¾ to 1½, incl.		70,000	90,000		20

Table 1.1 (Continued)
Specified Mechanical Properties of Structural Steels[1,2]

Heat-Treated Constructional Alloy Steel[e]

Brand Name	Steel ASTM Designation	Plate Thickness Range, inches	Web Thickness Range or ASTM Group for Structural Shapes	Yield Point or Yield Strength, psi	Tensile Strength, psi	Elongation,[a] percent In 8 Inches	In 2 Inches	Reduction of Area,[a] percent
USS "T-1"	A514 Grade F	3/16 to 3/4	f	100,000	115,000 to 135,000		18	40
		over 3/4 to 2½, incl.		100,000	115,000 to 135,000		18	40/50*
		over 2½ to 4, incl.		90,000	105,000 to 135,000		17	50*
	A517 Grade F	3/16 to 2½, incl.		100,000	115,000 to 135,000		16	35/45*
USS "T-1" type A	A514 Grade B	3/16 to 3/4, incl.	f	100,000	115,000 to 135,000		18	40
		over 3/4 to 1¼, incl.		100,000	115,000 to 135,000		18	40/50*
	A517 Grade B	3/16 to 2½, incl.		100,000	115,000 to 135,000		16	35/45*
USS "T-1" type B	A514 Grade H	3/16 to 3/4, incl.	f	100,000	115,000 to 135,000		18	40
		over 3/4 to 2, incl.		100,000	115,000 to 135,000		18	40/50*
	A517 Grade H	3/16 to 2, incl.		100,000	115,000 to 135,000		16	35/45*

Footnotes:

a. These values are modified for some thicknesses according to applicable ASTM or manufacturer's specification. Asterisked values are for ½ in. diameter specimens.

b. These steels are furnished in pressure vessel quality only.

c. For thicknesses over ½ inch to ¾ inch inclusive, the strength provided is slightly less than that required by ASTM A242.

d. Thickest part governs.

e. For these steels, A514 provides structural quality and A517 provides pressure vessel quality.

f. These steels available in many structural shapes; consult for availability.

General Notes:

1. Mechanical properties listed are specified minimum values except where a specified range of values (minimum to maximum) is given. Where value is omitted, no value is specified.

2. The following properties are approximate values for all of the structural steels:
   Modulus of Elasticity—29 × 10⁶ psi. Shear modulus—11 × 10⁶ psi.
   Poisson's Ratio—0.30.
   Yield Stress in Shear—0.57 times yield stress in tension.
   Ultimate Strength in Shear—⅔ to ¾ times tensile strength.
   Coefficient of Thermal Expansion—6.5 × 10⁻⁶ in./in./F for temperature range −50 F to +150 F.

Table 1.2

Typical Mechanical Properties for "T-1", "T-1" Type A, and "T-1" Type B Steel Plates Treated to Specified Minimum Brinell Hardness Values of 321 and 360*

Specified Minimum Brinell Hardness	Available Plate Thicknesses			Typical Mechanical Properties			
	"T-1"	"T-1" Type A	"T-1" Type B	Yield Strength, psi	Tensile Strength, psi	Elongation in 2 Inches, percent	Reduction of Area, percent
321	3/16 to 4	3/16 to 1¼	3/16 to 1¼	141,000	175,000	14	35
360	3/16 to 1½	3/16 to ½	3/16 to 1	145,000	184,000	13	35

* The typical mechanical properties and available plate thicknesses listed in this table are for the "T-1" steels furnished to the indicated specified minimum hardness values only. When the "T-1" steels are furnished to specified minimum Brinell hardness values, all other minimum mechnical properties are waived. Table 1.1 lists specified minimum mechanical properties for "T-1" steels that are not furnished to a minimum Brinell hardness.

Table 1.3

Typical Creep and Rupture Properties for Two Steels

Test Temperature, F	Stress (1000 psi) for a Creep Rate of		Stress (1000 psi) for Rupture in	
	0.0001% per hr (1% in 10,000 hr)	0.00001% per hr 1% in 100,000 hr)	1,000 hr	10,000 hr
Carbon Steel				
800	19.0	13.0	25.8	21.0
900	11.0	7.5	19.0	13.8
1000	5.0	3.5	11.7	6.8
"T-1" Steel				
700	78.0	65.0	100.0	95.0
800	68.5	58.0	83.5	72.0

Table 1.4

Transition Temperatures* for 1-Inch-Thick Plates Based on a Longitudinal Charpy V-Notch Impact-Test Value of 15 Foot-Pounds

	Typical* Temperature, F	Specified** Temperature, F
Carbon Steels		
A36	+30	
A285 Grade C	+45	
A515 Grade 70	+30	
A516 Grade 70***	−20	
High-Strength Low-Alloy Steels		
USS COR-TEN (Mn-Cr-Cu-V Type)	0	
USS TRI-TEN	+15	
USS MAN-TEN (A440)	+40	
USS EX-TEN 50	+30	
Heat-Treated Carbon Steels		
USS CHAR-PAC Normalized		−75
USS CHAR-PAC Quenched and tempered		−90
USS CON-PAC		−25
Heat-Treated Constructional Alloy Steels		
USS "T-1"		−50
USS "T-1" type A		−50
USS "T-1" type B		−50

* Where typical values are given, the values have been estimated for as rolled plate based on effects of carbon and manganese content, and of deoxidation practice. **The typical values are not guaranteed values.**

** The specified values represent the average of 3 specimens per standard ASTM procedure. The values for the constructional alloy steels can be specified for pressure vessel or higher quality material. For "T-1" steel, **20** foot-pounds at −50 F can be specified in plate thicknesses of ½ to 2½ inch (inclusive). For CON-PAC steel, **20** foot-pounds at −25 can be specified in plate thicknesses to 1½ inch (inclusive).

*** When furnished to ASTM A300 specifications, a Charpy **keyhole** value of 15 ft-lb (average of 3 specimens) at −50 F is guaranteed. If normalized, the tabulated V-notch temperature would be lowered approximately 40 F.

CHAPTER 2

Tension Members

2.1 Introduction

Tension members are the most efficient form for supporting loads. Unlike other load-carrying members, the load carrying capacity of a tension member is independent of the shape of the cross-section. This is a decided advantage because the member can be fabricated from a variety of steel products selecting that which best suits the architectural and structural functions.

The action of a tension member is primarily one of direct longitudinal stress, but when used as a truss member or eccentrically loaded it may be subjected additionally to bending stresses. In this instance, the shape of the cross-section to resist the bending action may become important and may dictate the optimum shape. Only direct tension action in the members will be discussed in this chapter; members under combined tension and bending are considered in Chapter 8.

The axial load, P_y, that causes initial yielding in a tension member is

$$P_y = Af_y \qquad (2.1)$$

where A is the cross-sectional area and f_y is the yield stress. The ultimate load, P_u, of the member is

$$P_u = Af_u \qquad (2.2)$$

where f_u is the tensile strength of the steel. The total elongation, Δ, in the elastic range is

$$\Delta = \frac{PL}{AE} \qquad (2.3)$$

where P is the axial load and L is the length of the member.

In the design of a tension member, the cross-sectional area required is

$$A = \frac{P}{f_a} \qquad (2.4)$$

where f_a is the allowable design stress. The allowable stress is usually determined by dividing the yield stress of the steel by a safety factor. For structural shapes and built-up members in buildings, the AISC[1] uses a safety factor of 1/.60 or 1.67, whereas for such members in bridges, AASHO[2] and AREA[3] uses approximately 1/.55 or 1.82. Allowable stresses based on these safety factors are given in Table 2.1 for various steel yield stresses.

It can be seen from Equation 2.4 and Table 2.1 that the area of a tension member is inversely proportional to the allowable design stress. Therefore, for any single factor of safety, the area is inversely proportional to the yield stress or strength of the steel.

The selection of an appropriate factor of safety depends upon the type of structure being designed. For buildings, bridges, and a few other special types of structures, standard specifications are available as noted above. However, for many structural applications in containers, equipment, machines, tanks, trailers, trucks, etc., the design engineer usually must establish the factor of safety based on his knowledge and experience with the conditions to be satisfied.

Although the ultimate strength of a tension member does not depend upon its slenderness ratio,* most specifications suggest or specify an upper limit to prevent lateral movement or vibration, and for safe handling during fabrication and erection. The maximum slenderness ratio allowed by various specifications ranges from 200 to 300.

Although the fundamental equations that govern tension behavior are simple, members may be fabricated in several different shapes, each exhibiting special characteristics which must be considered in design. These characteristics are discussed in detail below.

2.2 Structural Shapes and Built-Up Sections

When welded connections are used, structural shapes and built-up members are designed on the basis of their gross area. When bolted connections are used, the design is based on the nominal stress at the net section. The net section is the transverse section along a possible line of failure through the bolt holes, and may cross the member directly or may zigzag through a chain of holes when the holes are staggered on two or more gage lines. The area of the net section (net area) equals the net width times the material thickness. The smallest possible value of net width must be used if there are two or more possible lines of failure.

---

*The slenderness ratio of a member is equal to its length divided by its radius of gyration.

For any possible line of failure, the net width is determined by subtracting from the gross width the sum of the hole diameters through which the transverse section passes directly, and adding the quantity $s^2/4g$ for each diagonal portion of the chain, where s is the pitch (longitudinal spacing) and g is the gage (transverse spacing). Although the hole diameter is usually $\frac{1}{16}$ inch oversize, the diameter for design purposes is usually assumed as the diameter of the rivet or bolt plus $\frac{1}{8}$ inch, to account for possible damage to material surrounding the hole when it is made. Tests have shown that the ultimate strength of a tension member with holes usually will not exceed 85 percent of the calculated ultimate strength at the section; therefore, some specifications[1] limit the maximum value of the net section to 85 percent of the gross section.

Tension members that have holes for end connections only can be designed on the basis of their gross section if the ends are made by welding on a thicker section or a section made of a higher strength steel than that in the balance of the member. Of course, the end sections must be proportioned so that the strength of the net section equals the strength of the gross section elsewhere. The use of a higher-strength steel usually is preferable because it eliminates the stress concentration caused by the change in thickness, and also reduces weld size, welding time and cost, and simplifies details of construction.

2.3 Eyebars and Pin-Connected Plates

Flat plates with large diameter holes at the ends for pin connections are sometimes used as tension members. Plates of constant width are called pin-connected plates, and plates with widened ends are called eyebars. Tests of pin-connected plates[4] have demonstrated that three types of failure may occur in the ends or "heads" of such members.

1. A shearing failure behind the pin along planes parallel to the axis of the bar caused by insufficient edge distance.
2. A tensile failure, or excessive inelastic deformation due to stress concentration, across a transverse plane through the hole caused by insufficient net section.
3. A "dishing" failure of the plate behind the pin due to lateral instability that is caused by an excessive length-to-thickness ratio of the plate behind the pin.

Various specifications provide dimensional requirements and reduced allowable stresses on the net section that prevent the above-mentioned failures. For example, in addition to other requirements, the AISC[1] requires that the nominal tensile stress in the net section must be 25 percent less than the stress in the main body of the member. If it is necessary to utilize a steel with a higher yield stress than covered in design specifications, special attention should be given to the width-to-thickness ratio required to prevent dishing. In many design situations, where several members connect at the same pin, packing and external nuts generally will provide sufficient restraint against instability.

2.4 Rods

Tension rods can be made by threading the ends of either plain bars or bars with upset ends. The behavior of the two types of rods differs in several respects. A properly designed rod with upset ends yields first in the unthreaded portion, whereas a rod with plain ends yields first in the threaded portion. Also, when the threaded portion yields, lateral contraction in the yielded portion can reduce the bearing area on the threads and may cause failure by stripping of the threads. Thus, an upset rod that yields along its entire length is likely to absorb much more energy than a plain rod before failure. Furthermore, when an upset rod is loaded eccentrically, thus producing bending, the rigidity of the upset end tends to cause the main portion of the bar to flex thereby preventing overstress in the threaded portion.

Allowable stresses for rods are included in various specifications. Sometimes the allowable stress on the gross area rather than the net area is specified for plain rods, but a reduced value has been used so that the nominal stress on the net area will be approximately equal to the net area stress of other tension members.[1]

2.5 Strands and Wire Ropes

A strand is an assembly of wires formed helically around a center wire in one or more symmetrical layers.

A wire rope consists of a group of strands laid helically around a fiber core, a wire strand core, or an independent wire rope core. Wire ropes with fiber cores are used almost entirely for hoisting purposes. Wire ropes with strand cores or independent wire rope cores are used as either standing lines or hoisting ropes. The manufacturing practices for these several types of ropes vary depending upon the intended end use.

Because strands and ropes are fabricated from helically formed components, their behavior is somewhat different from that of rods, eyebars, or even the individual wires from which they are made. When a tensile load is applied to a strand or wire rope, the resulting elongation will consist of (1) structural stretch, which is caused by radial and axial adjustment of the wires and strands to the load, and (2) the elastic stretch of the wires.

The structural stretch varies with the number of wires per strand, the number of strands per rope, and the length of lay (pitch of helix) of the wires and strands. The stretch also varies with the magnitude of the load imposed and the amount of bending to which the rope is subjected.

Structural stretch is gradually lessened by service, with an accompanying increase in modulus of elasticity. For stationary strands and wire ropes where a limited amount of elongation under load is permissible, and where a stable modulus is necessary, removal of structural stretch by prestressing is employed. This is accomplished by subjecting the strand or rope to a predetermined load for a sufficient length of time to permit adjustment of the component parts to that load. Prestressed galvanized bridge strands and ropes, which are generally used for such applications, have the following minimum moduli of elasticity.

½" to 2¾₆" diam. Bridge Strand	24,000,000 psi
2⅝" and larger diam. Bridge Strand	23,000,000 psi
⅝" to 4" diam. Bridge Rope	20,000,000 psi

These moduli of elasticity are used to determine the elongation in the elastic range (Equation 2.3).

Strands and wire ropes, because they are manufactured from cold drawn wire, do not have a definite yield point. Therefore, a working load for strand or wire rope, unlike that for most other types of tension members, is usually established by dividing the minimum breaking strength (ultimate strength) of a specific size and construction of strand or rope by a safety factor. The safety factor to be used depends upon the particular end use and service conditions, but should in no case be less than three.

Specific information on the types of strands and wire ropes and their engineering properties is available from the United States Steel Corporation.[5]

References (Chapter 2)

1. American Institute of Steel Construction, "Specification for the Design, Fabrication, and Erection of Structural Steel for Buildings," 1963.

2. American Association of State Highway Officials, "Standard Specifications for Highway Bridges," 1965.

3. American Railway Engineering Association, "Standard Specifications for Steel Railway Bridges," 1966.

4. B. G. Johnston, "Pin-Connected Plate Links, "Transactions ASCE, 104, 1939.

5. "Wire Rope Engineering Handbook," U. S. Steel Corporation.

Table 2.1

Allowable Stresses in Tension for Structural Steels

Specified Minimum Yield Stress, ksi	Allowable Stress on Net Section Except at Pin Holes or Threaded Parts, ksi	
	0.60 Fy*	0.55 Fy*
36	22.0**	20.0+o
42	25.0**	23.0+
46	27.5**	25.0+
50	30.0**	27.0+o
60	36.0	33.0
70	42.0	38.5
80	48.0	44.0
90	54.0	49.5
100	60.0	55.0

* The allowable stresses noted may differ slightly from this value but are stated as listed in the indicated specification.

** AISC specification for buildings.

+ AASHO specification for bridges.

o AREA specification for bridges.

CHAPTER 3

Columns

3.1 Introduction

Straight members that are compressed by axial forces are known as columns and are usually limited in strength by buckling. In considering column buckling, the instability of the member as a whole, it is assumed that local buckling, the instability of an individual element of the member, does not occur prior to column buckling. Local buckling is considered in Chapter 4. Members that must simultaneously withstand axial forces and significant bending moments are known as "beam-columns" and are considered in Chapter 8.

3.2 Strength of a Perfect Column

A column that is (1) made of isotropic material, (2) free of residual stresses, (3) perfectly straight, and (4) loaded precisely at its centroid is referred to as a "perfect column." When an increasing load is applied, the column will shorten uniformly because of the uniform compressive strains on transverse cross sections. However, a load will eventually be reached at which the column is on the verge of deflecting laterally in a bending mode.* This "tangent modulus" load is the buckling load and, for practical purposes, is the maximum load that the column can withstand.

If the perfect column is made of a material that has a linear stress-strain curve, such as the idealized curve shown in Figure 3.1a, the buckling stress, f_c, is given within the elastic range by the Euler equation[1]

---

*Members that buckle in a twisting mode are discussed in Section 3.5.

41

$$f_c = \frac{\pi^2\, EI}{(KL)^2\, A} = \frac{\pi^2\, E}{(KL/r)^2} \qquad (3.1)$$

where K is an effective length coefficient, L is the column length between supports, r is the radius of gyration, and KL/r is the "effective slenderness ratio." The relationship between the buckling stress and the effective slenderness ratio is shown in Figure 3.1b. As indicated in the figure, when KL/r is less than $\sqrt{\pi^2 E/f_y}$, the column will buckle inelastically at a stress equal to f_y. At lower slenderness ratios, general yielding rather than buckling will occur. At variance with the ideal conditions discussed here, in actual columns with extremely small slenderness ratios, strain hardening may allow structural-steel columns to reach a somewhat greater stress than f_y.

If the perfect column is made from a material that has a stress-strain curve having a rounded portion such as that shown in Figure 3.1c, the buckling stress in the inelastic range is given by the Engesser equation

$$f_c = \frac{\pi^2\, E_t}{(KL/r)^2} \qquad (3.2)$$

where E_t, the tangent modulus, is the slope of the stress-strain curve at a stress equal to f_c. The value of E_t decreases with increasing stress. As shown in Figure 3.1d, f_c obtained from the Engesser and Euler equations is the same when f_c equals the proportional limit, since E_t is equal to E at that stress. Although the Engesser equation is generally not directly applicable to structural-steel columns because they are not "perfect," the tangent-modulus concept is important in determining the strength of actual columns.

3.3 Strength of an Actual Column

Because of the presence of residual stresses, initial column curvature, and accidental eccentricity of the applied load, the strength of an actual column is generally less than that of a perfect column. An explanation of these factors, each assumed to occur independently, is given below.

3.3.1 *Initial Curvature and Accidental Eccentricity*

Axially loaded columns that are not perfectly straight and eccentrically loaded straight columns will deflect laterally as they are loaded. For example, if an axially loaded column has an initial shape that approximates one-half of a sine wave having an initial ordinate (out-of-straightness), y_o, at midheight, the final midheight out-of-straightness, y, after a load, P, has been applied is[1]

$$y = y_o \left[\frac{1}{1 - P/P_e} \right] \qquad (3.3)$$

where P_e is the Euler load for buckling of the column in the plane of initial curvature. The bracketed term is the "amplification factor."

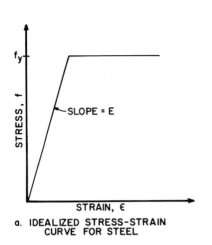

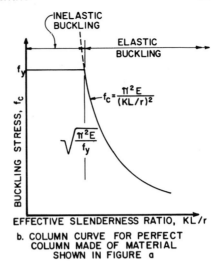

a. IDEALIZED STRESS-STRAIN
CURVE FOR STEEL

b. COLUMN CURVE FOR PERFECT
COLUMN MADE OF MATERIAL
SHOWN IN FIGURE a

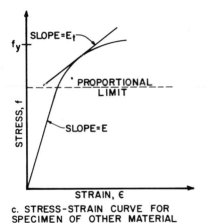

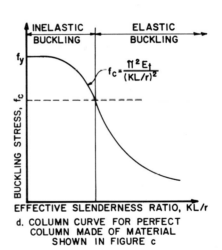

c. STRESS-STRAIN CURVE FOR
SPECIMEN OF OTHER MATERIAL

d. COLUMN CURVE FOR PERFECT
COLUMN MADE OF MATERIAL
SHOWN IN FIGURE c

FIGURE 3.1 COLUMN CURVES FOR PERFECT
COLUMNS OF DIFFERENT MATERIALS

The Euler load is the product of the Euler buckling stress, Equation 3.1, and the area. (In this case, the Euler load is not limited by f_y.) If the load at each end of an initially straight column is applied a distance "e" from the centroid, the total mid-height out-of-straightness after a load P is

$$y = e \sec \frac{\pi}{2} \sqrt{\frac{P}{P_e}} \qquad (3.4)$$

As shown in Figure 3.2, the deflection (midheight out-of-straightness) of such columns increases with increasing applied load and approaches infinity as P approaches P_e.

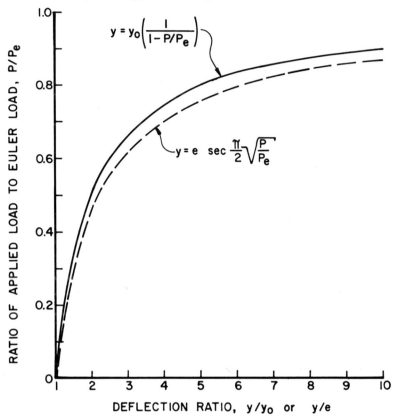

FIGURE 3.2 LATERAL DEFLECTION OF COLUMNS

The maximum stress in the column, f_m, is the sum of the axial stress and the bending stress. For the initially curved column

$$f_m = \frac{P}{A} + \frac{Pyc}{I} = \frac{P}{A}\left[1 + \frac{y_0 c}{r^2}\left(\frac{1}{1 - P/P_e}\right)\right]$$

(3.5)

where c is the distance from the column centroid to its outer fiber. For the eccentrically loaded straight column

$$f_m = \frac{P}{A}\left[1 + \frac{ec}{r^2}\sec\frac{\pi}{2}\sqrt{\frac{P}{P_e}}\right]$$

(3.6)

The load that causes initial yielding in the outer fibers of a given column can be calculated from the above equations by substituting

f_y for f_m. If the average stress at initial yielding is taken as f_y', the equations can be written in the dimensionless forms shown in Figure 3.3.

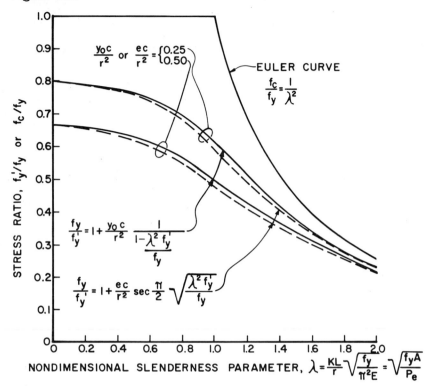

FIGURE 3.3 EFFECT OF INITIAL CURVATURE AND ACCIDENTAL ECCENTRICITY ON COLUMN STRENGTH

In Figure 3.3, the ratio of the average stress at the initial yield load and the yield stress, f_y'/f_y, is plotted versus a dimensionless slenderness parameter, λ, for two assumed values $\dfrac{y_o c}{r^2}$ or $\dfrac{ec}{r^2}$. The Euler curve is also shown in dimensionless form. The flexibility parameter, λ, is equal to the effective slenderness ratio of a column KL/r, divided by the slenderness ratio for which the Euler buckling stress equals the yield stress, $\sqrt{\dfrac{\pi^2 E}{f_y}}$. This latter slenderness ratio is a constant for a given yield stress. Dividing KL/r by this constant ratio and f_y' or f_c by the yield stress allows expressions for the strengths of columns of various steels to be plotted on the same coordinates.

Figure 3.3 shows that initial yielding occurs in the outer fibers of the column when the average stress is less than both the Euler stress and the yield stress. For a constant value of $\frac{c}{r^2}$, the effects of initial curvature and accidental eccentricity are similar for equal values of y_o and e. The effects have greatest significance for columns having small and intermediate slenderness parameters. Also, with a constant value of $\frac{y_o c}{r^2}$ or $\frac{ec}{r^2}$, f_y'/f_y decreases as f_y increases.

If the initial maximum out-of-straightness of a column is given as a function of the column length, y_o/L, as is often done when specifying out-of-straightness tolerances, Equation 3.5 can be written as

$$f_m = \frac{P}{A}\left[1 + \frac{y_o}{L}\frac{c}{r}\frac{L}{r}\left(\frac{1}{1 - P/P_e} \right)\right]\qquad (3.7)$$

By expressing L/r as $\dfrac{\lambda}{K\sqrt{\dfrac{f_y'}{\pi^2 E}}}$ the average stress at initial yield-

ing was calculated and plotted in a dimensionless form in Figure 3.4 for the following values: y_o/L = 1/1000, c/r = 2.00, and f_y = 36,000 and 100,000 psi. For wide-flange column shapes, c/r equals approximately 2.00 about the weak axis and 1.17 about the strong axis. Thus, the curves shown are for weak-axis buckling. Curves for strong-axis buckling would have higher average stresses at initial yielding. The value of y_o/L = 1/1000 is the maximum value permitted by the AISC.[2]

Figure 3.4 shows again that initial yielding occurs when the average stress is less than both the yield stress and the Euler stress and that out-of-straightness has greatest significance for columns with intermediate slenderness ratios. Also, the effect of the initial curvature increases as the yield stress increases. (Note that the curve for columns made of 100,000 psi yield strength steel is below that for columns of 36,000 psi yield point steel.) Although the figure indicates that f_y'/f_y decreases only slightly with increasing f_y when columns of equal λ are compared, it can be shown that f_y'/f_y decreases considerably with increasing f_y when columns of equal KL/r are compared. The dashed line, CRC curve, shown in Figure 3.4 is based on the effect of residual stresses and will be discussed in Section 3.4.

The ultimate strength of the column is not reached until a portion of the cross section has yielded and, thus, is somewhat greater than that at initial yielding shown in Figures 3.3 and 3.4. For strong axis buckling of wide-flange columns, the ultimate strength is only slightly above the initial yield strength, but the increase may be larger for solid round or square cross sections.

In the past, the secant formula, Equation 3.6, was widely used, since by assuming an arbitrary "equivalent eccentricity," $\frac{ec}{r^2}$, of 0.25 to account for initial crookedness and unintentional eccentric

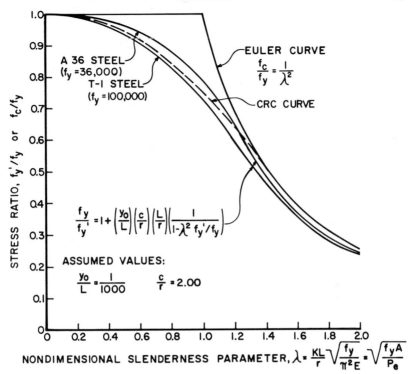

FIGURE 3.4 EFFECT OF INITIAL OUT-OF-STRAIGHTNESS ON COLUMN STRENGTH OF TWO STEELS

application of load, and by assuming that the maximum column strength is reached when f_m reaches f_y, computed loads would approximate the maximum loads observed in column tests made in the past. However, later research has shown that the influence of residual stresses on column strength is often greater than that of initial crookedness and unintentional eccentricity. When used in design, the secant equation is usually written as

$$F_a = \frac{f_y}{N \left[1 + \frac{ec}{r^2} \sec \frac{L}{2r} \sqrt{\frac{NF_a}{E}} \right]} \qquad (3.8)$$

where F_a is the allowable stress and N is a safety factor.

3.3.2 *Residual Stress*

Stresses that remain in structural members after rolling or fabrication are known as "residual stresses." To satisfy the conditions of equilibrium, the axial force and moment obtained by integrating the residual stresses acting on any cross section must be zero. In hot-rolled structural shapes and in welded sections, the residual stresses result from uneven cooling of portions of the sections after rolling or welding; the portion of the member that cools most slowly develops residual tension that is balanced by residual compression in other portions of the member. The average hot-rolled wide-flange beam has residual compression in its flange tips, as shown in Figure 3.5a, and residual tension in the vicinity of the flange-web junction which cools slowly. Residual stresses can also result from localized plastic deformation caused by fabrication operations such as cold forming and straightening. Residual stresses from cooling are approximately constant along the length of a column, whereas cold-straightening stresses frequently occur only at particular locations where the member has been straightened. For most columns, the maximum compressive residual stresses caused by cold straightening are about the same magnitude as those caused by cooling, but have an antisymmetric rather than a symmetric distribution. Because studies[3] have shown that the residual stresses that result from cooling are the most important from the standpoint of column strength, only the effect of cooling residual stresses on column strength are considered here.

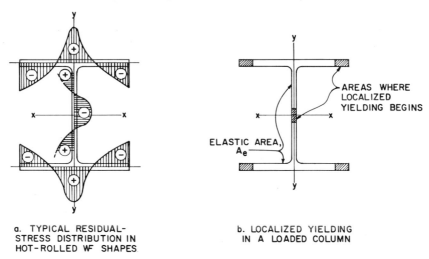

a. TYPICAL RESIDUAL-
STRESS DISTRIBUTION IN
HOT-ROLLED WF SHAPES

b. LOCALIZED YIELDING
IN A LOADED COLUMN

FIGURE 3.5 RESIDUAL STRESSES IN WF SHAPES

The portions of a column that contain compressive residual stresses will begin to yield when the sum of the stress from an applied load and the maximum compressive residual stress equals the yield stress of the material. Thus, as indicated in Figure 3.5b, the loaded column will contain areas that have yielded, even though the average applied stress is less than the yield stress.

On the basis of an idealized stress-strain relationship for individual fibers,[4] the stiffness of the yielded portion of the column is zero and the stiffness of the cross section is limited to the stiffness of the elastic portion, EI_e, in which I_e is the moment of inertia of the elastic portion. Thus, the buckling strength of a column that

RESIDUAL-STRESS DISTRIBUTION

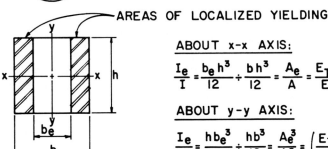

AREAS OF LOCALIZED YIELDING

ABOUT x-x AXIS:

$$\frac{I_e}{I} = \frac{b_e h^3}{12} \div \frac{b h^3}{12} = \frac{A_e}{A} = \frac{E_T}{E}$$

ABOUT y-y AXIS:

$$\frac{I_e}{I} = \frac{h b_e^3}{12} \div \frac{h b^3}{12} = \frac{A_e^3}{A^3} = \left(\frac{E_T}{E}\right)^3$$

a. SOLID RECTANGULAR BAR

RESIDUAL-STRESS DISTRIBUTION

AREA OF LOCALIZED YIELDING

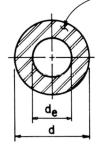

ABOUT ANY AXIS:

$$\frac{I_e}{I} = \frac{\pi d_e^4}{64} \div \frac{\pi d^4}{64} = \frac{A_e^2}{A^2} = \left(\frac{E_T}{E}\right)^2$$

b. SOLID ROUND BAR

RESIDUAL-STRESS DISTRIBUTION

AREAS OF LOCALIZED YIELDING

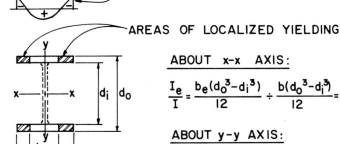

ABOUT x-x AXIS:

$$\frac{I_e}{I} = \frac{b_e(d_o^3 - d_i^3)}{12} \div \frac{b(d_o^3 - d_i^3)}{12} = \frac{b_e}{b} = \frac{A_e}{A} = \frac{E_T}{E}$$

ABOUT y-y AXIS:

$$\frac{I_e}{I} = \frac{(d_o - d_i) b_e^3}{12} \div \frac{(d_o - d_i) b^3}{12} = \frac{b_e^3}{b^3} = \frac{A_e^3}{A^3} = \left(\frac{E_T}{E}\right)^3$$

c. WIDE FLANGE SHAPE (WEB NEGLECTED)

FIGURE 3.6 RELATIONS BETWEEN I_e/I AND E_T/E

contains residual stresses may be determined by substituting I_e for I in Equation 3.1 to give

$$f_c = \frac{\pi^2 \, EI_e}{(KL)^2 \, A} = \frac{\pi^2 \, E}{(KL/r)^2}\left(\frac{I_e}{I}\right) \tag{3.9}$$

I_e, of course, varies with f_c; therefore, to use Equation 3.9, the relationship between I_e and f_c must be established. As shown in Figure 3.6, for a given cross-sectional shape and residual-stress distribution, a relationship can be mathematically established between I_e/I and A_e/A. Furthermore, as illustrated in Figure 3.7, A_e/A equals E_T/E, where E_T is the tangent modulus for the total column cross section and can be determined from a "stub-column" test. In such a test, a short length of column is axially compressed, and the load and axial shortening are recorded. The tangent modulus is determined from the average stress-strain curve for this column section, and therefore includes the combined effects of

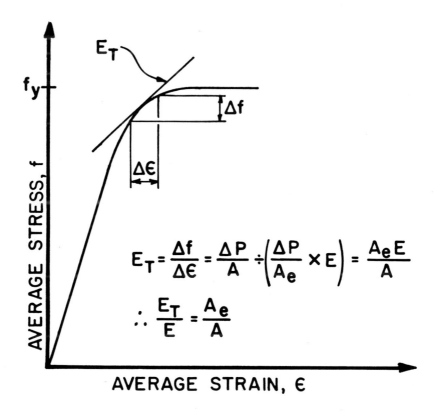

$$E_T = \frac{\Delta f}{\Delta \epsilon} = \frac{\Delta P}{A} \div \left(\frac{\Delta P}{A_e} \times E\right) = \frac{A_e E}{A}$$

$$\therefore \frac{E_T}{E} = \frac{A_e}{A}$$

FIGURE 3.7 STRESS-STRAIN CURVE
FROM STUB COLUMN TEST

applied stress and residual stresses on yielding. Thus, Equation 3.9 may be written in terms of E_T for a specific cross-sectional shape and residual-stress distribution as indicated in the following section.

3.4 Column Strength of Hot-Rolled Wide-Flange Shapes

As a result of many full-scale tests and theoretical investigations performed under the direction of the Column Research Council (CRC), better understanding of the behavior of hot-rolled wide-flange shapes has been obtained. This work has shown that for practical hot-rolled wide-flange columns of carbon and high-strength steel, the effects of residual stress from cooling are more important in considering column strength than the effects of initial curvature or accidental eccentricities. Thus, as explained below, a column curve including the effects of residual stresses can be established, and the smaller effects of unintentional curvature and eccentricity can be accounted for by treating the member as a beam-column or by including the effect in the safety factor.

If the contribution of the web to the moment of inertia is neglected, the I_e/I ratios for a wide-flange shape are those given in Figure 3.6c. More exact relationships that include the effect of the web have been derived.[5] However, for practical wide-flange shapes, the exact relationships do not differ significantly from the approximate relationships. Thus, for bending about the strong axis, $I_e/I = E_T/E$, f_c is given by the approximate equation

$$f_c = \frac{\pi^2 E}{(KL/r)^2} \left(\frac{E_T}{E} \right) = \frac{\pi^2 E_T}{(KL/r)^2} \tag{3.10}$$

Similarly, bending about the weak axis, $I_e/I = (E_T/E)^3$, f_c is given by the approximate equation

$$f_c = \frac{\pi^2 E}{(KL/r)^2} \left(\frac{E_T}{E} \right)^3 \tag{3.11}$$

Although Equation 3.10 is similar to Equation 3.2, E_T in Equation 3.10 is the tangent modulus of a column cross section that contains residual stresses, whereas E_t in Equation 3.2 is the tangent modulus of a material that is free of residual stresses. E_T must be determined from a stub-column test, but E_t can be determined from a small specimen.

Equations 3.10 and 3.11 have been plotted in dimensionless form in Figure 3.8, the E_T/E relation being determined for the residual stress shown in the lower portion of the figure. The maximum compressive residual stress at the flange tips, $0.3 f_y$, is a typical value for structural carbon steel and a conservative value for the other structural steels. Also, the linear distribution of residual stresses closely approximates patterns measured in hot-rolled wide-flange shapes. Thus, the E_T/E relation used would be typical of that determined from a stub-column test of a structural carbon-steel hot-rolled wide-flange shape.

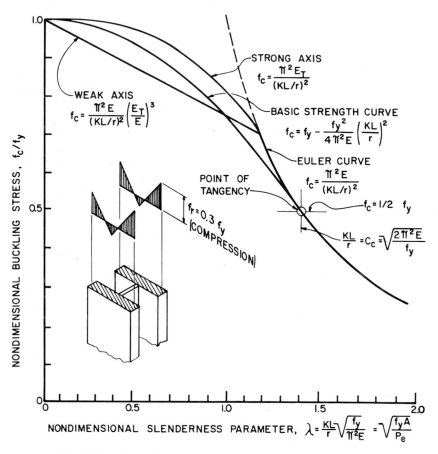

FIGURE 3.8 EFFECT OF RESIDUAL STRESS ON COLUMN STRENGTH OF WIDE-FLANGE SHAPE

As indicated in Figure 3.8, when f_c is less than 0.7 f_y, no localized yielding occurs, $E_T/E = 1.0$, and both Equations 3.10 and 3.11 reduce to the Euler equation. However, when f_c is greater than 0.7 f_y, the weak-axis bending strength of a column is less than the strong-axis bending strength of a column with the same slenderness parameter. Thus, yielding in the flange tips caused by residual stresses is more detrimental for weak-axis bending than for strong-axis bending. This behavior has been confirmed by the CRC column tests referred to above.

Figure 3.8 also shows the curve suggested by the CRC to serve as a single "basic strength curve" for hot-rolled wide-flange shapes.[6] To simplify design specifications, a single curve was suggested that was conservative for strong-axis buckling and slightly unconservative for weak-axis buckling. In design, the usual safety factor takes care of the slight unconservativeness of the design formula for weak-axis buckling. The basic strength curve is defined by the equation

$$f_c = f_y - \frac{f_y^2}{4\pi^2\,E}\left(\frac{KL}{r}\right)^2 \quad \text{when} \frac{KL}{2} \le C_c \qquad (3.12)$$

and by the Euler equation, Equation 3.1, when $\dfrac{KL}{r} \ge C_c$. C_c corre-sponds to the point of tangency on the Euler curve and is defined as

$$C_c = \sqrt{\frac{2\pi^2\,E}{f_y}} \qquad (3.13)$$

Most of the tests that led to the development of the basic strength curve were on structural carbon-steel columns. Measurements have shown that residual compressive stresses in hot-rolled high-strength steel wide-flange columns are of about the same magnitude as the residual stresses in similar carbon-steel columns and, therefore, are a smaller percentage of the yield point. For rolled wide-flange shapes of constructional alloy steel, residual stresses are smaller than those in structural carbon steel and are almost a negligible percentage of the 100,000-psi yield strength. Therefore, since the effect of residual stress on column buckling is related to the per-centage of the yield stress rather than to the actual magnitude, residual stresses have a smaller effect on column strength for steels with yield stresses higher than carbon steel. Conversely, as illus-trated in Figure 3.4, the effect of initial curvature on column strength is greater for steels with yield stresses higher than those of carbon steel. However, the basic strength curve, which is shown as a dashed line in Figure 3.4, lies close to the curve based on initial curvature for the strongest structural steel. Consequently, as verified by tests of carbon steel, high-strength steel, and con-structional-alloy-steel columns, the basic strength curve gives a good approximation of the strength of practical columns for all the structural steels.

Table 3.1 gives values of f_c corresponding to the basic strength curve for structural steels with specified minimum yield stresses of 33,000 to 100,000 psi and for KL/r values from 0 to 160. Allow-able stresses for design purposes can be obtained by dividing the tabulated stresses by an appropriate factor of safety, as discussed in Section 3.7. Table 3.1 also gives values of the Euler buckling stress for KL/r values to 160. These values may be used in the design of members subjected to combined bending and axial load, as discussed in Chapter 8, and are listed here for convenience.

3.5 Column Strength of Other Sections

In addition to hot-rolled wide-flange shapes,[*] many other sections such as hot-rolled tubes, welded box and H sections, round bars,

---

*The behavior of other hot-rolled beam shapes such as American Standard beams is essentially the same as the behavior of wide-flange shapes.

and angles are used as columns. Although the CRC basic strength curve was not developed specifically for these other sections, the column strengths of such sections are compared here with that predicted by the basic strength curve. Tests on hot-rolled structural tubes indicate that although residual stresses are very low and initial out-of-straightness is the more important parameter, the CRC curve gives a conservative approximation of the buckling strength.[7]

Research on the column strength of welded box and H sections is not yet complete. The thickness of plates, type of plates (sheared, flame cut or rolled to width), and size of welds affect the residual stress distribution and, thus, the column strength. Design specifications do not usually consider it necessary to distinguish between welded and rolled shapes, but allow the safety factor to account for any slight differences in strength.

Extensive research on round bars of both structural carbon and constructional alloy steel has shown that if such members are to be efficiently and economically used as columns they should be ordered to a maximum out-of-straightness* of ⅛ inch in any 5 feet, or ⅛ inch times the total length in feet divided by 5, and a final thermal stress-relief treatment after straightening should be specified. Although initial curvature is more important than residual stress in affecting the strength of the stress-relieved columns, the AISC equations,[2] which are based on the CRC column curve and are discussed in Section 3.7 of this manual, provide a reasonable and conservative design basis. Round bars that are ordered to the straightness tolerance mentioned above but are not stress-relieved generally have high antisymmetric residual stresses, and therefore, the AISC formulas should be modified by using a higher safety factor. Reference 8 gives the appropriate formulas for such columns.

The column sections discussed thus far are members that fail by buckling in the plane of one of their two axes of symmetry without twisting. However, columns of "open" cross section that have only one axis of symmetry — such as angles, tees, zees, and channels — as well as some with two axes of symmetry — such as cruciform sections — may fail by twisting or by twisting and bending simultaneously. This behavior, caused by the relatively small torsional rigidity of such sections, is called torsional buckling and may result in a lower column strength than that predicted for in-plane bending. Because the torsional rigidity of such members is approximately proportional to the cube of their material thickness, torsional buckling is particularly significant for thin open members such as those formed from light-gage steel sheets. Torsional buckling is not usually significant for hot-rolled structural steel channels, but may be significant for rolled tee sections or for tee sections fabricated from angles. For single equal-leg angles and cruciform sections, torsional buckling of the section is equivalent to local buckling of the legs, and therefore, safe design against local buckling** automatically results in safe design against torsional buckling.

---

*This maximum out-of-straightness is within that allowed by AISC, L/1000.
**See Chapter 4.

For those members susceptible to torsional buckling, Reference 9 and 10 provide adequate design information.

The shear deformation that occurs when a laced column, battened column, or column with perforated cover plates buckles about an axis perpendicular to the lacing or perforations (the laced column deforms like a truss with diagonals and the perforated column deforms somewhat like a Vierendeel truss) reduces its buckling strength; however, Bleich[9] and White and Thurlimann[11] have shown that this reduction is small enough to be neglected for practical columns of structural carbon steel and high-strength low-alloy steel. For constructional alloy steels, however, the effect of shear deformation, although often negligible, should be investigated. The strength and local-buckling requirements of the component parts should also be investigated. The lacing or open web is frequently designed to carry a shear force equal to 2 percent of the axial compressive force plus the shear due to dead weight if the column is in a horizontal position. Reference 6 covers the design of such members in more detail.

3.6 Effective Column Length[6]

The effective column length, KL, which has been used in the buckling equations given in this chapter, is the length between points of inflection of the buckled column. Restraint against both rotation and translation of the column ends influences the location of the inflection points. Theoretical K values for several combinations of idealized end conditions are given in Figure 3.9. If the column ends are not completely fixed against rotation, the actual K value is generally larger than the theoretical value. Since complete end fixity is not usually obtained, the CRC has recommended design values that are generally greater than the theoretical values. The design values are also given in the figure.

A base fully fixed against rotation (conditions a, b, c, and e in Figure 3.9) can be obtained only when a column is rigidly anchored to a footing that does not rotate significantly under an overturning moment. A column top fully fixed against rotation (conditions a, c, and f in Figure 3.9) can be approached when the top of the column is rigidly connected by welding or bolting (friction joint) to a heavy girder that is many times stiffer than the column. The translation of the column top relative to the base can be prevented (conditions a, b, and d in Figure 3.9) by the lateral support provided by rigid walls or diagonal bracing. If the amount of restraint against either rotation or translation is uncertain, it may be conservatively assumed to be nonexistent.

For columns in continuous frames, such as building frames, where the ideal conditions discussed above are not approached and the rigidity, I/L, of adjacent members has a significant effect, effective length factors can be determined from the charts in Figure 3.10. These charts are based on an elastic analysis that includes the effect of column load and assumes, conservatively, that all columns in the portion of the framework under consideration reach

	(a)	(b)	(c)	(d)	(e)	(f)
BUCKLED SHAPE OF COLUMN IS SHOWN BY DASHED LINE	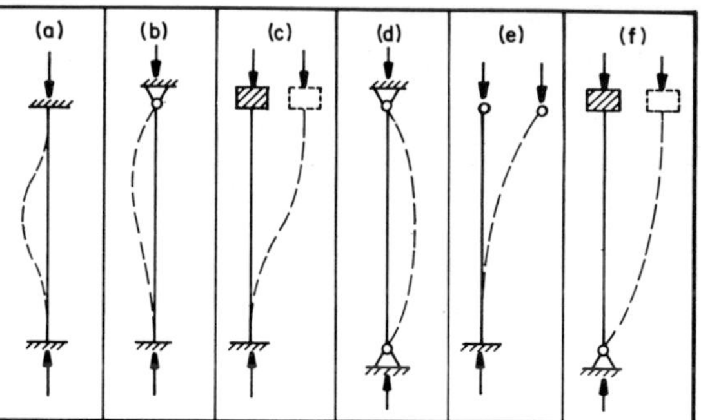					
THEORETICAL K VALUE	0.5	0.7	1.0	1.0	2.0	2.0
DESIGN VALUE OF K WHEN IDEAL CONDITIONS ARE APPROXIMATED	0.65	0.80	1.2	1.0	2.1	2.0
END CONDITION CODE		ROTATION FIXED TRANSLATION FIXED				
		ROTATION FREE TRANSLATION FIXED				
		ROTATION FIXED TRANSLATION FREE				
		ROTATION FREE TRANSLATION FREE				

FIGURE 3.9 EFFECTIVE LENGTH FACTORS FOR COLUMNS

their buckling loads simultaneously. The chart can be used in the following manner.

At each end of the column, designated arbitrarily by the subscripts "A" and "B," determine the relative stiffness value, G, which is defined as

$$G = \frac{\Sigma I_c / L_c}{\Sigma I_g / L_g} \tag{3.14}$$

In this equation, Σ indicates a summation of all members that are rigidly connected at the joint and lie in the plane of buckling. The subscripts "c" and "g" refer, respectively, to the column and the girders, and the moments of inertia are taken about an axis perpendicular to the plane of buckling. L is the actual length of the member. After the G values are determined, K is found at the intersection of a straight line that joins G_a and G_b in the appropriate portion of the chart, depending upon whether sidesway is prevented or permitted. The following suggestions from Reference 6 are appropriate for the determination of G values.

"For a column base connected to a footing by a frictionless hinge, G is theoretically infinite but should be taken as 10 in design practice. If the column base is rigidly attached to a properly designed footing, G approaches a theoretical value of zero but should be taken as 1.0. Other values may be justified by analysis.

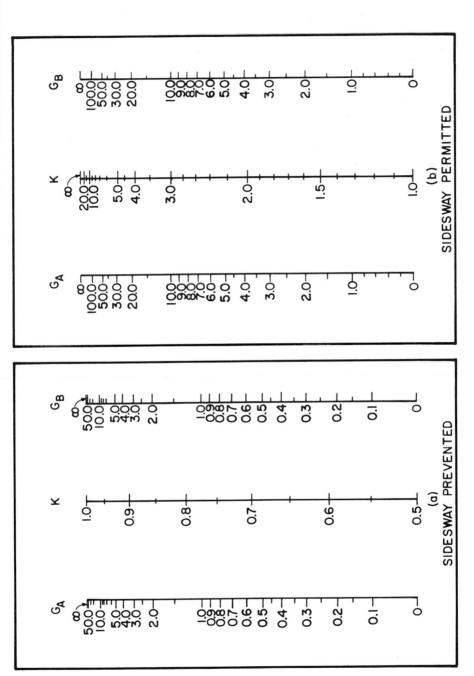

FIGURE 3.10 CHARTS FOR EFFECTIVE LENGTH OF COLUMNS IN CONTINUOUS FRAMES

"The girder stiffness $_gI/L_g$ should be multiplied by a factor when certain conditions at the far end are known to exist. For the case with sidesway prevented (Figure 3.10a), the appropriate multiplying factors are as follows:

1.5 for far end of girder hinged, and

2.0 for far end of girder fixed against rotation

For the case with sidesway not prevented (Figure 3.10b), the multiplying factors are:

0.5 for far end of girder hinged, and

0.67 for far end of girder fixed."

3.7 Design of Columns for Buildings

The allowable column stresses given in the AISC specification[2] are applicable for the design of all types of structural-steel columns for buildings. For columns with $KL/r \geq C_c$, allowable stresses are determined by dividing the Euler equation, Equation 3.1, by a safety factor of 1.92. For shorter columns with $KL/r \leq C_c$, allowable stresses are calculated by dividing the CRC equation, Equation 3.10, by the following:

$$\text{Safety Factor} = \frac{5}{3} + \frac{3}{8} \frac{(KL/r)}{C_c} - \frac{(KL/r)^3}{8C_c^3} \qquad (3.15)$$

This safety factor varies from 1.67, when KL/r is equal to 0, to 1.92, when KL/r is equal to C_c. For the convenience of the designer, allowable stresses for columns in buildings, calculated according to the AISC specification, are presented in Table 3.2 for steels with specified minimum yield stresses of 36,000 to 100,000 psi.

The AISC permits the use of a rational method for determining K, such as that discussed in Section 3.6. A maximum KL/r value of 200 is permitted, and supplementary formulas for the design of secondary compression members are given in the AISC specification.

3.8 Design of Columns for Bridges

In the bridge-design specifications of the American Association of State Highway Officials (AASHO)[12] and the American Railway Engineering Association (AREA)[13] allowable column stresses are determined by using a form of the secant formula similar to Equation 3.8, with an arbitrary eccentricity ratio, $ec/r^2 = 0.25$, and an applied factor of safety, N, of approximately 1.80.* Also, for design purposes, the term "L" is replaced by "KL."

Because the secant formula requires a trial and error solution to obtain allowable stresses, AASHO and AREA permit the use of simple allowable-stress formulas as an alternative to using the secant formula. Although derived to approximate the secant formula, these alternative formulas can be derived from the CRC basic

---

*Because of the form of Equation 3.8, the safety factor (ratio of yield stress to allowable stress) when $KL/2r = 0$ is 1.25N or 2.25 for an N of 1.80.

column-strength formula, Equation 3.12, by using a factor of safety of 2.25 and a K value of 0.75 for riveted columns and 0.875 for columns with pinned ends. The AASHO specification allows a maximum L/r of 120 for main members, whereas the AREA allows 100.

Since bridge members are usually part of a truss in which no applicable lateral sidesway of the individual member is possible, and since riveted and bolted connections provide some end fixity, the use of an effective length factor less than 1.0 is appropriate. However, if the formulas are used for other types of members where sidesway may be present, it would be desirable to determine K by a rational means such as that discussed in Section 3.6.

Suggested allowable stresses for axially loaded columns for bridges are given in Table 3.3 for steels with specified minimum yield points of 36,000 to 100,000 psi. The stresses were calculated from Equation 3.8, with an N factor of 1.80 and a value of ec/r² of 0.25.

3.9 Design Examples

Example 3.1

A 10-foot-long rolled wide-flanged column supports a 510-kip axial load in the interior of a single-story building. The column base is not rigidly connected (for moment transfer) to the foundation, but the top of the column has flanges rigidly connected to a very stiff girder. Bracing prevents sidesway in the weak direction of the column, but sidesway in the strong direction is not prevented. Using AISC allowable stress criteria, select a column of A36 steel, EX-TEN 50 steel, and "T-1" type A steel.

Solution:

For buckling about the y-y (weak) axis, from Figure 3.9d, K = 1.0, and therefore, KL = 120 in.

For buckling about the x-x (strong) axis, from Figure 3.9f, K = 2.0, and therefore, KL = 240 in.

A36 Steel

Try a 12WF92 section. $A = 27.06$ sq in. $r_y = 3.08$ in. $r_x = 5.40$ in.

$$\text{y-y axis:} \quad \frac{KL}{r} = \frac{120}{3.08} = 39.0$$

$$\text{x-x axis:} \quad \frac{KL}{r} = \frac{240}{5.40} = 44.4 \quad f_a = 18.8 \text{ ksi (Table 3.2)}$$

Design Load = $F_a \times A = 18.8 \times 27.06 = 509$ kips   **O.K.**

EX-TEN 50 Steel

Try a 12WF72 section. $A = 21.16$ sq in. $r_y = 3.04$ in. $r_x = 5.31$ in.

$$\text{y-y axis:} \quad \frac{KL}{r} = \frac{120}{3.04} = 39.5$$

$$\text{x-x axis:} \quad \frac{KL}{r} = \frac{240}{5.31} = 45.2 \quad f_a = 25.1 \text{ ksi (Table 3.2)}$$

Design Load = $25.1 \times 21.16 = 531$ kips   **O.K.**

"T-1" type A Steel

Try a 12WF50 section. $A = 14.71$ sq. in. $r_y = 1.96$ in. $r_x = 5.18$ in.

$$y\text{-y axis: } \frac{KL}{r} = \frac{120}{1.96} = 61.2 \quad f_a = 35.3 \text{ (Table 3.2)}$$

$$x\text{-x axis: } \frac{KL}{r} = \frac{240}{5.18} = 46.3$$

Design Load $= 35.3 \times 14.71 = 519$ kips **O.K.**

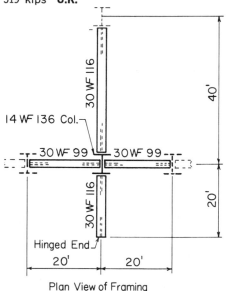

Example 3.2

An interior column of an intermediate story in a building frame has girders rigidly connected at top and bottom. All stories are spaced at 12 feet and adjacent stories have the same column section. A plan view of the top of the column is shown. The girder arrangement at the bottom of the column is similar except that the 20-foot-long 30WF116 girder does not have a hinged end. Sidesway is permitted in both directions. The column has been tentatively selected as a 14WF136 rolled shape of EX-TEN 42 steel. Determine the allowable axial column load using AISC allowable stress criteria.

Plan View of Framing

Solution:

Use Figure 3.10 to determine effective length factors. Girder stiffness can be multiplied by 0.50 when far end is hinged. The 14WF136 column has the following properties: $A = 39.98$ in.^{2}, $I_{xx} = 1593.0$ in.^{4}, $r_{xx} = 6.31$ in., $I_{yy} = 567.7$ in.^{4}, and $r_{yy} = 3.77$ in. For the 30WF99 girder, $I_{xx} = 3988.6$ in.^{4}. For the 30WF116 girder, $I_{xx} = 4919.1$ in.^{4}.

x - x Axis

At column top, $G_A = \sum \dfrac{I_c}{L_c} \div \sum \dfrac{I_g}{L_g}$

$$= \left(\frac{1593}{12} + \frac{1593}{12} \right) \div \left(\frac{4919 \times .5}{20} + \frac{4919}{40} \right)$$

$$= 1.08$$

At column bottom, $G_B = \left(\frac{1593}{12} + \frac{1593}{12} \right) \div \left(\frac{4919}{20} + \frac{4919}{40} \right)$

$$= 0.720$$

From Figure 3.10, K$= 1.28$

$$\frac{KL}{r} = \frac{1.28 \times 144}{6.31} = 29.2$$

y-y Axis

At column top, $G_A = \left(\dfrac{567.7}{12} + \dfrac{567.7}{12} \right) \div \left(\dfrac{3989 \times 2}{20} \right)$

$= 0.237$

At column bottom, $G_B = 0.237$

From Figure 3.10, K = 1.08

$\dfrac{KL}{r} = \dfrac{1.08 \times 144}{3.77} = 41.3$

From Table 3.2, $F_a = 21.95$

Allowable axial load = $F_a \times A$

$= 21.95 \times 39.98$

$= $ **878 kips**

Example 3.3

A 15-foot-long compression member of a truss with high-strength bolted connections has a design load of 230 kips. Select a rolled wide-flange section in A36 steel according to AAHSO specifications.

Solution:

Try a 10WF54 section: A = 15.88 in.^{2}, r_{xx} = 4.39 in., r_{yy} = 2.56 in. Since the member is part of a truss and has high-strength bolted end connections, a K of 0.75 will be used.

$\dfrac{KL}{r} = \dfrac{.75 \times 15 \times 12}{2.56} = 52.7$

F_a = 14.7 psi (Table 3.3)

Design Load = $f_a \times A$ = 14.7 $\times$ 15.88 = 233 kips **O.K.**

Example 3.4*

A special-purpose framework, such as may be found in a drilling platform, includes a column with an effective length, KL, of 20 feet. The column is to be designed to support a 100-kip load and provide a safety factor of 3.0 against failure. If an 8-inch-square tubular section with a yield point of 36,000 psi is used for the column, determine the required thickness of tube.

Solution:

Try a ⅜-inch wall thickness: A = 10.83 in.^{2} r = 3.06 in.

$\dfrac{KL}{r} = \dfrac{20 \times 12}{3.06} = 78.4$

f_c = 29.0 ksi (Table 3.1)

Design Load = $\dfrac{f_c x A}{N} = \dfrac{29.0 \times 10.83}{3.00}$ = 105 kips **O.K.**

---

*For most structures not covered by specifications, design procedures of AISC may be followed, but with the safety factor adjusted to suit the conditions present.

References (Chapter 3)

1. S. P. Timoshenko and J. M. Gere, **Theory of Elastic Stability,** McGraw-Hill Book Company, New York City, 1961.

2. American Institute of Steel Construction, "Specification for the Design, Fabrication, and Erection of Structural Steel for Buildings," 1963.

3. L. S. Beedle and L. Tall, "Basic Column Strength," **Journal of the Structural Division, Proceedings** ASCE, **86,** No. ST7, July 1960.

4. C. H. Yang, L. S. Beedle, and B. G. Johnston. "Residual Stress and the Yield Strength of Steel Beams," **The Welding Journal, 31,** 1952.

5. A. W. Huber and L. S. Beedle, "Residual Stress and the Compressive Strength of Steel," **The Welding Journal, 33,** 1954.

6. Column Research Council, "Guide to Design Criteria for Metal Compression Members," 2nd Ed. 1966, John Wiley & Sons, publisher.

7. G. Haaijer, "Significant Research Data for Use in Steel Design," U. S. Steel Corporation, ADUSS 91-1008, Design and Engineering Seminar, 1964.

8. T. V. Galambos, "Strength of Round Steel Columns," **Journal of the Structural Division, Proceedings** ASCE, **91,** No. ST1, February 1965.

9. F. Bleich, **Buckling Strength of Metal Structures,** McGraw-Hill Book Company, New York City, 1952.

10. A Chajes and G. Winter, "Torsional-Flexural Buckling of Thin-Walled Members," **Journal of the Structural Division, Proceedings** ASCE, **91,** No. ST4, August 1965.

11. M. White and B. Thurlimann, "Study of Columns With Perforated Cover Plates," **Proceedings** American Railway Engineering Association, **58,** 1957.

12. American Association of State Highway Officials, "Standard Specifications for Highway Bridges," 1965.

13. American Railway Engineering Association, "Standard Specifications for Steel Railway Bridges," 1966.

Table 3.1
Buckling Stresses for Steel Columns

Effective Slenderness Ratio, KL/r	Euler Buckling Stress, ksi	Basic Column Buckling Stress, ksi, for Indicated Steel Yield Stress, ksi								
		36.00	42.00	46.00	50.00	60.00	70.00	80.00	90.00	100.00
5		35.97	41.96	45.95	49.95	59.92	69.89	79.86	89.82	99.78
10		35.89	41.84	45.82	49.78	59.69	69.57	79.44	89.29	99.13
15		35.75	41.65	45.59	49.55	59.29	69.04	78.74	88.41	98.03
20	715.55	35.55	41.38	45.26	49.13	58.74	68.29	77.76	87.17	96.51
25	457.95	35.29	41.04	44.85	48.64	58.03	67.32	76.51	85.58	94.54
30	318.02	34.98	40.61	44.33	48.04	57.17	66.15	74.97	83.63	92.14
35	233.65	34.61	40.11	43.74	47.33	56.15	64.76	73.15	81.33	89.30
40	178.89	34.19	39.53	43.04	46.51	54.97	63.15	71.06	78.68	86.02
45	141.34	33.71	38.88	42.26	45.58	53.63	61.33	68.68	75.67	82.32
50	114.49	33.17	38.15	41.38	44.54	52.14	59.30	66.02	72.31	78.16
55	94.62	32.58	37.34	40.41	43.40	50.49	57.05	63.09	68.60	73.58
60	79.51	31.93	36.45	39.35	42.14	48.68	54.59	59.87	64.53	68.56
65	67.74	31.22	35.49	38.19	40.78	46.71	51.92	56.38	60.11	63.10
70	58.41	30.45	34.45	36.94	39.30	44.59	49.03	52.61	55.33	57.20
75	50.88	29.63	33.33	35.60	37.72	42.31	45.92	48.55	50.20	50.87
80	44.72	28.76	32.14	34.17	36.03	39.87	42.61	44.22	44.72	44.72
85	39.61	27.82	30.87	32.65	34.23	37.28	39.08	39.61	39.61	39.61
90	35.34	26.83	29.52	31.03	32.32	34.53	35.33	35.33	35.34	35.34
95	31.71	25.78	28.09	29.32	30.30	31.62	31.71	31.71	31.71	31.71
100	28.62	24.68	26.59	27.52	28.17	28.62	28.62	28.62	28.62	28.62
105	25.96	23.52	25.01	25.62	25.93	25.96	25.96	25.96	25.96	25.96
110	23.65	22.30	23.36	23.63	23.65	23.65	23.65	23.65	23.65	23.65
115	21.64	21.03	21.62	21.64	21.64	21.64	21.64	21.64	21.64	21.64
120	19.88	19.70	19.88	19.88	19.88	19.88	19.88	19.88	19.88	19.88
125	18.32	18.31	18.32	18.32	18.32	18.32	18.32	18.32	18.32	18.32
130	16.94	16.94	16.94	16.94	16.94	16.93	16.93	16.93	16.94	16.94
135	15.70	15.70	15.70	15.70	15.70	15.70	15.70	15.70	15.70	15.70
140	14.60	14.60	14.60	14.60	14.60	14.60	14.60	14.60	14.60	14.60
145	13.61	13.61	13.61	13.61	13.61	13.61	13.61	13.61	13.61	13.61
150	12.72	12.72	12.72	12.72	12.72	12.72	12.72	12.72	12.72	12.72
155	11.91	11.91	11.91	11.91	11.91	11.91	11.91	11.91	11.91	11.91
160	11.18	11.18	11.18	11.18	11.18	11.18	11.18	11.18	11.18	11.18

Table 3.2
Allowable Stresses for Steel Columns in Buildings

Allowable Column Stress, ksi, for Indicated Steel Yield Stress, ksi

Effective Slenderness Ratio, KL/r	36.00	42.00	46.00	50.00	60.00	70.00	80.00	90.00	100.00
1	21.56	25.15	27.54	29.94	35.92	41.89	47.87	53.84	59.82
2	21.52	25.10	27.48	29.87	35.83	41.78	47.73	53.68	59.62
3	21.48	25.05	27.42	29.80	35.74	41.67	47.59	53.51	59.42
4	21.44	24.99	27.36	29.73	35.64	41.55	47.44	53.33	59.21
5	21.39	24.94	27.30	29.66	35.54	41.42	47.29	53.15	58.99
6	21.35	24.88	27.23	29.58	35.44	41.29	47.13	52.95	58.76
7	21.30	24.82	27.16	29.50	35.34	41.16	46.96	52.75	58.53
8	21.25	24.76	27.09	29.42	35.23	41.02	46.79	52.55	58.28
9	21.21	24.70	27.02	29.34	35.12	40.88	46.62	52.33	58.03
10	21.16	24.63	26.95	29.26	35.01	40.73	46.44	52.11	57.77
11	21.10	24.57	26.87	29.17	34.89	40.58	46.25	51.89	57.50
12	21.05	24.50	26.79	29.08	34.77	40.43	46.06	51.65	57.22
13	21.00	24.43	26.72	28.99	34.65	40.27	45.86	51.41	56.93
14	20.95	24.36	26.63	28.90	34.52	40.11	45.66	51.17	56.64
15	20.89	24.29	26.55	28.80	34.40	39.94	45.45	50.92	56.34
16	20.83	24.22	26.47	28.71	34.27	39.78	45.24	50.66	56.03
17	20.78	24.15	26.38	28.61	34.13	39.60	45.02	50.39	55.72
18	20.72	24.07	26.29	28.51	34.00	39.43	44.80	50.12	55.39
19	20.66	24.00	26.21	28.40	33.86	39.24	44.57	49.85	55.06
20	20.60	23.92	26.11	28.30	33.71	39.06	44.34	49.56	54.72
21	20.54	23.84	26.02	28.19	33.57	38.87	44.11	49.28	54.38
22	20.48	23.76	25.93	28.08	33.42	38.68	43.87	48.98	54.03
23	20.41	23.68	25.83	27.97	33.27	38.49	43.62	48.68	53.67
24	20.35	23.59	25.73	27.86	33.12	38.29	43.37	48.38	53.30
25	20.28	23.51	25.64	27.75	32.96	38.09	43.12	48.07	52.93
26	20.22	23.42	25.54	27.63	32.81	37.88	42.86	47.75	52.55
27	20.15	23.33	25.43	27.52	32.65	37.67	42.60	47.43	52.17
28	20.08	23.24	25.33	27.40	32.48	37.46	42.33	47.10	51.78
29	20.01	23.15	25.23	27.28	32.32	37.24	42.06	46.77	51.38
30	19.94	23.06	25.12	27.15	32.15	37.03	41.79	46.43	50.97
31	19.87	22.97	25.01	27.03	31.98	36.80	41.51	46.09	50.56

Table 3.2 (Continued)
Allowable Stresses for Steel Columns in Buildings

Effective Slenderness Ratio, KL/r	Allowable Column Stress, ksi, for Indicated Steel Yield Stress, ksi								
	36.00	42.00	46.00	50.00	60.00	70.00	80.00	90.00	100.00
32	19.80	22.88	24.90	26.90	31.81	36.58	41.22	45.74	50.15
33	19.73	22.78	24.79	26.77	31.63	36.35	40.94	45.39	49.72
34	19.65	22.69	24.68	26.64	31.45	36.12	40.64	45.03	49.29
35	19.58	22.59	24.56	26.51	31.28	35.88	40.35	44.67	48.86
36	19.50	22.49	24.45	26.38	31.09	35.65	40.05	44.30	48.42
37	19.42	22.39	24.33	26.25	30.91	35.41	39.75	43.93	47.97
38	19.35	22.29	24.21	26.11	30.72	35.16	39.44	43.55	47.51
39	19.27	22.19	24.10	25.97	30.53	34.92	39.13	43.17	47.05
40	19.19	22.08	23.97	25.83	30.34	34.67	38.81	42.78	46.59
41	19.11	21.98	23.85	25.69	30.15	34.41	38.49	42.39	46.12
42	19.03	21.87	23.73	25.55	29.95	34.16	38.17	42.00	45.64
43	18.95	21.77	23.60	25.40	29.75	33.90	37.84	41.59	45.16
44	18.86	21.66	23.48	25.26	29.55	33.64	37.51	41.19	44.67
45	18.78	21.55	23.35	25.11	29.35	33.37	37.18	40.78	44.17
46	18.70	21.44	23.22	24.96	29.15	33.10	36.84	40.36	43.67
47	18.61	21.33	23.09	24.81	28.94	32.83	36.50	39.94	43.17
48	18.53	21.22	22.96	24.66	28.73	32.56	36.15	39.51	42.65
49	18.44	21.10	22.83	24.51	28.52	32.28	35.80	39.08	42.14
50	18.35	20.99	22.69	24.35	28.31	32.00	35.45	38.65	41.61
51	18.26	20.87	22.56	24.19	28.09	31.72	35.09	38.21	41.08
52	18.17	20.76	22.42	24.04	27.87	31.44	34.73	37.77	40.55
53	18.08	20.64	22.28	23.88	27.66	31.15	34.37	37.32	40.00
54	17.99	20.52	22.14	23.72	27.43	30.86	34.00	36.86	39.46
55	17.90	20.40	22.00	23.55	27.21	30.56	33.63	36.41	38.90
56	17.81	20.28	21.86	23.39	26.98	30.27	33.25	35.94	38.35
57	17.71	20.16	21.72	23.22	26.76	29.97	32.87	35.47	37.78
58	17.62	20.03	21.57	23.06	26.53	29.67	32.49	35.00	37.21
59	17.53	19.91	21.43	22.89	26.29	29.36	32.10	34.52	36.63
60	17.43	19.79	21.28	22.72	26.06	29.05	31.71	34.04	36.05
61	17.33	19.66	21.13	22.55	25.82	28.74	31.32	33.56	35.46
62	17.24	19.53	20.98	22.37	25.58	28.43	30.92	33.06	34.87

Columns

Table 3.2 (Continued)

Allowable Stresses for Steel Columns in Buildings

Effective Slenderness Ratio, KL/r	Allowable Column Stress, ksi, for Indicated Steel Yield Stress, ksi								
	36.00	42.00	46.00	50.00	60.00	70.00	80.00	90.00	100.00
63	17.14	19.40	20.83	22.20	25.34	28.11	30.52	32.57	34.26
64	17.04	19.27	20.68	22.02	25.10	27.79	30.11	32.07	33.66
65	16.94	19.14	20.53	21.85	24.86	27.47	29.70	31.56	33.04
66	16.84	19.01	20.37	21.67	24.61	27.15	29.29	31.05	32.42
67	16.74	18.88	20.22	21.49	24.36	26.82	28.87	30.53	31.80
68	16.64	18.75	20.06	21.31	24.11	26.49	28.45	30.01	31.16
69	16.53	18.61	19.90	21.12	23.86	26.15	28.03	29.48	30.52
70	16.43	18.48	19.74	20.94	23.60	25.82	27.60	28.95	29.88
71	16.33	18.34	19.58	20.75	23.34	25.48	27.17	28.41	29.22
72	16.22	18.20	19.42	20.56	23.08	25.14	26.73	27.87	28.56
73	16.12	18.06	19.26	20.38	22.82	24.79	26.29	27.32	27.90
74	16.01	17.92	19.10	20.19	22.56	24.44	25.84	26.77	27.22
75	15.90	17.78	18.93	19.99	22.29	24.09	25.39	26.21	26.54
76	15.79	17.64	18.76	19.80	22.02	23.73	24.94	25.65	25.80
77	15.69	17.50	18.60	19.61	21.75	23.38	24.48	25.08	25.13
78	15.58	17.35	18.43	19.41	21.48	23.02	24.02	24.50	24.49
79	15.47	17.21	18.26	19.21	21.21	22.65	23.56	23.92	23.87
80	15.36	17.06	18.08	19.01	20.93	22.29	23.08	23.28	23.28
81	15.24	16.92	17.91	18.81	20.65	21.91	22.61	22.71	22.71
82	15.13	16.77	17.74	18.61	20.37	21.54	22.13	22.16	22.16
83	15.02	16.62	17.56	18.41	20.09	21.16	21.65	21.63	21.63
84	14.90	16.47	17.39	18.20	19.80	20.78	21.16	21.12	21.12
85	14.79	16.32	17.21	17.99	19.51	20.40	20.62	20.62	20.62
86	14.67	16.17	17.03	17.79	19.22	20.01	20.15	20.15	20.15
87	14.56	16.01	16.85	17.58	18.93	19.62	19.69	19.69	19.69
88	14.44	15.86	16.67	17.37	18.63	19.23	19.24	19.24	19.24
89	14.32	15.71	16.48	17.15	18.34	18.83	18.81	18.81	18.81
90	14.20	15.55	16.30	16.94	18.04	18.43	18.40	18.40	18.40
91	14.09	15.39	16.12	16.72	17.73	17.99	17.99	17.99	17.99
92	13.97	15.23	15.93	16.50	17.43	17.60	17.60	17.60	17.60
93	13.84	15.07	15.74	16.29	17.12	17.23	17.23	17.23	17.23

Table 3.2 (Continued)
Allowable Stresses for Steel Columns in Buildings

Effective Slenderness Ratio, KL/r	Allowable Column Stress, ksi, for Indicated Steel Yield Stress, ksi								
	36.00	42.00	46.00	50.00	60.00	70.00	80.00	90.00	100.00
94	13.72	14.91	15.55	16.06	16.81	16.86	16.86	16.86	16.86
95	13.60	14.75	15.36	15.84	16.50	16.51	16.51	16.51	16.51
96	13.48	14.59	15.17	15.62	16.19	16.17	16.17	16.17	16.17
97	13.35	14.43	14.97	15.39	15.87	15.84	15.84	15.84	15.84
98	13.23	14.26	14.78	15.17	15.51	15.51	15.51	15.51	15.51
99	13.10	14.09	14.58	14.94	15.20	15.20	15.20	15.20	15.20
100	12.98	13.93	14.39	14.71	14.90	14.90	14.90	14.90	14.90
101	12.85	13.76	14.19	14.47	14.61	14.61	14.61	14.61	14.61
102	12.72	13.59	13.99	14.24	14.32	14.32	14.32	14.32	14.32
103	12.59	13.42	13.79	14.00	14.04	14.04	14.04	14.04	14.04
104	12.47	13.25	13.58	13.77	13.78	13.78	13.78	13.78	13.78
105	12.33	13.08	13.38	13.53	13.51	13.51	13.51	13.51	13.51
106	12.20	12.90	13.17	13.29	13.26	13.26	13.26	13.26	13.26
107	12.07	12.73	12.96	13.01	13.01	13.01	13.01	13.01	13.01
108	11.94	12.55	12.75	12.77	12.77	12.77	12.77	12.77	12.77
109	11.81	12.37	12.54	12.54	12.54	12.54	12.54	12.54	12.54
110	11.67	12.19	12.33	12.31	12.31	12.31	12.31	12.31	12.31
111	11.54	12.01	12.12	12.09	12.09	12.09	12.09	12.09	12.09
112	11.40	11.83	11.88	11.88	11.88	11.88	11.88	11.88	11.88
113	11.26	11.65	11.67	11.67	11.67	11.67	11.67	11.67	11.67
114	11.13	11.47	11.47	11.47	11.47	11.47	11.47	11.47	11.47
115	10.99	11.28	11.27	11.27	11.27	11.27	11.27	11.27	11.27
116	10.85	11.10	11.07	11.07	11.07	11.07	11.07	11.07	11.07
117	10.71	10.88	10.88	10.88	10.88	10.88	10.88	10.88	10.88
118	10.57	10.70	10.70	10.70	10.70	10.70	10.70	10.70	10.70
119	10.43	10.52	10.52	10.52	10.52	10.52	10.52	10.52	10.52
120	10.28	10.35	10.35	10.35	10.35	10.35	10.35	10.35	10.35

Table 3.3
Allowable Stresses for Steel Columns in Bridges

Effective Slenderness Ratio, KL/r	Allowable Column Stress, Ksi, for Indicated Steel Yield Stress, ksi								
	36.00	42.00	46.00	50.00	60.00	70.00	80.00	90.00	100.00
0	16.00	18.67	20.44	22.22	26.67	31.11	35.56	40.00	44.44
5	15.99	18.65	20.43	22.20	26.64	31.07	35.51	39.94	44.37
10	15.96	18.61	20.38	22.15	26.56	30.96	35.36	39.75	44.13
15	15.91	18.54	20.30	22.05	26.41	30.77	35.10	39.43	43.73
20	15.84	18.45	20.18	21.91	26.21	30.49	34.73	38.95	43.14
25	15.74	18.32	20.02	21.72	25.94	30.11	34.24	38.32	42.35
30	15.63	18.15	19.82	21.49	25.59	29.63	33.60	37.50	41.31
35	15.48	17.95	19.58	21.20	25.17	29.03	32.80	36.46	40.01
40	15.31	17.71	19.29	20.85	24.65	28.31	31.82	35.19	38.41
45	15.11	17.43	18.95	20.44	24.03	27.44	30.66	33.68	36.51
50	14.87	17.10	18.55	19.95	23.31	26.42	29.30	31.93	34.34
55	14.60	16.72	18.08	19.39	22.47	25.26	27.76	30.00	31.97
60	14.30	16.29	17.55	18.76	21.54	23.97	26.09	27.92	29.50
65	13.95	15.81	16.96	18.06	20.51	22.59	24.34	25.82	27.04
70	13.57	15.27	16.31	17.28	19.41	21.15	22.57	23.72	24.67
75	13.14	14.69	15.61	16.46	18.27	19.70	20.83	21.73	22.46
80	12.69	14.06	14.87	15.60	17.12	18.28	19.17	19.88	20.44
85	12.20	13.41	14.11	14.73	15.98	16.92	17.63	18.18	18.61
90	11.68	12.74	13.33	13.85	14.88	15.64	16.20	16.63	16.97
95	11.16	12.07	12.57	13.00	13.84	14.45	14.90	15.23	15.51
100	10.62	11.40	11.82	12.18	12.87	13.36	13.72	13.99	14.21
105	10.09	10.74	11.10	11.39	11.96	12.36	12.65	12.88	13.05
110	9.56	10.12	10.41	10.66	11.12	11.45	11.69	11.87	12.01
115	9.05	9.52	9.77	9.97	10.36	10.63	10.82	10.98	11.09
120	8.56	8.95	9.16	9.33	9.65	9.88	10.04	10.16	10.26
125	8.09	8.42	8.60	8.74	9.01	9.20	9.33	9.43	9.52
130	7.64	7.93	8.07	8.20	8.42	8.58	8.69	8.79	8.85
135	7.22	7.47	7.59	7.69	7.88	8.02	8.12	8.18	8.25
140	6.83	7.03	7.14	7.23	7.39	7.51	7.59	7.66	7.70
145	6.46	6.64	6.73	6.80	6.94	7.04	7.11	7.16	7.21
150	6.11	6.27	6.34	6.41	6.53	6.61	6.68	6.73	6.76

Table 3.3 (Continued)
Allowable Stresses for Steel Columns in Bridges

Effective Slenderness Ratio, KL/r	Allowable Column Stress, ksi, for Indicated Steel Yield Stress, ksi									
	36.00	42.00	46.00	50.00	60.00	70.00	80.00	90.00	100.00
155	5.79	5.92	5.99	6.05	6.15	6.22	6.28	6.31	6.35
160	5.49	5.60	5.66	5.71	5.80	5.87	5.91	5.95	5.98
165	5.20	5.31	5.36	5.40	5.48	5.54	5.58	5.60	5.63
170	4.94	5.03	5.08	5.11	5.18	5.23	5.27	5.30	5.32
175	4.70	4.78	4.82	4.85	4.91	4.95	4.99	5.01	5.03
180	4.47	4.54	4.57	4.60	4.66	4.70	4.72	4.75	4.76
185	4.26	4.32	4.35	4.37	4.42	4.46	4.48	4.50	4.52
190	4.06	4.11	4.14	4.16	4.20	4.24	4.26	4.28	4.29
195	3.87	3.92	3.94	3.96	4.00	4.03	4.05	4.06	4.08
200	3.69	3.74	3.76	3.78	3.81	3.84	3.86	3.87	3.88

CHAPTER 4

Local Buckling of Plates

4.1 Introduction

Most structural members and fabrications are composed of connected elements that, for purposes of analysis and design, may be treated as plates. When a plate is subjected to direct compression, bending, or shear, the plate may buckle locally before the member as a whole becomes unstable. This chapter considers local buckling of flat plates, stiffened flat plates, and tubes. The buckling of stiffened girder webs is considered in Chapter 5.

4.2 Behavior of Flat Plates Under Various Edge Loadings

4.2.1 *Uniform Compression*

a. Buckling Behavior

A plate that is (1) made of isotropic material, (2) free of residual stresses, (3) perfectly flat, and (4) subjected to loads in its plane is referred to as a "perfect plate." When an increasing uniform compressive load is applied along opposite edges of a perfect rectangular plate, the plate shortens uniformly in its plane, and compressive stresses are uniformly distributed over all transverse cross sections. However, when the buckling stress is reached, the plate deflects from its initial plane in a series of waves, and the compressive stresses are redistributed over transverse cross sections. As subsequently explained in Section 4.2.1.b, the buckling stress of a plate is not usually the maximum stress a plate can withstand.

Within the elastic range, the buckling stress, f_{cr}, is[1]

$$f_{cr} = \frac{k_c \pi^2 E}{12 (1 - u^2) (b/t)^2} = \frac{26.2 \times 10^6 \, k_c}{(b/t)^2} \tag{4.1}$$

where b/t is the plate width-to-thickness ratio and k_c is a nondimensional plate buckling coefficient that depends primarily on the type of edge supports and the length-to-width ratio, a/b, of the plate. The width is measured perpendicular to the direction of the applied load. The above equation, similar to the Euler equation for columns, is shown in Figure 4.1 as a nondimensional plate buckling curve. The dimensionless quantities chosen for the ordinate and abscissa in Figure 4.1 are analogous to those used for columns in Figure 3.8.

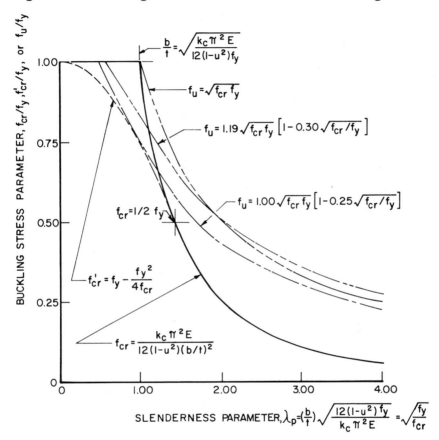

FIGURE 4.1 NONDIMENSIONAL BUCKLING CURVE FOR PLATES UNDER UNIFORM EDGE COMPRESSION

If f_y is substituted for f_{cr}, Equation 4.1 may be solved for the theoretical maximum b/t that would allow the plate to reach the yield stress before buckling:

$$\frac{b}{t} = \sqrt{\frac{k_c \pi^2 E}{12 \, (1 - u^2) \, f_y}} \qquad (4.2)$$

However, as explained for columns, residual stresses and initial imperfections can cause premature yielding, and thus, an actual plate may buckle inelastically at an average stress less than that given by Equation 4.1. Therefore, the maximum b/t ratio that would allow an actual plate to reach an average stress equal to its yield stress without buckling is less than that given by Equation 4.2.

A precise determination of the inelastic buckling stress for a given plate would require a detailed knowledge of the residual stresses and out-of-flatness of the plate. However, it is likely that these factors will have approximately the same effect on plate buckling as on column buckling and, therefore, the CRC equation for inelastic buckling of columns, Equation 3.12, will give a reasonable estimate of the inelastic buckling stress of plates. Equation 3.12 can be written as

$$f'_c = f_y - \frac{f_y^2}{4f_c} \tag{4.3}$$

where f_c is the calculated elastic column buckling stress and f'_c is the actual buckling stress in the inelastic range. If the elastic plate buckling stress, Equation 4.1, is substituted for f_c in Equation 4.3, the following equation for the plate buckling stress in the inelastic range, f'_{cr}, is obtained:

$$f'_{cr} = f_y - \frac{f_y^2}{4f_{cr}} = f_y - \frac{3(1-u^2) f_y^2 (b/t)^2}{k_c \pi^2 E} \tag{4.4}$$

when $f_{cr} \geqq f_y/2$

As indicated by the dashed line in Figure 4.1, the inelastic plate-buckling equation developed above is based on the conservative assumption that a plate will always buckle before reaching the yield stress. However, theoretical and experimental work have established maximum width-to-thickness ratios that allow plates of structural carbon or high-strength steel to reach the yield point and deform plastically without buckling.[2] Values of these ratios are given in Section 4.4.1. Actually, strain hardening may allow some plates with small slenderness parameters to reach a buckling stress somewhat greater than the yield stress.[3]

Figure 4.2 gives curves for theoretically determined k_c values for 10 different ideal edge support conditions.[4] Each curve is actually a lower envelope of an infinite family of curves; each member of the family is a curve for the number of half waves into which the plate buckles. The k_c values have been plotted versus a/b with solid lines and dashed lines indicating; respectively, simple supports and fixed supports along loaded edges. Fixing the loaded edges causes an increase in k_c for small a/b values but the effect becomes insignificant as a/b increases. Therefore, for most plates, k_c depends primarily on the type of support along the unloaded edges.

Because the supported edges of actual plates are not completely free to rotate (simply supported) or completely rigid (fixed), the

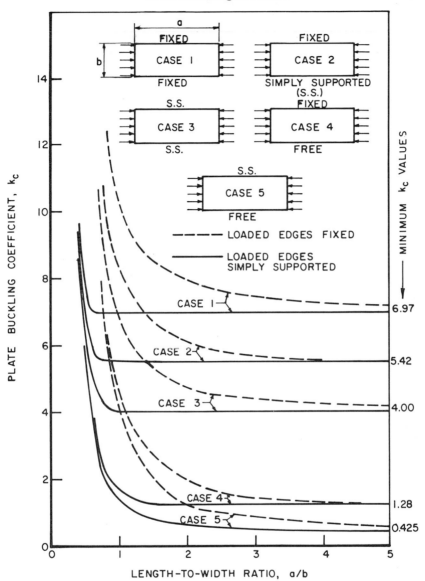

FIGURE 4.2 BUCKLING COEFFICIENTS FOR FLAT
PLATES UNDER UNIFORM COMPRESSION

ideal edge conditions referred to above are seldom achieved. Conservative buckling loads can be obtained by assuming that a supported edge is free to rotate. However, information is available that
gives theoretical k_c values as a function of the amount of edge

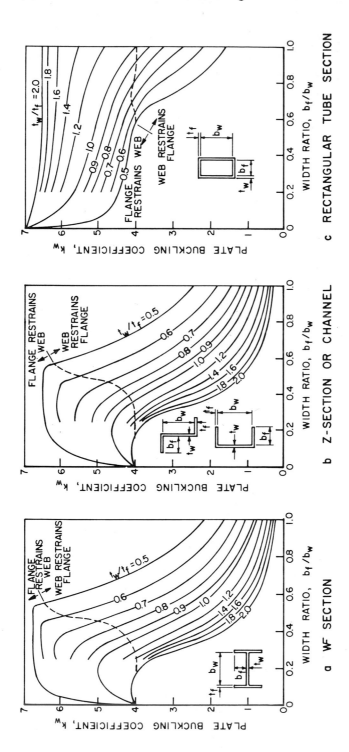

FIGURE 4.3 BUCKLING COEFFICIENTS FOR PLATE ELEMENTS OF STRUCTURAL MEMBERS UNDER UNIFORM COMPRESSION

rotational restraint.[4] In structural members or sections comprising several plates, the edge rotational restraint of each plate depends on the relative stiffnesses, $\dfrac{k_c}{(b/t)^2}$, of the adjacent plates. If the entire section is under uniform compression, the plate having the smallest stiffness will tend to buckle first. However, the stiffer plate will retard buckling of the plate having the lower stiffness until the two plates buckle together. This is because the angle between the plates resists change.

Based on theoretical determinations of the interaction of adjacent long plates, Figure 4.3 gives a modified compressive buckling coefficient, k_w, that may be used to determine the stress at which local buckling first occurs in three types of structural sections under uniform compression.[5] As indicated by the chart, the relative dimensions of the individual plates determine whether the flange or the web is the restraining element. However, the chart has been constructed so that k_w must be used with the width-to-thickness ratio of the web, b_w/t_w, to determine the local buckling stress from the previously given equations.

b. Postbuckling Behavior

Unlike a column, a plate does not usually attain its maximum load-carrying capacity at the buckling load, but usually shows significant "postbuckling strength." This behavior is illustrated in Figure 4.4, where longitudinal and transverse bars represent a plate that is simply supported along all edges.[6] As the uniformly distributed end load, such as that which might be applied through a rigid transverse member, is gradually increased, the longitudinal bars are equally stressed and reach their buckling load simultaneously. However, as the longitudinal bars buckle, the transverse bars develop tension in restraining the lateral deflection of the longitudinal bars. Thus, the longitudinal bars do not collapse when they reach their buckling load but are able to carry additional load because of the transverse restraint. The longitudinal bars nearest the center can deflect more than the bars near the edge, and therefore, the edge bars carry higher loads after buckling than do the center bars.

The postbuckling behavior of a simply supported plate is similar to that of the grid model. However, the ability of a plate to resist the shear strains that develop during buckling also contributes to its postbuckling strength. Although the grid shown in Figure 4.4a buckled into only one longitudinal half-wave, a longer plate may buckle into several waves as illustrated in Figure 4.4b. For long plates, the half-wave length approaches the width b.

After a simply supported plate buckles, the compressive stress will vary from a maximum near the supported edges to a minimum at the mid-width of the plate as shown by line 1 of Figure 4.4c. As the load is increased, the edge stresses will increase but the stress in the mid-width of the plate may decrease slightly. The maximum load is reached and collapse is initiated when the edge stress reaches the yield stress, a condition indicated by line 2 of Figure 4.4c.

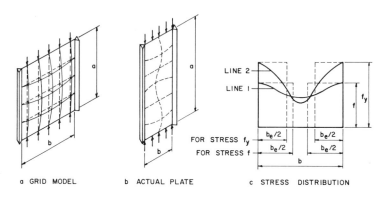

a GRID MODEL   b ACTUAL PLATE   c STRESS DISTRIBUTION

FIGURE 4.4   POSTBUCKLING PHENOMENON FOR PLATES IN UNIFORM EDGE COMPRESSION

The postbuckling strength of a plate can be conveniently determined by assuming that after buckling, the total load is carried by strips adjacent to the supported edges which are at a uniform stress equal to the actual maximum edge stress. These strips are indicated by the dashed lines in Figure 4.4c. The total width of the strips, known as the "effective width" of the plate, b_e, is selected so that the product of b_e and the maximum edge stress equals the actual stresses integrated over the entire width. At maximum load the stress on the effective width is the yield stress.

The behavior of plates with other edge-support conditions is generally similar to that discussed above. However, a plate supported along only one edge will develop only one effective strip. Plates with fixed edges theoretically develop greater effective widths than do similar plates with simply supported edges.

A theoretical equation derived by von Karman[7] for the effective width of a perfect plate can be expressed in a generalized form as

$$b_e = b\sqrt{\frac{f_{cr}}{f}} \qquad (4.5)$$

where f is the uniform stress on the effective width. The corresponding value of the average stress at ultimate load (ultimate load divided by total area), f_u, is

$$f_u = \left(b\sqrt{\frac{f_{cr}}{f_y}}\right) t f_y \left(\frac{1}{bt}\right) = \sqrt{f_{cr} f_y} \qquad (4.6)$$

Winter conducted a large number of tests of light-gage cold-formed members to develop the following modified equations for the effective width of plates that are simply supported along both edges or one longitudinal edge, respectively:[6, 8]

$$b_e = b\sqrt{\frac{f_{cr}}{f}}\left[1 - 0.25\sqrt{\frac{f_{cr}}{f}}\right] \qquad (4.7)$$

$$b_e = 1.19\ b\sqrt{\frac{f_{cr}}{f}}\left[1 - 0.30\sqrt{\frac{f_{cr}}{f}}\right] \qquad (4.8)$$

Corresponding equations for the average stress at maximum load are, for simple supports along both edges,

$$f_u = \sqrt{f_{cr}\ f_y}\left[1 - 0.25\sqrt{\frac{f_{cr}}{f_y}}\right] \qquad (4.9)$$

and, for simple supports along one edge,

$$f_u = 1.19\ \sqrt{f_{cr}\ f_y}\left[1 - 0.30\sqrt{\frac{f_{cr}}{f_y}}\right] \qquad (4.10)$$

Equations 4.6, 4.9, and 4.10 are shown in a nondimensional form in Figure 4.1. As shown in the figure, the ultimate strength of edge-supported plates is significantly greater than their elastic buckling strength for most values of λ_p.

By inserting the expression for f_{cr} given by Equation 4.1, and taking $K_c = 4.00$, equation 4.7 for plates supported along both edges may be rewritten in the following form, where f is in psi:

$$b_e/t = \frac{10{,}320}{\sqrt{f}}\left[1 - \frac{2580}{b/t\ \sqrt{f}}\right] \qquad (4.11)$$

The equation is valid when $b/t > 5160/\sqrt{f}$; the effective width is equal to the actual width for smaller b/t values.

Similarly, Equation 4.8 for plates supported along one edge may be written as:

$$b_e/t = \frac{4340}{\sqrt{f}}\left(1 - \frac{1090}{b/t\ \sqrt{f}}\right) \qquad (4.12)$$

where f is in psi. The equation is valid when $b/t > 2170/\sqrt{f}$; the effective width is equal to the actual width for smaller values of b/t. As discussed in Reference 6, plates supported along only one edge and loaded into the postbuckling range generally tend to show larger distortions than similarly stressed plates supported along both longitudinal edges. Thus, in design, special care must be taken to select a suitable safety factor for use with Equation 4.12 so that undesirable distortions will not occur at design load.

The stress in a plate for a given load can be calculated only by trial, since b_e is a function of f. Similarly, the deflection of a plate or a shape in which one or more elements are in the postbuckling range can be calculated only by trial. The effective width at the given load must be obtained by trial from Equation 4.11 or 4.12

and must be used to calculate the stiffness of the plate or shape at that load.

Sections consisting entirely of plates supported along one edge only, such as angles and cruciform sections, tend to twist when the

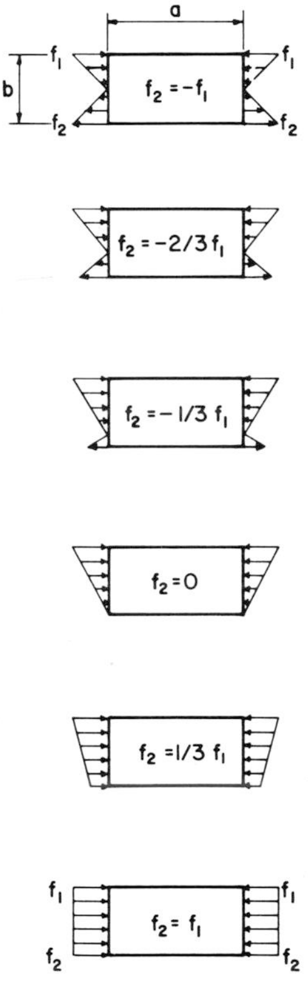

LOADING	RATIO OF BENDING STRESS TO UNIFORM COMPRESSION STRESS, f_b/f_c	MINIMUM BUCKLING COEFFICIENT,[*] k_1	
		UNLOADED EDGES SIMPLY SUPPORTED	UNLOADED EDGES FIXED
$f_2 = -f_1$	∞ (PURE BENDING)	23.9	39.6
$f_2 = -2/3 f_1$	5.00	15.7	
$f_2 = -1/3 f_1$	2.00	11.0	
$f_2 = 0$	1.00	7.8	13.6
$f_2 = 1/3 f_1$	0.50	5.8	
$f_2 = f_1$	0.00 (PURE COMPRESSION)	4.0	6.97

[*] VALUES GIVEN ARE BASED ON PLATES HAVING LOADED EDGES SIMPLY SUPPORTED AND ARE CONSERVATIVE FOR PLATES HAVING LOADED EDGES FIXED.

FIGURE 4.5 BUCKLING COEFFICIENTS FOR FLAT PLATES UNDER COMPRESSION AND BENDING

plates reach their local buckling load. Thus, local buckling of the individual plates corresponds to torsional buckling of the member as a whole, and the sections are not usually considered to have significant postbuckling strength. However, some recent investigators[9] have shown that cruciform sections made from plates do have significant postbuckling strength, and that the strength of such a section is given conservatively by Equation 4.6.

4.2.2 *Compression and Bending*

When in-plane bending stresses act simultaneously with uniform compression stresses, the sum of the applied edge stress varies along the loaded edges of the plate from a maximum compressive stress, f_1, to a minimum stress f_2, as shown in Figure 4.5. The behavior of plates under these loading conditions is generally similar to that discussed in the preceding section. For the elastic range, the value of f_1 at buckling, f_{cr1}, is

$$f_{cr1} = \frac{k_1 \pi^2 E}{12 (1 - u^2) (b/t)^2} = \frac{26.2 \times 10^6 \ k_1}{(b/t)^2} \qquad (4.13)$$

where k_1 is a nondimensional plate buckling coefficient that depends primarily on the type of edge support and on the ratio of bending stress to uniform compressive stress, f_b/f_c. Minimum values of k_1 for two edge conditions are given in Figure 4.5.[10] The plate buckling coefficient, k_1 is independent of a/b for values of $a/b \geq 1.0$, and are conservative for $a/b < 1.0$. For stress ratios not shown in Figure 4.5, values of k_1 can be obtained by linear interpolation or by the method given in Section 4.2.4.

For the inelastic range, a reasonable estimate of the value of f_1 at buckling can be obtained from Equation 4.4 by substituting k_1 for k_c. Specific information on the postbuckling strength of plates under simultaneous bending and compression is not available.

4.2.3 *Shear*

As illustrated by the sketch in Figure 4.6, a plate subjected to uniformly distributed shear stress along all four edges develops internal tension and compression stresses that are a maximum on planes at 45° to the edges and equal to the edge shear stress. Thus, when increasing shear stresses are applied, the internal compression stress increases and the plate eventually buckles.

Within the elastic range the value of the shear stress at buckling, f_{crs}, is

$$f_{crs} = \frac{k_s \pi^2 E}{12 (1 - u^2) (b/t)^2} = \frac{26.2 \times 10^6 \ k_s}{(b/t)^2} \qquad (4.14)$$

where k_s is a nondimensional plate buckling coefficient that depends primarily on the type of edge supports and the a/b ratio. A plot of k_s as a function of a/b is shown in Figure 4.6 for three sets of edge conditions. Except for small a/b ratios, plates with long edges fixed and short edges simply supported have the same buckling strength as plates with all edges fixed. Although not shown in the figure, if long edges are simply supported and short edges fixed, the buckling strength of long plates will be the same as if all edges were simply supported.

Early yielding due to residual stresses and initial out-of-flatness may also cause shear-loaded plates to buckle inelastically when the shear stress is less than the yield stress in shear and less than

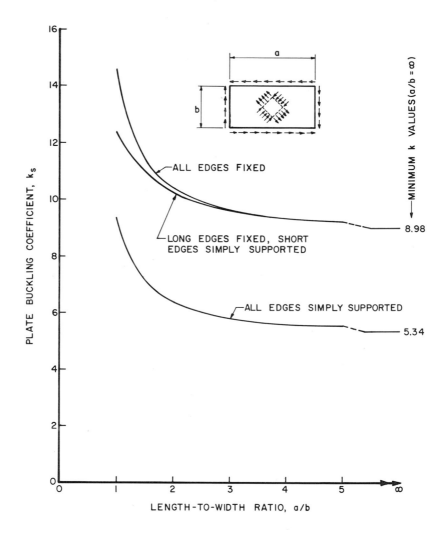

FIGURE 4.6 BUCKLING COEFFICIENTS FOR FLAT PLATES IN SHEAR

the elastic buckling stress. From the Hencky-von Mises yield criterion, the yield stress in shear, f_{ys}, is

$$f_{ys} = f_y/\sqrt{3} \qquad (4.15)$$

Thus, if f_y is replaced by $f_y/\sqrt{3}$, Equation 4.4 may be used in the following form to estimate the inelastic shear buckling stress, f'_{crs}:

$$f'_{crs} = \frac{1}{\sqrt{3}}\left[f_y - \frac{3(1 - u^2) f_y^2}{k_s \pi^2 E}\left(\frac{b}{t}\right)^2\right] \qquad (4.16)$$

4.2.4 *Shear and Other Loadings*

When shear is simultaneously applied with bending and/or uniform compression, a plate will buckle before the applied stress reaches the lowest critical value calculated for independent load-

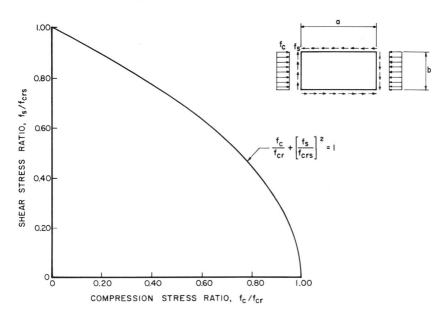

FIGURE 4.7 INTERACTION CURVE FOR BUCKLING OF FLAT PLATES UNDER SHEAR AND UNIFORM COMPRESSION

ings. Curves giving stress combinations that will cause buckling for three different combinations of loading and the interaction equations that define them are shown in Figures 4.7, 4.8, and 4.9. The curves and equations are given in terms of stress ratios, that is, ratios of applied stress to buckling stress for independent loadings. For simultaneous loadings of shear, compression, and bending, a series of curves is given in Figure 4.9 for various shear-stress ratios. The curve for zero shear stress ratio is an interaction curve for compression and bending.

Each curve has been derived for plates having $a/b \geq 1/2$, and are conservative for smaller a/b ratios. The curves are based on elastic behavior, but will give approximate results in the inelastic range if the inelastic buckling stresses are calculated by the equations given in the preceding sections.

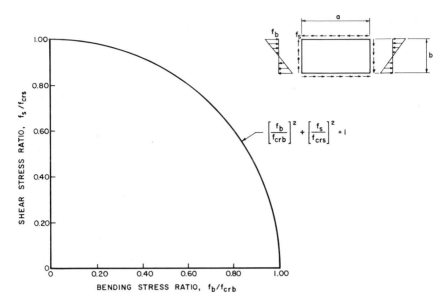

FIGURE 4.8 INTERACTION CURVE FOR BUCKLING OF
FLAT PLATES UNDER SHEAR AND BENDING

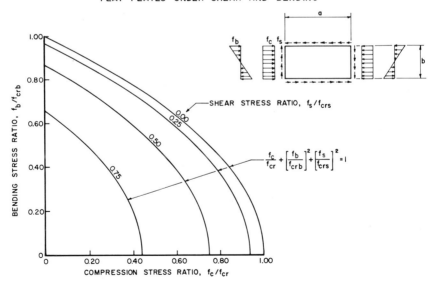

FIGURE 4.9 INTERACTION CURVE FOR BUCKLING OF FLAT
PLATES UNDER SHEAR, COMPRESSION, AND BENDING

4.3 Behavior of Longitudinally Stiffened Flat Plates Under Uniform Edge Compression

4.3.1 *Plates With Longitudinal Stiffeners Between Simply Supported Edges*

a. Buckling Behavior

The buckling behavior of a stiffened plate[10] depends on the relative stiffness of the plate and the stiffeners. If the stiffener has a relatively small stiffness, the simply supported plate and the stiffener(s) will buckle together in the mode of an unstiffened plate, although at a higher buckling stress, as illustrated by mode "a" in Figure 4.10. However, if the stiffener has sufficient bending stiffness,* the plate will buckle between the stiffeners as a series of simply supported plates, as illustrated by mode "b" in Figure 4.10. The maximum local buckling strength is obtained for the latter condition.

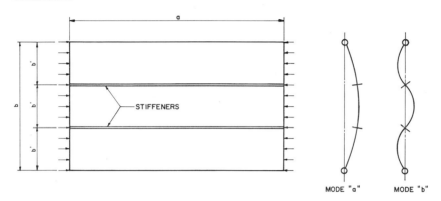

MODE "a"   MODE "b"

FIGURE 4.IO BUCKLING MODES OF A STIFFENED PLATE

The equation for the buckling strength of a stiffened plate in edge compression is the same as that for a plain plate, Equations 4.1 and 4.4, with appropriate values of k_c. The value of k_c for a stiffened plate must satisfy the theoretically derived equation

$$\gamma = \phi + \left[\left(\frac{a}{b} \right)^2 \left(\frac{A_s}{bt} \right) \right] k_c \qquad (4.17)$$

where ϕ is a nondimensional parameter that depends on a/b and k_c, A_s is the area of one stiffener, and γ is the ratio of the moment of inertia of one stiffener, I_s, to the moment of inertia of the entire plate. Thus, γ may be expressed as

$$\gamma = \frac{12 (1 - u^2) I_s}{bt^3} = \frac{10.9 I_s}{bt^3} \qquad (4.18)$$

Because part of the adjacent plate tends to act with the stiffener, I_s may be taken as the moment of inertia of a section composed of the stiffener and an effective portion of the plate having a width[10]

---

*The torsional stiffness of the stiffener is conservatively neglected in this discussion.

of $6000t/\sqrt{f_y}$ about the centroidal axis parallel to the plane of the plate.

The relation between ϕ, k_c, and a/b is shown in Figures 4.11, 4.12, and 4.13, respectively, for plates with one, two, or three equally spaced longitudinal stiffeners. Since ϕ and k_c are not independent terms, the following procedure must be used to determine the buckling stress of a given stiffened plate:

1. Calculate γ from Equation 4.18.
2. Calculate the bracketed term in Equation 4.17.
3. For the known a/b ratio, choose corresponding values of k_c and ϕ from the appropriate figure that will satisfy Equation 4.17. This may be done by a trial-and-error procedure or by the direct graphical method illustrated in Design Example 4.5.
4. Use the value of k_c obtained to calculate f_{cr} from Equation 4.1 or 4.4.

The maximum k_c values given in Figures 4.11, 4.12, and 4.13 (that is, 16, 36, and 64, respectively) will give the local buckling stress of the plate when the plate buckles as individual plates between stiffeners — the maximum buckling stress of the plate. The minimum I_s required to obtain this maximum local buckling strength can be determined as follows:

1. Select a trial stiffener section and compute A_s/bt and I_s.
2. From the appropriate figure, find the value of ϕ for the known a/b ratio and the maximum k_c shown in the figure.
3. Use the value of ϕ thus determined, the maximum k_c, and the trial value of A_s/bt to calculate γ from Equation 4.17 and I_s from Equation 4.18.
4. Repeat the procedure until the I_s of the trial stiffener section equals or exceeds the value calculated by using Equation 4.18. The local buckling strength of the plate cannot be increased by increasing I_s above this value.

b. Postbuckling Behavior

The bending stiffness of the stiffener required to ensure that a stiffened plate can reach the ultimate strength of the plate between stiffeners as calculated from Equation 4.9,* is greater than that required to develop the maximum local buckling stress of these plates. The required value of I_s has been determined experimentally to be the larger of the following values:[11)

$$I_s = 3.66 \ t^4 \ \sqrt{(b'/t)^2 - 144} \qquad (4.19)$$

$$I_s = 18.4 \ t^4 \qquad (4.20)$$

---

*A stiffened plate that is not loaded by actual compressive end forces but is subjected to compressive stresses that arise in bending (for example, a longitudinal stiffened compression flange of a box girder) will have a lower strength than that predicted by Equation 4.9 because of a "shear lag" effect. This is discussed in References 6 and 11.

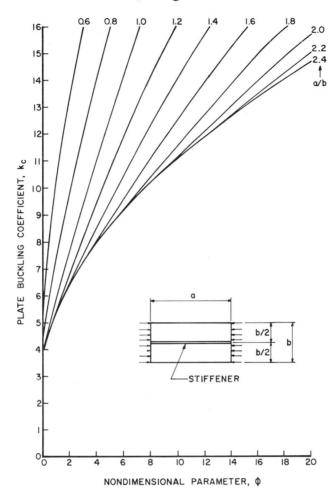

FIGURE 4.II BUCKLING COEFFICIENTS FOR STIFFENED PLATES UNDER UNIFORM COMPRESSION (ONE LONGITUDINAL STIFFENER AT MID – POINT)

where b' is the plate width between stiffeners. When postbuckling strength is considered, I_s must be calculated for the stiffener only about its centroidal axis because at ultimate load, the plate adjacent to the stiffener has yielded, and thus does not contribute to bending stiffness.

4.3.2 *Plates Stiffened Along One Longitudinal Edge*
a. Buckling Behavior

The behavior of an edge-stiffened plate is generally similar to that discussed in the previous section. If the edge stiffener has a relatively small stiffness, the plate and stiffener will buckle together in the mode of a plate with a free longitudinal edge as shown

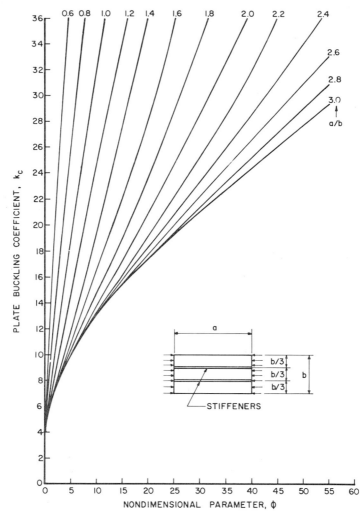

FIGURE 4.12 BUCKLING COEFFICIENTS FOR STIFFENED PLATES UNDER UNIFORM COMPRESSION (TWO LONGITUDINAL STIFFENERS AT THIRD POINTS)

in Figure 4.14a. However, the maximum local buckling strength is obtained when the edge stiffener has sufficient bending stiffness to cause the plate to buckle in the mode of a plate simply supported along both longitudinal edges as shown in Figure 4.14b. The buckling stress for mode b can be calculated from Equation 4.1 or 4.4 with $k_c = 4.0$.

The required value of I_s for maximum local buckling strength has been theoretically determined as the larger of the following values:[10]

$$I_s = 1.85bt^3 + 2.73\,A_s t^2 \tag{4.21}$$

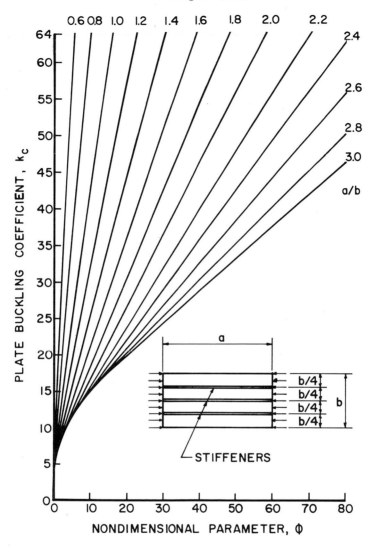

FIGURE 4.13 BUCKLING COEFFICIENTS FOR STIFFENED PLATES UNDER UNIFORM COMPRESSION (THREE LONGITUDINAL STIFFENERS AT QUARTER POINTS)

$$I_s = 1.18bt^3 \left(\frac{a}{b} - 0.41 \right)^2 + 0.47t^2 + 0.43A_s t^2 \left(\frac{a}{b} \right)^2 \quad \textbf{(4.22)}$$

I_s may be calculated for a section comprising the stiffener (along one edge) and an effective plate width of $3000t/\sqrt{f_y}$.

The local buckling strength of an edge-stiffened plate with I_s

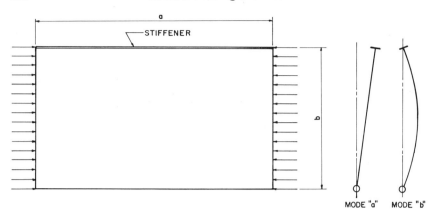

FIGURE 4.14 BUCKLING MODES OF AN EDGE-STIFFENED PLATE

smaller than the required value can be determined by the method given in Reference 10 or it may be determined from Equation 4.1 or 4.4 by conservatively assuming that k_c is equal to 0.425—the value for a plate with a free longitudinal edge.

b. Postbuckling Behavior

The moment of inertia of the stiffener that is required to develop the full postbuckling strength of a long plate has been experimentally determined as the larger of the following values:[11]

$$I_s = 1.83t^4 \sqrt{(b/t)^2 - 144} \qquad \textbf{(4.23)}$$

$$I_s = 9.2t^4 \qquad \textbf{(4.24)}$$

The value of I_s must be calculated for the stiffener only, since the plate material will yield and not contribute to stiffness when ultimate load is reached. If the above stiffness is furnished, the ultimate buckling strength of the plate will be that given by Equation 4.10 for a plate with simply supported longitudinal edges when the plate is loaded by compressive end forces.*

4.4 Design of Flat Plates

4.4.1 *Design Based on Local Buckling Strength*

a. Elastic Design

If the width-to-thickness ratios of the various plate elements of structural members are limited so that local buckling cannot occur before the yield stress is reached, such members may be designed according to the usual elastic theory in which the sectional properties of the full section are considered. This design method is usually followed for hot-rolled structural shapes and fabricated shapes such as those used in the principal members of buildings

---

*See footnote preceding.

and bridges. Limiting width-to-thickness ratios for plate elements in such elastically designed members are given in Tables 4.1 and 4.2. As indicated in the tables, the ratios listed are based on the requirements of AISC,[12] AASHO,[13] or AREA.[14] However, the listed values may differ slightly from those given in the specifications because the specifications generally give "rounded-off" values. These limiting allowable b/t values are smaller than the theoretical values for perfect plates given by Equation 4.2 to compensate for the effects of residual stresses and initial imperfection. AISC and AASHO allow larger width-to-thickness ratios for perforated cover plates than for solid plates because the stress in the solid portion of a plate between perforations is considerably less than the average stress. AISC also allows greater ratios for the stems of tees than for projecting girder flanges because the edge restraint present in the tee is greater.

From the requirements of AISC, a relation is given in Table 4.1 for limiting width-to-thickness ratios that allow webs without stiffeners to reach the shearing yield stress without buckling. As indicated in Table 4.2, both AASHO and AREA give limiting width-to-thickness ratios for webs of beams without stiffeners that allow the web to be stressed to the yield stress in shear or bending or both without buckling. Greater ratios can be used when the webs are stiffened or when the stresses are less than the basic allowable stress.

b. Elastic Design of Compact Sections

The limiting width-to-thickness ratios given above enable plate elements to reach their yield stress without buckling. However, more restrictive ratios have been determined that will allow the plate elements of members not only to reach the yield stress but also to undergo large plastic strains. Structural members consisting of plate elements not exceeding these more restrictive ratios are referred to as "compact sections." Because such sections can reach an ultimate bending moment that is greater than the yield moment (the plastic moment*) the AISC permits an increased allowable stress of $0.66f_y$ for "laterally supported"** beams that meet the requirements for a compact section given in Table 4.3. In other words, members that have plate elements that do not exceed the maximum ratios listed in Table 4.3 may be designed in the usual elastic manner but an allowable stress of $0.66f_y$ instead of the allowable stress of $0.60f_y$ for noncompact sections. Sufficient information is not presently available on similar local buckling requirements for steels having yield stresses higher than those listed in the table.

4.4.2 *Design Based on Postbuckling Strength*

The **ultimate** load, P_u, of a plate loaded in edge compression may be expressed as

---

*See Chapter 5 for a discussion of this behavior.
**See Chapter 6 for lateral support requirements.

$$P_u = \left(\frac{b_e}{t}\right) t^2 f_y \qquad \textbf{(4.25)}$$

To calculate the ultimate load, the effective width, b_e, must be calculated at a stress of f_y, that is, with $f = f_y$ in Equation 4.11 or 4.12. Values of b_e/t for plates loaded in compression and supported along both longitudinal edges are listed in Table 4.4 for various steel yield stresses and b/t ratios. Although these b_e/t ratios were developed for light-gage members, Equation 4.11 may be used conservatively for thicker plate elements. The ultimate load may be divided by a safety factor to obtain a design load.

4.5 Design of Stiffened Plates Under Uniform Edge Compression

Where wide plates are required in structural members, it is often structurally efficient to use longitudinal stiffeners and thereby minimize the plate thickness. Although the design method may vary with the type of structure, the following procedures are generally applicable.*

If the design is based on buckling strength and the maximum buckling strength is desired, select the number of stiffeners and the plate thickness so that local buckling between stiffeners (or between a stiffener and a supported edge) is prevented. This may be done by limiting the width-to-thickness ratio between stiffeners to an appropriate value such as those given in Table 4.1 or 4.2 for plates supported along both edges. Then, proportion the stiffeners so that the minimum I_s is provided in accordance with the procedure given in Section 4.3.1a or 4.3.2a. The design load is then equal to the product of the design stress and the area.

If the design is based on postbuckling strength, select a trial plate thickness and number of stiffeners. Calculate the minimum I_s by the equations given in Section 4.3.1b or 4.3.2b. A design load based on the effective width between stiffeners may then be determined as explained in Section 4.4.2.

4.6 Circular Tubes

4.6.1 *Uniform Compression*

When the elastic local buckling load is reached, the walls of a cylindrical tube loaded in uniform axial compression will deflect into a pattern of diamond-shaped dimples. According to elastic theory, the buckling stress for a long perfect tube of radius R is

$$f_{cr} = \frac{E}{\sqrt{3\,(1-u^2)}}\frac{t}{R} = 0.60\,\frac{Et}{R} \qquad \textbf{(4.26)}$$

where t is the tube wall thickness. Because of the influence of the end supports, short tubes theoretically have a greater buckling stress. However, such short tubes are not generally of interest in structural applications and will not be considered in this manual.

---

*Shear lag must be considered in certain multiple-stiffened elements. See References 6 and 11.

The information presented in succeeding paragraphs may be used conservatively for all tube lengths.

When a tube subjected to longitudinal compressive stresses buckles, transverse (circumferential) compressive stresses develop in the tube wall. Because the buckled form of a tube is unstable and cannot resist these stresses, the tube has no usable post-buckling strength. For the same reason, a tube is generally sensitive to initial imperfections and may buckle at a stress smaller than the theoretical elastic local buckling stress.

Shown in Figure 4.15 is a nondimensional plot of the theoretical elastic local buckling curve, as well as curves based on test data.[6] The test curves show that tubes with a slenderness parameter, $\dfrac{f_v}{E}\dfrac{R}{t}$, of 0.064 or less can be stressed to their yield stress without buckling, whereas tubes with larger slenderness parameters will buckle at lower stresses. Generally, tubes for most structural applications will have a slenderness parameter less than 0.20. The portion of the test curve for slenderness parameters greater than 0.20 is shown as a dashed line because its location is not definitely established. Available data indicate that the dashed-line curve may be overconservative for hot-rolled tubes, but may not be conservative for tubes fabricated from plates because of their inherent initial imperfections.

4.6.2 *Bending*

The local buckling behavior of the compressed portion of a cylindrical tube in bending is similar to that of a tube under axial compression. Some information[15] suggests that because of the beneficial effect of the stress gradient, the elastic buckling stress of tubes is about 1.3 times the local buckling stress for axial compression. However, the information given in the preceding section can be conservatively applied to tubes in bending.

As previously explained, structural sections that have sufficient stiffness do not buckle upon reaching the yield stress, but can undergo large plastic strains and reach an ultimate or plastic moment that is greater than the yield moment. Tests have shown that structural steel tubes with a slenderness parameter of 0.060 or less can reach their full plastic moment and, thus, may be treated as "compact sections."

4.6.3 *Shear*

Shear buckling can occur in tubes that are loaded in torsion or in transverse (beam) shear. Within the elastic range, the local buckling strength of tubes in torsion with a radius R is given by the equations

$$f_{crs} = 0.632E\left(\frac{t}{R}\right)^{5/4}\left(\frac{R}{L}\right)^{1/2} \tag{4.27}$$

$$\text{when } 10\left(\frac{t}{R}\right)^{1/2} < \frac{L}{R} < 3\left(\frac{R}{t}\right)^{1/2}$$

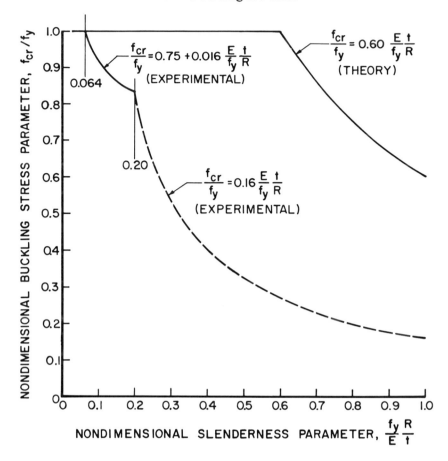

FIGURE 4.15 NONDIMENSIONAL BUCKLING CURVE
FOR CIRCULAR TUBES IN COMPRESSION

and

$$f_{crs} = 0.248E\left(\frac{t}{R}\right)^{3/2} \tag{4.28}$$

$$\text{when } \frac{L}{R} > 3\left(\frac{R}{t}\right)^{1/2}$$

Both equations have been derived from theory, but contain a 15 percent reduction, since test values generally are about 15 percent below the theoretical values for perfect tubes. Equation 4.27, which depends in part on the tube length, was derived for tubes having pinned ends. Tubes with fixed ends would theoretically have a buckling stress about 10 percent higher. Equation 4.27 may also be used conservatively for tubes having $L/R < 10\left(\dfrac{t}{R}\right)^{1/2}$. The yield stress in shear, $f_y/\sqrt{3}$, is considered the upper limit of shear buckling strength, f_{crs}.

For tubes loaded in transverse shear, the buckling stress may be considered conservatively as 1.3 times the buckling stress in torsion, but again, no greater than $f_y/\sqrt{3}$. The increase results from the beneficial effect of the stress gradient that is present in transverse shear.

4.6.4 *Shear and Other Loadings*

For tubes subjected to combined loadings, the stresses that will cause buckling can be estimated conservatively from the interaction equation

$$\frac{f_c}{f_{cr}}+\left(\frac{f_s}{f_{crs}}\right)^2 = 1 \qquad\qquad (4.29)$$

where f_c is the maximum compressive stress that results from uniform compression or bending or both, f_{cr} is the critical stress for uniform compression only (Figure 4.15), f_s is the maximum shear stress that results from torsion or transverse shear or both, and f_{crs} is the critical stress for torsion only (Equation 4.27 or 4.28).

4.7 Design Examples

Example 4.1

The welded box section shown at the right is a long axial loaded compression member that has been laterally supported to prevent column buckling. The section has been fabricated from USS EX-TEN 50 steel. Determine a design load for the section by the following four methods:

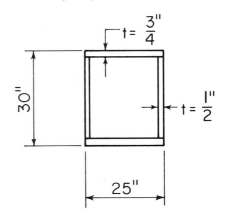

a. Assume that the plate elements are simply supported at the corners and a safety factor of 1.65 against local buckling is desired.

b. Consider the interaction of adjacent elements and provide a safety factor of 1.65 against local buckling.

c. Use the limiting width ratios and the basic allowable stress corresponding to AISC requirements given in Table 4.1.

d. Assume that a safety factor of 1.65 against ultimate failure is desired.

Solution:

a. For the ½-inch-thick plate, $b/t = 28.5/.50 = 57.0$
For the ¾-inch-thick plate, $b/t = 24.0/.75 = 32.0$

By using the larger b/t and $k_c = 4.0$, Figure 4.2, the following value for f_{cr} is obtained:

$$f_{cr} = \frac{26.2 \times 10^6 \, k_c}{(b/t)^2} = \frac{26.2 \times 10^6 \times 4.0}{(57.0)^2} = 32,300 \text{ psi} \quad \textbf{(Equation 4.1)}$$

Since $f_{cr} > f_y/2$ (Figure 4.1), buckling will occur in the inelastic range. Therefore,

$$f'_{cr} = f_y - \frac{f_y^2}{4f_{cr}} = 50,000 - \frac{(50,000)^2}{4 \times 32,300} = 30,600 \text{ psi} \qquad \textbf{(Equation 4.4)}$$

Total area of section is 66.0 in.²

$$\text{Design load} = \frac{30,600 \times 66.0}{1.65} = \textbf{1220 kips}$$

b. $\dfrac{b_f}{b_w} = \dfrac{24.0}{28.5} = 0.842 \qquad \dfrac{t_f}{t_w} = \dfrac{0.75}{0.50} = 1.50$

$k_w = 5.9$ (Figure 4.3c)

$$f_{cr} = \frac{26.2 \times 10^6 \times 5.9}{(57.0)^2} = 47,600 \text{ psi} > f_y/2 \qquad \textbf{(Equation 4.1)}$$

Therefore, $f_{cr} = 50,000 - \dfrac{(50,000)^2}{4 \times 47,600} = 36,900 \text{ psi}$ \qquad **(Equation 4.4)**

$$\text{Design load} = \frac{36,900 \times 66.0}{1.65} = \textbf{1480 kips}$$

c. From Table 4.1, the limiting b/t permitted for stress calculations is 35.8. For the ½-inch-thick plate, b/t > 35.8; therefore, calculate load for $b = 35.8 \times ½ = 17.9$ in.

For the ¾-in-thick plate, b/t < 35.8; therefore, full width is effective. Area for stress calculation = $(17.9 \times ½ \times 2) + (25.0 \times ¾ \times 2) = 55.4$ in.²

Design load = $30,000 \times 55.4 = \textbf{1660 kips}$

d. From Table 4.4, for b/t = 57.0, $b_e/t = 36.8$
for b/t = 32.0, $b_e/t = 29.2$

Effective area = $\Sigma[b_e/t]t^2 + \Sigma$ corner areas = $(36.8 \times ½ \times ½ \times 2) +$

$(29.2 \times ¾ \times ¾ \times 2) + (½ \times ¾ \times 4) = 52.7$ in.²

$$\text{Design load} = \frac{50,000 \times 52.7}{1.65} = \textbf{1600 kips}$$

Comment on Solution:

Solution "a" and "b" provide a safety factor of 1.65 against local buckling and, therefore, give smaller design loads than do solutions "c" and "d" because solution "c," indirectly, and solution "d," directly, provide a safety factor of 1.65 against ultimate failure. The design load given by "b" is greater than that given by "a'" because of the beneficial effect of the edge restraint of adjacent plates.

Example 4.2

A 20-inch-wide by ½-inch-thick steel plate is simply supported along both longitudinal unloaded edges and is subjected to a uniform end compression loading. Determine the load that will cause local buckling and the load that will cause **ultimate** failure if the plate is (a) USS TRI-TEN steel and (b) USS "T-1" steel.

Solution:

a. TRI-TEN Steel

$$b/t = 20 \div \tfrac{1}{2} = 40 \qquad\qquad b_e/t = 32.7 \qquad\qquad \textbf{(Table 4.4)}$$

$$f_{cr} = \frac{26.2 \times 10^6 \times 4.00}{(40)^2} = 65{,}500 \text{ psi} > f_y/2 \qquad\qquad \textbf{(Equation 4.1)}$$

$$f'_{cr} = 50{,}000 - \frac{(50{,}000)^2}{4 \times 65{,}500} = 40{,}500 \text{ psi} \qquad\qquad \textbf{(Equation 4.4)}$$

Local buckling load $= 40{,}500 \times 20 \times \tfrac{1}{2} = $ **405 kips**
Ultimate load $= 50{,}000 \times 32.7 \times \tfrac{1}{2} \times \tfrac{1}{2} = $ **409 kips** $\qquad$ **(Equation 4.25)**

b. "T-1 Steel

$b_e/t = 25.8$ (Table 4.4)
$f_{cr} = 41{,}900 \text{ psi} < f_y/2$ $\qquad\qquad\qquad\qquad\qquad\qquad$ **(Equation 4.1)**
Local buckling load $= 41{,}900 \times 20 \times \tfrac{1}{2} = $ **419 kips**
Ultimate load $= 100{,}000 \times 25.8 \times \tfrac{1}{2} \times \tfrac{1}{2} = $ **645 kips** $\qquad$ **(Equation 4.25)**

Example 4.3

Determine the maximum total outstanding width of a ¾-inch-thick flange for a welded A36 steel plate girder to meet each of the following three requirements:

a. AISC requirements for a compact section.
b. AISC requirements for a noncompact section.
c. AASHO requirements.

Solution:

a. From Table 4.3, projecting width ÷ thickness $= 8.5$
   Total outstanding width is $2 \times \tfrac{3}{4} \times 8.5 = $ **12.75 in.**
b. From Table 4.1, projecting width ÷ thickness $= 15.8$
   Total outstanding width is $2 \times \tfrac{3}{4} \times 15.8 = $ **23.7 in.**
c. From Table 4.2, projecting width ÷ thickness $= 11.5$
   Total outstanding width is $2 \times \tfrac{3}{4} \times 11.5 = $ **17.25 in.**

Example 4.4

A rectangular plate of A36 steel has the following dimensions: width—30 in., length—60 in., and thickness—¼ in. The plate is subjected to an edge shear stress of 3000 psi and a uniform compression stress of 4000 psi. Determine the bending stress that will cause buckling. The uniform compression stress and bending stress are both applied along the width of the plate. All edges are simply supported.

Solution:

Buckling stresses for the individual loading must be calculated.

$b/t = 30 \div \tfrac{1}{4} = 120 \qquad a/b = 60/30 = 2.00$
$k_s = 6.34$ **(Figure 4.6)** $\qquad k_c = 4.00$ **(Figure 4.2)**
$k_b = 23.9$ **(Figure 4.5)**

$$f_{crs} = \frac{26.2 \times 10^6 \times 6.34}{(120)^2} = 11{,}500 \text{ psi} < \frac{1}{2}f_{ys} \qquad\qquad \textbf{(Equation 4.14)}$$

$$f_{cr} = \frac{26.2 \times 10^6 \times 4.00}{(120)^2} = 7280 \text{ psi} < \frac{1}{2}f_y \qquad\qquad \textbf{(Equation 4.13)}$$

$$f_{crb} = \frac{26.2 \times 10^6 \times 23.9}{(120)^2} = 43{,}500 \text{ psi} > \frac{1}{2}f_y \qquad\qquad \textbf{(Equation 4.13)}$$

$$f'_{crb} = 36{,}000 - \frac{(36{,}000)^2}{4 \times 43{,}500} = 28{,}500 \text{ psi} \qquad\qquad \textbf{(Equation 4.4)}$$

$$\frac{f_c}{f_{cr}} = \frac{4000}{7280} = 0.549 \qquad \frac{f_s}{f_{crs}} = \frac{3000}{11500} = 0.261$$

$$\frac{f_b}{f_{crb}} = 0.618 \qquad\qquad\qquad\qquad\qquad \textbf{(Figure 4.9)}$$

Therefore, the bending stress that will cause buckling for the combined loading is $0.618 \times 28{,}500 = $ **17,600 psi**

Example 4.5

A simply supported USS EX-TEN 42 steel plate having a width of 57 in., a length of 114 in., and a thickness of ½ in. is subjected to a uniform end compression loading.

   a. Determine the location and size of angle stiffeners to develop the **maximum ultimate** load (yield load) of the plate. (Assume that the stiffened plate is part of a building framework.)

   b. Determine the buckling load of the plate when stiffened at third points by angles with dimensions of 4 in. by 3 in. by ¼ in.

   c. Determine the size of stiffener required to develop the postbuckling strength of the plate when only one stiffener is used at the midpoint of the plate. Determine the ultimate load of the plate.*

Solution:

   a. From Table 4.1, the maximum width-to-thickness ratio for a solid USS EX-TEN 42 steel plate simply supported along both edges is 39.0. Therefore, the maximum unsupported plate width is $39.0 \times ½ = 19.5$ in. Place stiffeners at third points as shown below.

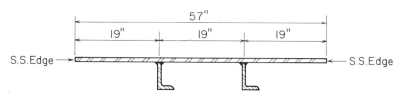

Try stiffener angles $6 \times 3½ \times ¼$ made of USS EX-TEN 42 steel.

For vertical leg, $b/t = 6 \div ¼ = 24 < 39.0$ O.K. **(Table 4.1)**

For other leg, $b/t = 3.5 \div ¼ = 14 < 14.6$ O.K. **(Table 4.1)**

As shown below, a plate width of $6000\ t/\sqrt{f_y}$ or 14.6 in. may be assumed to act with the angle when I_s is computed.

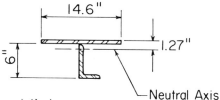

$I_s = 40.8$ in.⁴ (from statics)

$$\frac{A_s}{bt} = \frac{2.31}{57 \times ½} = 0.0810$$

$a/b = 114/57 = 2.0 \qquad k_c = 36$ and $\phi = 38$ \qquad\qquad **(Figure 4.12)**

---

* The load carried by the stiffeners may be added to that carried by the plate.

$$\gamma = \phi + \left[\left(\frac{a}{b}\right)^2 \left(\frac{A_s}{bt}\right)\right] k_c = 38 + 2 \times 2 \times .0810 \times 36 = 49.7$$

(Equation 4.17)

$$I_s = \frac{\gamma bt^3}{10.9} = \frac{49.7 \times 57 \times (\frac{1}{2})^3}{10.9} = 32.5 \text{ in.}^4$$

(Equation 4.18)

The I_s furnished, 40.8 in.^{4}, is greater than the minimum required I_s, 32.5. Therefore, the angles selected are satisfactory. The buckling stress of the plate may be considered to be the yield stress, 42,000 psi, and the ultimate load of the plate is 42,000 × 57 × ½ = **1200 kips.**

b. The section for determining the moment of inertia is as shown below.

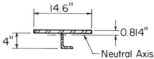

$I_s = 15.3$ in.^{4} (from statics)

$$\frac{A_s}{bt} = \frac{1.69}{57 \times \frac{1}{2}} = 0.0593$$

$$\gamma = \frac{10.9 \, I_s}{bt^3} = \frac{10.9 \times 15.3}{57 \times (\frac{1}{2})^3} = 23.4$$

(Equation 4.19)

$$\left[\left(\frac{a}{b}\right)^2 \left(\frac{A_s}{bt}\right)\right] = 2 \times 2 \times .0593 = 0.237$$

$$23.4 = \phi + 0.237 \, k_c$$

(Equation 4.17)

This equation relating ϕ and k_c is that of a straight line. Therefore, select two arbitrary values of k_c and calculate corresponding values of ϕ from the equation. Locate these two points in Figure 4.12 and connect with a straight line. The intersection of the straight line with the line for $a/b = 2.0$ gives the correct value of k_c as illustrated below.

If $k_c = 4.0$, $\phi = 23.4 - .237 \times 4.0 = 22.5$
If $k_c = 36.0$, $\phi = 23.4 - .237 \times 36.0 = 14.9$

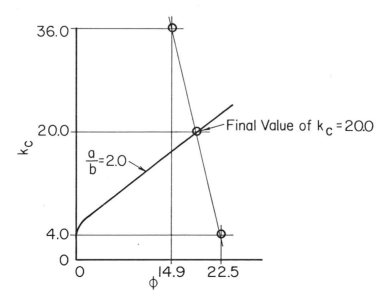

$$f_{cr} = \frac{26.2 \times 10^6 \times 20.0}{(57 \div \frac{1}{2})^2} = 40{,}300 \text{ psi} > f_y/2 \qquad \textbf{(Equation 4.1)}$$

$$f'_{cr} = 42{,}000 - \frac{(42{,}000)^2}{4 \times 40{,}300} = 31{,}100 \text{ psi} \qquad \textbf{(Equation 4.4)}$$

The buckling stress of the plate is 31,000 psi and the buckling load of the plate is $31{,}100 \times 57 \times \frac{1}{2} =$ **886 kips.**

c. The minimum I_s is the larger value given by the following two equations:

$$I_s = 3.66 \, t^4 \sqrt{(b'/t)^2 - 144}$$

$$= 3.66 \left(\frac{1}{2}\right)^4 \sqrt{(28.5 \div \frac{1}{2})^2 - 144} \qquad \textbf{(Equation 4.19)}$$

$$= 12.7 \text{ in.}^4$$

$$I_s = 18.4 \, t^4 = 18.4 \left(\frac{1}{2}\right)^4 = 1.15 \qquad \textbf{(Equation 4.20)}$$

Therefore, the minimum I_s is 12.7 in.⁴ Plate material cannot be considered effective for moment of inertia in postbuckling strength calculations.

Select a **6⊏8.2** having $I = 13.0$ in.⁴

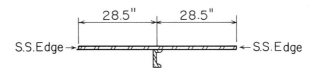

$$b/t = 28.5/0.50 = 57$$

$$b_e/t = 39.2 \qquad \textbf{(Table 4.4)}$$

The ultimate load of the plate is $2 \times 42{,}000 \times 39.2 \times \frac{1}{2} \times \frac{1}{2} =$ **824 kips**

Example 4.6

Determine the maximum design load that will provide a safety factor of 1.65 against local buckling for a round tubular column made of a steel having a yield stress of 52,000 psi, an outside diameter of 24 in., and a wall thickness of 0.250 in.

Solution:

$$\frac{f_y R}{Et} = \frac{52{,}000 \times 11.875}{29 \times 10^6 \times 0.250} = 0.0852$$

$$\frac{f_{cr}}{f_y} = 0.938 \qquad \textbf{(Figure 4.15)}$$

$$f_{cr} = 0.938 \times 52{,}000 = 48{,}800 \text{ psi}$$

$$\text{Design load} = \frac{48{,}800 \times 18.6}{1.65} = \textbf{550 kips}$$

Note: This member must also be checked for column buckling.

References (Chapter 4)

1. S. P. Timoshenko and J. M. Gere, **Theory of Elastic Stability,** McGraw-Hill Book Company, 1961.

2. G. Haaijer and B. Thurlimann, "On Inelastic Buckling in Steel," **Journal of the Engineering Mechanics Division, Proceedings** ASCE, **84,** No. EM2, April 1958.

3. G. Haaijer, "Plate Buckling in the Strain-Hardening Range," **Journal of the Engineering Mechanics Division, Proceedings** ASCE, **83,** No. EM2, April 1957.

4. G. Gerard and H. Becker, **Handbook of Structural Stability, Part I—Buckling of Flat Plates,** NACA TN 3781, July 1957.

5. E. Z. Stowell, G. J. Heimerl, C. Libove, and E. E. Lundquist, "Buckling Stresses for Flat Plates and Sections," **Transactions** ASCE, 1951.

6. G. Winter, Commentary on the 1962 edition of **Light Gage Cold-Formed Steel Design Manual,** American Iron and Steel Institute, 1962.

7. T. von Karman, E. F. Sechler, and L. H. Donnell, "The Strength of Thin Plates in Compression," **Transactions** ASME, 54, No. 2, January 30, 1932.

8. J. R. Jombock and J. W. Clark, "Post Buckling Behavior of Flat Plates," **Journal of the Structural Division, Proceedings** ASCE, **87,** No. ST5, June, 1961.

9. G. Haaijer, "Significant Research Data for Use in Steel Design," U. S. Steel Corporation, Design and Engineering Seminar, ADUSS 91-1008, 1964.

10. F. Bleich, **Buckling Strength of Metal Structures,** McGraw-Hill Book Company, 1952.

11. American Iron and Steel Institute, **Light Gage Cold-Formed Steel Design Manual,** 1962.

12. American Institute of Steel Construction, "Specification for the Design, Fabrication, and Erection of Structural Steel for Buildings." 1963.

13. American Association of State Highway Officials, "Standard Specifications for Highway Bridges," 1965.

14. American Railway Engineering Association. "Standard Specifications for Steel Railway Bridges," 1965.

15. G. Gerard and H. Becker, **Handbook of Structural Stability, Part III—Buckling of Curved Plates and Shells,** NACA TN 3783, August 1957.

Table 4.1

Maximum Width-to-Thickness Ratios for Plate Elements in Elastically Designed Structural Members of Buildings*

Specified Minimum Yield Stress, psi	Plates in Compression Supported Along One Edge			Plates in Compression Supported Along Both Edges		Plates in Shear Supported Along Both Edges (Unstiffened Girder Webs)
	Single Angle Struts	Outstanding Flanges or Plates, Double Angle Struts, and Plate Girder Stiffeners	Stems of Tees	Solid Plates	Perforated Plates	
	$\dfrac{2400}{\sqrt{f_y}}$	$\dfrac{3000}{\sqrt{f_y}}$	$\dfrac{4000}{\sqrt{f_y}}$	$\dfrac{8000}{\sqrt{f_y}}$	$\dfrac{10{,}000}{\sqrt{f_y}}$	$\dfrac{12{,}000}{\sqrt{f_y}}$
36,000	12.6	15.8	21.1	42.2	52.7	63.2
42,000	11.7	14.6	19.5	39.0	48.8	58.6
46,000	11.2	14.0	18.6	37.3	46.6	56.0
50,000	10.7	13.4	17.9	35.8	44.7	53.7
60,000	9.8	12.2	16.3	32.7	40.8	49.0
70,000	9.1	11.3	15.1	30.2	37.8	45.4
80,000	8.5	10.6	14.1	28.3	35.4	42.4
90,000	8.0	10.0	13.3	26.7	33.3	40.0
100,000	7.6	9.5	12.6	25.3	31.6	37.9

* The ratios are based on the requirements of AISC. The AISC specifies a basic allowable stress of 0.60 f_y in compression and 0.40 f_y in shear, where f_y is the yield stress in psi. When the ratios listed for plates in compression are exceeded, members are considered satisfactory if stress requirements are satisfied by a portion of the width not exceeding the ratio listed times the plate thickness. Double-angle struts with spacers are regarded as single-angle struts. The ratios listed for plates in shear are for unstiffened webs of girders that can be stressed to the basic allowable shear stress. As explained in Chapter 5, higher ratios may be used when stiffeners are provided or when the shear stress is less than 0.40 f_y. "The width of plates shall be taken from the free edge to the first row of rivets, bolts, or welds; the width of legs of angles, channels, and zees, and of the stems of tees, shall be taken as the full nominal dimension; the width of flanges of beams and tees shall be taken as one-half the full nominal width. The thickness of a sloping flange shall be measured halfway between a free edge and the corresponding face of the web."[12]

Table 4.2
Maximum Width-to-Thickness Ratios for Plate Elements in Elastically Designed Structural Members of Bridges*

Specified Minimum Yield Stress, psi	Plates in Compression Supported Along One Edge		Plates in Compression Supported Along Both Edges			Webs of Solid Rib Arches and Gusset Plates+	Plates in Shear Supported Along Both Edges (Unstiffened Girder Webs)+
	Outstanding Flanges of Main Members and Bearing Stiffeners+0	Outstanding Flanges of Secondary Railway Members0	Principal Elements+0	Connecting Elements Such as Column webs+0	Perforated Column Cover Plates+		
	$\dfrac{2180}{\sqrt{f_y}}$	$\dfrac{2540}{\sqrt{f_y}}$	$\dfrac{6030}{\sqrt{f_y}}$	$\dfrac{7540}{\sqrt{f_y}}$	$\dfrac{9080}{\sqrt{f_y}}$	$\dfrac{10{,}900}{\sqrt{f_y}}$	$\dfrac{13{,}000}{\sqrt{f_y}}$
36,000	11.5	13.4	31.8	39.8	47.9	57.4	68.5
42,000	10.6	12.4	29.4	36.8	44.3	53.2	63.4
46,000	10.2	11.8	28.1	35.1	42.3	50.8	60.6
50,000	9.7	11.4	27.0	33.8	40.6	48.7	58.1
60,000	8.9	10.4	24.6	30.8	37.1	44.5	53.1
70,000	8.2	9.6	22.8	28.4	34.3	41.2	49.1
80,000	7.7	9.0	21.3	26.6	32.1	38.5	46.0
90,000	7.3	8.5	20.1	25.1	30.3	36.3	43.3
100,000	6.9	8.0	19.1	23.8	28.7	34.5	41.1

* Columns marked "+" are based on the requirements of AASHO, and those marked "0" are based on the requirements of AREA. Both AAHSO and AREA generally specify a basic allowable stress of 0.55 f_y in compression and approximately 0.33 f_y in shear, where f_y is the yield stress in psi. See Specifications for provisions for greater width-to-thickness ratios when the calculated stress is less than the basic allowable stress. For angles, b may be taken as the nominal leg dimension. The width of rolled-beam or welded-girder flanges may be taken as one-half of the nominal width.

Table 4.3

Maximum Width-to-Thickness Ratios for Plate Elements of Compact Sections*

Specified Minimum Yield Point, psi	Plates in Compression Supported Along One Edge	Plates in Compression Supported Along Both Edges	Plates in Bending With Support Along Both Edges	Plates in Combined Compression and Bending With Support Along Both Edges (Minimum Value**)
	$\dfrac{1600}{\sqrt{f_y}}$	$\dfrac{6000}{\sqrt{f_y}}$	$\dfrac{13{,}300}{\sqrt{f_y}}$	$\dfrac{8000}{\sqrt{f_y}}$
36,000	8.5	31.6	70.1	42.2
42,000	7.8	29.3	64.9	39.0
46,000	7.5	28.0	62.0	37.3
50,000	7.2	26.8	59.5	35.8
60,000	6.5	24.5	54.3	32.7

* The ratios are based on the requirements of AISC.

** The maximum b/t for such plates equals the value tabulated, $\dfrac{8000}{\sqrt{f_y}}$,

or $\dfrac{13{,}300}{\sqrt{f_y}}\left(1 - 1.43\,\dfrac{f_a}{F_a}\right)$, whichever is larger, where f_a/F_a is the ratio of the computed axial stress to the allowable axial stress in the absence of bending.

Table 4.4
Effective Width-to-Thickness Ratios for Flat Plates in Compression Supported Along Both Longitudinal Edges*

Effective Width-to-Thickness Ratio, b_e/t, for Indicated Yield Stress in ksi

Actual Width Ratio, b/t	36.0	42.0	46.0	50.0	60.0	70.0	80.0	90.0	100.0
16	16.0	16.0	16.0	16.0	16.0	16.0	16.0	16.0	16.0
18	18.0	18.0	18.0	18.0	18.0	18.0	18.0	18.0	17.8
20	20.0	20.0	20.0	20.0	20.0	20.0	19.8	19.6	19.3
22	22.0	22.0	22.0	22.0	22.0	21.7	21.4	21.0	20.5
24	24.0	24.0	24.0	24.0	23.6	23.2	22.6	22.1	21.5
26	26.0	26.0	25.9	25.7	25.1	24.4	23.7	23.0	22.4
28	28.0	27.7	27.4	27.1	26.3	25.4	24.6	23.8	23.1
30	29.7	29.2	28.8	28.4	27.3	26.3	25.4	24.5	23.8
32	31.3	30.5	30.0	29.5	28.3	27.1	26.1	25.2	24.3
34	32.6	31.7	31.1	30.5	29.1	27.8	26.7	25.7	24.8
36	33.8	32.7	32.0	31.4	29.8	28.4	27.2	26.2	25.2
38	34.9	33.7	32.9	32.1	30.5	29.0	27.7	26.6	25.6
40	35.9	34.5	33.6	32.8	31.0	29.5	28.2	27.0	26.0
42	36.8	35.3	34.3	33.5	31.6	29.9	28.6	27.4	26.3
44	37.6	35.9	35.0	34.0	32.0	30.4	28.9	27.7	26.6
46	38.3	36.6	35.5	34.6	32.5	30.7	29.3	28.0	26.8
48	39.0	37.1	36.1	35.1	32.9	31.1	29.6	28.2	27.1
50	39.6	37.7	36.5	35.5	33.3	31.4	29.8	28.5	27.3
52	40.2	38.2	37.0	35.9	33.6	31.7	30.1	28.7	27.5
54	40.7	38.6	37.4	36.3	33.9	32.0	30.3	28.9	27.7
56	41.2	39.0	37.8	36.6	34.2	32.2	30.5	29.1	27.9
58	41.6	39.4	38.1	37.0	34.5	32.4	30.7	29.3	28.0
60	42.1	39.8	38.5	37.3	34.7	32.7	30.9	29.5	28.2
62	42.5	40.1	38.8	37.6	35.0	32.9	31.1	29.6	28.3
64	42.8	40.5	39.1	37.8	35.2	33.1	31.3	29.8	28.5
66	43.2	40.8	39.3	38.1	35.4	33.2	31.4	29.9	28.6
68	43.5	41.0	39.6	38.3	35.6	33.4	31.6	30.0	28.7
70	43.8	41.3	39.8	38.5	35.8	33.6	31.7	30.2	28.8
72	44.1	41.6	40.1	38.8	36.0	33.7	31.9	30.3	28.9
74	44.4	41.8	40.3	39.0	36.1	33.9	32.0	30.4	29.0

*The ratios are based on the requirements of AISI.

Table 4.4 (Continued)
Effective Width-to-Thickness Ratios for Flat Plates in Compression Supported Along Both Longitudinal Edges

Actual Width Ratio, b/t	Effective Width-to-Thickness Ratio, b_c/t, for Indicated Yield Stress in ksi								
	36.0	42.0	46.0	50.0	60.0	70.0	80.0	90.0	100.0
76	44.7	42.0	40.5	39.1	36.3	34.0	32.1	30.5	29.1
78	44.9	42.2	40.7	39.3	36.4	34.1	32.2	30.6	29.2
80	45.1	42.4	40.9	39.5	36.6	34.3	32.3	30.7	29.3
82	45.4	42.6	41.1	39.7	36.7	34.4	32.4	30.8	29.4
84	45.6	42.8	41.2	39.8	36.8	34.5	32.5	30.9	29.5
86	45.8	43.0	41.4	40.0	37.0	34.6	32.6	31.0	29.5
88	46.0	43.2	41.5	40.1	37.1	34.7	32.7	31.0	29.6
90	46.2	43.3	41.7	40.2	37.2	34.8	32.8	31.1	29.7
92	46.4	43.5	41.8	40.4	37.3	34.9	32.9	31.2	29.7
94	46.5	43.6	42.0	40.5	37.4	35.0	32.9	31.3	29.8
96	46.7	43.8	42.1	40.6	37.5	35.0	33.0	31.3	29.9
98	46.8	43.9	42.2	40.7	37.6	35.1	33.1	31.4	29.9
100	47.0	44.0	42.3	40.8	37.7	35.2	33.2	31.4	30.0
110	47.7	44.6	42.9	41.3	38.1	35.5	33.5	31.7	30.2
120	48.2	45.1	43.3	41.7	38.4	35.8	33.7	31.9	30.4
130	48.7	45.5	43.7	42.1	38.7	36.1	33.9	32.1	30.6
140	49.1	45.8	44.0	42.3	39.0	36.3	34.1	32.3	30.7
150	49.5	46.1	44.3	42.6	39.2	36.5	34.3	32.4	30.9
160	49.8	46.4	44.5	42.8	39.4	36.6	34.4	32.6	31.0
170	50.0	46.6	44.7	43.0	39.5	36.8	34.5	32.7	31.1
180	50.3	46.8	44.9	43.2	39.7	36.9	34.6	32.8	31.2
190	50.5	47.0	45.1	43.3	39.8	37.0	34.7	32.8	31.2
200	50.7	47.2	45.2	43.5	39.9	37.1	34.8	32.9	31.3
210	50.9	47.3	45.4	43.6	40.0	37.2	34.9	33.0	31.4
220	51.0	47.5	45.5	43.7	40.1	37.3	35.0	33.1	31.4
230	51.2	47.6	45.6	43.8	40.2	37.4	35.0	33.1	31.5
240	51.3	47.7	45.7	43.9	40.3	37.4	35.1	33.2	31.5
250	51.4	47.8	45.8	44.0	40.4	37.5	35.2	33.2	31.6
260	51.5	47.9	45.9	44.1	40.4	37.5	35.2	33.3	31.6
270	51.7	48.0	46.0	44.2	40.5	37.6	35.3	33.3	31.6

Table 4.4 (Continued)
Effective Width-to-Thickness Ratios for Flat Plates in Compression Supported Along Both Longitudinal Edges

Effective Width-to-Thickness Ratio, b_c/t, for Indicated Yield Stress in ksi

Actual Width Ratio, b/t	36.0	42.0	46.0	50.0	60.0	70.0	80.0	90.0	100.0
280	51.7	48.1	46.1	44.3	40.5	37.6	35.3	33.3	31.7
290	51.8	48.2	46.1	44.3	40.6	37.7	35.3	33.4	31.7
300	51.9	48.2	46.2	44.4	40.7	37.7	35.4	33.4	31.7
310	52.0	48.3	46.3	44.4	40.7	37.8	35.4	33.4	31.7
320	52.1	48.4	46.3	44.5	40.7	37.8	35.4	33.5	31.8
330	52.1	48.4	46.4	44.5	40.8	37.9	35.5	33.5	31.8
340	52.2	48.5	46.4	44.6	40.8	37.9	35.5	33.5	31.8
350	52.3	48.5	46.5	44.6	40.9	37.9	33.5	33.6	31.9
360	52.3	48.6	46.5	44.7	40.9	37.9	35.6	33.6	31.9
370	52.4	48.6	46.6	44.7	40.9	38.0	35.6	33.6	31.9
380	52.4	48.7	46.6	44.8	41.0	38.0	35.6	33.6	31.9
390	52.5	48.7	46.6	44.8	41.0	38.0	35.6	33.6	32.0
400	52.5	48.8	46.7	44.8	41.0	38.1	35.7	33.7	32.0
410	52.6	48.8	46.7	44.9	41.0	28.1	35.7	33.7	32.0
420	52.6	48.8	46.7	44.9	41.1	38.1	35.7	33.7	32.0
430	52.7	48.9	46.8	44.9	41.1	38.1	35.7	33.7	32.0
440	52.7	48.9	46.8	44.9	41.1	38.1	35.7	33.7	32.0
450	52.7	48.9	46.8	45.0	41.1	38.2	35.7	33.7	32.0
460	52.8	49.0	46.9	45.0	41.2	38.2	35.8	33.8	32.1
470	52.8	49.0	46.9	45.0	41.2	38.2	35.8	33.8	32.1
480	52.9	49.0	46.9	45.1	41.2	38.2	35.8	33.8	32.1
490	52.9	49.1	46.9	45.1	41.2	38.2	35.8	33.8	32.1
500	52.9	49.1	47.0	45.1	41.2	38.2	35.8	33.8	32.1

CHAPTER 5

Bending Members with Full Lateral Support

5.1 Introduction

Structural members that support transverse loads primarily by means of their bending strength are known as beams, and large beams fabricated from plates may be further designated as girders. This chapter will consider the behavior and design of beams and girders that (1) have all loads perpendicular to one principal axis and thus are not subject to biaxial bending, (2) have all loads passing through their shear center and thus are not subject to torsion, and (3) have sufficient lateral support to prevent lateral buckling. Bending members that do not meet these requirements will be considered in Chapters 6 and 7. Unless otherwise stated, it is also assumed that the members have been proportioned to prevent local buckling.

5.2 Behavior of Homogeneous Beams

The behavior of a homogeneous beam in bending is illustrated by the bending moment versus curvature* relationship shown in Figure 5.1. The solid line curve is for a wide-flange beam that is free of residual stresses. During the application of an increasing moment, the beam passes through three stages of behavior. Stage I represents entirely elastic behavior, Stage II represents the range in which yielding begins at the outer fibers and progresses through the section, and Stage III represents the range in which the entire section has yielded. Zones of yielding and stress distributions over

---

*A load versus deflection curve would have the same general shape as the moment versus curvature curve shown.

the beam cross section during each of the stages are illustrated in the figure. The bending moment that causes first yielding, M_y, is the moment at the end of Stage I, and the moment during Stage III is the plastic moment, M_p.

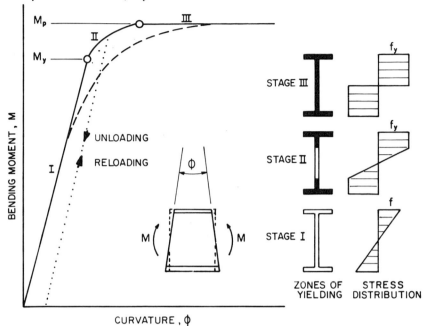

FIGURE 5.I   MOMENT-CURVATURE
RELATIONSHIP FOR A HOMOGENEOUS BEAM

The dotted line in the figure shows the behavior of a beam that is loaded with a moment greater than its yield moment and then unloaded. Elastic behavior is observed during both unloading and subsequent reloading and a small residual curvature remains in the beam.

In actual beams, the presence of residual stresses will contribute to yielding, and as indicated by the dashed line in the figure, inelastic behavior will occur before the calculated M_y is reached. However, the residual stresses will not reduce the plastic bending moment of the beam. Also, because elastic behavior is observed during unloading and subsequent reloading, the effect of the residual stress is only observed during the initial application of load provided that subsequent loads do not exceed the previously applied maximum moment.

Within the elastic range the bending stress, f_b, at any distance, y, from the neutral axis (on which bending stresses are zero) is related to the bending moment, M, by

$$f_b = \frac{My}{I} \qquad (5.1)$$

If "*c*" denotes the distance from the neutral axis to the most extreme fiber, the maximum bending stress is

$$f_b = \frac{Mc}{I} = \frac{M}{S} \tag{5.2}$$

where S is the elastic section modulus of the beam. The moment that causes first yielding is

$$M_y = f_y S \tag{5.3}$$

The neutral axis is the transverse axis on which bending stresses are zero. For elastic stresses, the neutral axis is the centroidal axis, that is, the axis about which the statical moment of the compressively stressed portion of the cross-sectional area equals that of the tensile area. For equilibrium, the total compressive force resulting from the compression stresses on the cross section must equal the total tensile force resulting from the tensile stresses. Therefore, since all areas of the beam cross section are equally stressed when the plastic moment is reached, the neutral axis at plastic moment is an axis that divides the cross section into two equal areas. For symmetrical sections, this plastic neutral axis has the same location as the elastic neutral axis. However, as illustrated in Figure 5.2, the location of the elastic and plastic neutral axes is different for unsymmetrical sections. For any section, the plastic moment may be obtained by summing moments about the plastic netural axis for the fully plastic stress distribution. This moment may be expressed as

$$M_p = f_y Z \tag{5.4}$$

where Z, the plastic section modulus, is equal to the statical moment of the cross section about the plastic neutral axis.[1]

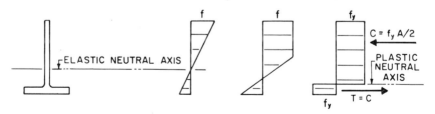

FIGURE 5.2   DISTRIBUTION OF BENDING
STRESS IN UNSYMMETRICAL SECTION

The ratio of the plastic moment to the yield moment, Z/S, is the shape factor. The shape factor varies with the geometry of the cross section and is an index of reserve strength after initial yielding. Generally, the shape factor is smaller for cross sections that have material concentrated near the outer fibers. Thus, as shown by the values given in Figure 5.3, the shape factor for solid sections is larger than that of similar open sections, and the shape factor for wide-flange shapes is larger about the weak axis than about the strong axis.

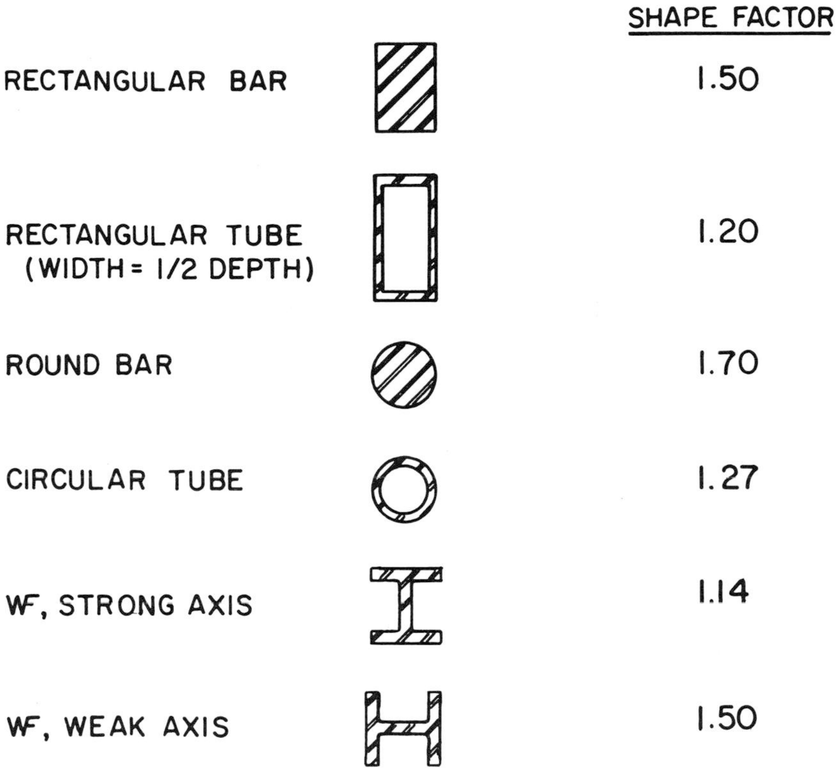

SHAPE FACTOR

RECTANGULAR BAR		1.50
RECTANGULAR TUBE (WIDTH = 1/2 DEPTH)		1.20
ROUND BAR		1.70
CIRCULAR TUBE		1.27
WF, STRONG AXIS		1.14
WF, WEAK AXIS		1.50

FIGURE 5.3   SHAPE FACTORS FOR VARIOUS CROSS SECTIONS

At any transverse cross section in a beam, the algebraic summation of the applied loads and reactions on either side of the cross section is the shear force, V, at that section. This shear force is resisted by internal shear stresses that are a maximum on vertical and horizontal planes through the neutral axis of the section. Within the elastic range the shear stress, f_v, is

$$f_v = \frac{VQ}{It} \tag{5.5}$$

where Q is the statical moment of the cross-sectional area beyond the point where the shear stress is calculated taken about the neutral axis of the beam, and t is the thickness of the beam where the shear stress is calculated.

neutral axis of the beam, and t is the thickness of the beam where the shear stress is calculated.

Figure 5.4 illustrates the elastic-shear-stress distribution in a wide-flange beam. For this section, the shear stress in the flange is small and the variation of shear stress in the web is small. Thus, the shear stress is usually approximated as

$$f_v = \frac{V}{A_w} = \frac{V}{t_w d} \qquad (5.6)$$

where A_w is the web area, t_w is the web thickness, and d is the beam depth. The load causing complete yielding in shear is the plastic shear force, V_p, which is

$$V_p = A_w f_{ys} = \frac{A_w f_y}{\sqrt{3}} \qquad (5.7)$$

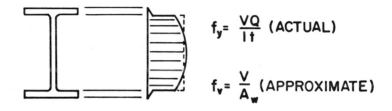

$$f_y = \frac{VQ}{It} \text{ (ACTUAL)}$$

$$f_v = \frac{V}{A_w} \text{ (APPROXIMATE)}$$

FIGURE 5.4 ELASTIC-STRESS DISTRIBUTION IN SHEAR

Although a bending member can be subjected to "pure bending," shear can only occur in the presence of bending, and therefore, a member cannot be subjected to "pure shear." If high values of moment and shear occur together, the web may yield locally because of the combined stresses. However, tests have shown that for most bending members* the localized yielding does not significantly reduce either bending strength or shear strength.[1] For wide-flange beams, the plastic moment will not be reduced if the concurrent shear does not exceed 95 percent of the value given by Equation 5.7. In elastic design, bending and shear are usually considered independently.

Within the elastic range, the deflection, Δ, caused by bending is

$$\Delta = k_{bd} \frac{WL^3}{EI} \qquad (5.8)$$

where W is the total load, L is the length of the beam, and k_{bd} is

---

*The combined effects of bending and shear must be considered for girders subject to tension field action. See Section 5.5.1b.

a numerical factor that depends on the manner of loading and support. The elastic deflection caused by shear is

$$\Delta = k_{sd} \frac{WL}{AG} \qquad (5.9)$$

where k_{sd} is a numerical factor that depends on the manner of loading and support and on the shape of the cross section. Shear deflection, usually much smaller than bending deflection, is insignificant except for beams having large depth-to-length ratios.

5.3 Behavior of Hybrid Beams

Beams that have flanges of a steel having a higher yield stress than that of the web are known as hybrid beams. The behavior of a hybrid beam in bending is illustrated by the bending moment versus curvature relationship shown in Figure 5.5 for a wide-flange hybrid beam that is free of residual stresses.[2] During the application of an increasing moment, the beam passes through four stages of behavior. Stage I represents entirely elastic behavior, Stage II represents the range in which yielding develops in the web while the flanges remain elastic, Stage III represents the range in which yielding progresses through the flanges while the web remains partly elastic, and Stage IV represents the range in which the entire section has yielded. Zones of yielding and stress distributions over the beam cross section during each stage are illustrated in the figure.

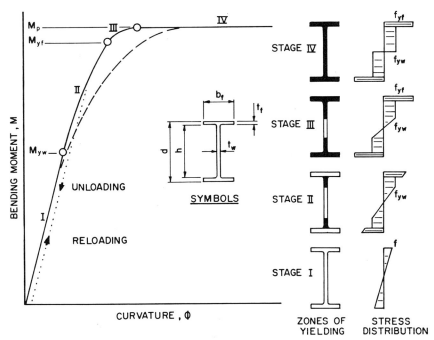

FIGURE 5.5   MOMENT-CURVATURE
RELATIONSHIP FOR A HYBRID BEAM

The dotted line in Figure 5.5 indicates the behavior of a hybrid beam that is unloaded and then reloaded. As with homogeneous beams, elastic behavior occurs during unloading.* Consequently, if the yield stress in the web was exceeded during the initial loading, a small residual curvature will remain in the beam. However, under all subsequent loading and unloading cycles, the beam will behave in a completely elastic manner if the reloading moment does not exceed the previously applied maximum moment.

Like homogeneous beams, residual stresses present in actual hybrid beams will contribute to yielding, and as indicated by the dashed line in the figure, inelastic behavior will occur at moments that are less than the calculated moments. However, the residual stresses will not reduce the ultimate bending moment of the beam and, generally, will only cause inelastic behavior during the initial application of maximum load.

The moment that causes initial yielding in the web, M_{yw}, the moment that causes initial yielding in the flange, M_{yf}, and the plastic bending moment, M_p, can all be calculated from the geometry of the cross section. The resulting equations are

$$M_{yw} = f_{yw}S\ (d/h) \tag{5.10}$$

$$M_{yf} = \frac{b_f t_f (d + h)^2}{4d} f_{yf} + \frac{t_w h^2}{4} f_{yw} - \frac{t_w d^2}{12} \left(\frac{f^3_{yw}}{f^2_{yf}} \right) \tag{5.11}$$

$$M_p = \frac{b_f t_f}{2} (d + h)\ f_{yf} + \frac{t_w h^2}{4} f_{yw} \tag{5.12}$$

where f_{yf} and f_{yw} are the yield stress of the flange and web, respectively; the other symbols are identified in Figure 5.5.

The equations for shear given for homogeneous beams are also appropriate for hybrid beams. Tests have shown that when bending and shear occur simultaneously, the reduction in bending strength of hybrid beams caused by shear is very small. Thus, hybrid beams may be designed independently for bending and shear, even when the maximum bending moment and maximum shear occur at the same cross section.

Like homogeneous beams, appropriate dimensional limitations must be followed to prevent premature local buckling of hybrid beams. When the design is based on the plastic moment, the maximum width-to-thickness ratios for compact sections, Table 4.3, must not be exceeded. When the design is based on the initial yielding of the flange, the maximum width-to-thickness ratios for elastic design, Table 4.1 or 4.2, must not be exceeded for the flange. Elastic-design rules for proportioning the web and for maximum web shear stress may generally follow rules for homogeneous bending members. However, web shear must be resisted by beam shear

---

*Under some conditions a hybrid beam may unload unelastically, but these conditions are not usually encountered in design.

action alone, and the maximum web depth should not exceed $41,000/\sqrt{f_{yf}}$. Also, a web that has yielded in bending should not be considered effective in assisting a bearing stiffener to resist concentrated loads.

5.4 Behavior of Composite Beams

When a steel beam acts integrally with another material to support transverse loads, the combined section is known as a composite beam. The behavior of a composite beam made up of a steel beam and a concrete slab will be considered below; the behavior of other types of composite beams is similar.

The elastic behavior of a steel-concrete composite beam is similar to that of an equivalent homogeneous steel beam that is composed of the actual steel beam and a "transformed area" of the concrete slab. The transformed area of the slab is equal to its effective area divided by n, the ratio of the modulus of elasticity of steel to that of concrete. The effective area of a concrete slab is equal to its effective width times the slab thickness. Design values for the effective width are given in Sections 5.6 and 5.7.

Sectional properties of the equivalent homogeneous beams are usually referred to as properties of the "transformed section." Thus, if I_{tr} is the moment of inertia of the transformed section about its neutral axis, the bending stress at any point in the steel, f_s, is

$$f_s = \frac{My}{I_{tr}} \tag{5.13}$$

The bending stress at any point in the slab, f_c, is

$$f_c = \frac{My}{nI_{tr}} \tag{5.14}$$

In the equations, y is the distance from the neutral axis of the transformed section. The bending deflection is

$$\Delta = k_{bd} \frac{WL^3}{EI_{tr}} \tag{5.15}$$

The method of construction affects the elastic stress distribution in steel-concrete composite beams.[3] If the concrete slab is independently supported or "shored" along its entire length during construction until it attains 75 percent or more of its 28-day compressive strength, the composite beam is subjected — after the support is removed — to both the moment caused by the weight of the slab and the steel beam, M_d, and the moment from live loads, M_l. Thus, the bending stresses are

$$f_s = \frac{(M_d + M_l)\, y}{I_{tr}} \tag{5.16}$$

$$f_c = \frac{(M_d + M_l)\, y}{n I_{tr}} \qquad (5.17)$$

If the concrete forms are supported on the steel beams and these beams are not shored during construction, the steel beam alone must carry the dead-load moments, and the composite beam is subjected to the live-load moment only. Thus, the bending stresses are

$$f_s = \frac{M_d y}{I} + \frac{M_l y}{I_{tr}} \qquad (5.18)$$

$$f_c = \frac{M_l y}{n I_{tr}} \qquad (5.19)$$

Elastic-stress distributions for these two conditions are illustrated in Figure 5.6.

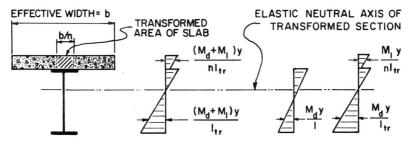

a. COMPOSITE BEAM　　**b. SHORED CONSTRUCTION**　　**c. UNSHORED CONSTRUCTION**

FIGURE 5.6　ELASTIC STRESS DISTRIBUTION IN COMPOSITE BEAMS

The stress distribution at ultimate load is independent of the manner in which the stresses are induced into the beam. Consequently, although the elastic stress distribution at the design-load level differs, the ultimate load is the same for shored and unshored construction. Also, creep and shrinkage may change the internal-stress distribution at the design-load level, but have no effect on the ultimate moment.

As shown in Figure 5.7b, the composite beam with the usual properties reaches its ultimate bending moment when the steel beam is uniformly stressed in tension to its yield stress and all compressive stresses are resisted by the concrete slab. The compressive stresses are assumed to have a magnitude of 0.85 times the ultimate compressive strength of concrete, f'_c, because concrete, unlike steel, does not have a plastic zone in its stress-strain relationship and, thus, cannot flow freely and develop a uniform stress of f'_c. Tensile stresses in the concrete are usually neglected.

The stress distribution at ultimate moment shown in Figure 5.7b occurs when $0.85 \, f'_c t_c b \geq f_y A_s$ and the ultimate moment is

$$M_u = f_y A_s \left(\frac{d}{2} + t_c - \frac{f_y A_s}{1.70 \, f'_c b} \right) \tag{5.20}$$

where A_s is the area of the steel beam, d is the depth of the steel beam, and t_c is the thickness of the slab. When the concrete slab alone does not have the load capacity to resist the tensile force; that is, when $0.85 \, f'_c t_c b < f_y A_s$, a portion of the steel beam will be stressed in compression and the stress distribution will be as shown in Figure 5.7c. For this condition, the ultimate moment is

$$M_u = 0.85 f_c b t_c y_1 - \left(\frac{f_y A_s - 0.85 f'_c t_c b}{2} \right) y_2 \tag{5.21}$$

where y_1 and y_2 are the distances between centroids (as shown in the figure) and may be determined from the cross sectional geometry.

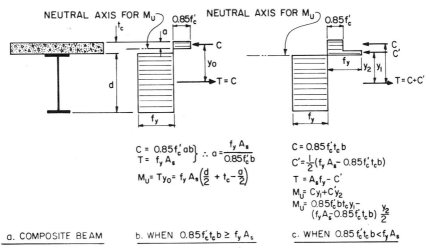

FIGURE 5.7 STRESS DISTRIBUTION AT
ULTIMATE MOMENT IN COMPOSITE BEAMS

To behave as a composite beam, the horizontal shear that develops during bending must be transmitted between the slab and the steel beam. Until yielding occurs in shear, this shear force per unit length, v_h, is given by

$$v_h = \frac{VQ}{I_{tr}} \tag{5.22}$$

where Q is the statical moment of the transformed area of the concrete slab about the neutral axis of the beam. If shear connectors are spaced to resist this elastic shear force, their spacing will vary along the beam, because V generally varies along the beam. At ultimate load, however, the total shear force that must be transmitted between the slab and the steel beam is equal to the compressive force in the slab, C, Figure 5.7. Static tests have shown that if the shear connectors are capable of yielding and re-distributing the shear force, their exact location along the length of the beam is unimportant provided that their total load capacity is not less than C.

The vertical shear force is assumed to be resisted by the web of the steel beam. The combined effects of bending and shear stresses are not usually critical for design.

5.5 Behavior of Girders with Stiffened Webs

5.5.1 *Transversely Stiffened Webs*

a. Girders in Bending

The buckling behavior of a typical web panel in bending such as that shown in Figure 5.8a, is similar to that of a flat plate pre-sented in Chapter 4. If the plate were perfect, it would deflect laterally from its initially flat position when the buckling load is reached. However, tests have shown that because of the initial im-perfections usually present, the lateral deflection in most web plates will increase progressively throughout the entire range of applied bending moment as shown in Figure 2b, and a distinct buckling load cannot be observed.[4] Thus, like other plates, web plates in bending do not collapse when the buckling load is reached, but have significant post buckling strength.

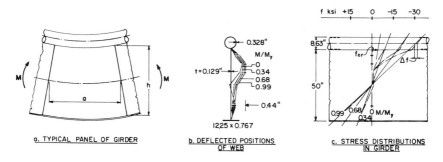

a. TYPICAL PANEL OF GIRDER   b. DEFLECTED POSITIONS OF WEB   c. STRESS DISTRIBUTIONS IN GIRDER

FIGURE 5.8 BENDING BEHAVIOR OF GIRDER
HAVING TRANSVERSELY STIFFENED WEB

Stress distributions through the girder at various loading values are shown in Figure 5.8c. As shown in the figure, the stress in the compression portion of the web that deflects laterally is less than that calculated for a linear distribution, and the stress in the com-pression flange is greater than the calculated value for a given moment. Thus, yielding may begin in the compression flange of the girder before the yield moment calculated from elementary beam theory is reached. However, tests have shown that the overstressing of the compression flange is slight and, due to the favorable redistribution of stresses that accompanies localized yielding, a girder can reach an ultimate bending moment that equals or slightly exceeds the calculated yield moment when the width-to-thickness ratio of the web does not exceed

$$\frac{h}{t} = 5.7 \sqrt{\frac{E}{f_y}} = 31,000/\sqrt{f_y} \qquad (5.23)$$

For larger $\frac{h}{t}$ values, tests have shown that the ultimate moment is less than the calculated yield moment and is given by the approximate theoretical relationship

$$\frac{M_u}{M_y} = 1 - 0.0005 \frac{A_w}{A_t} \left(\frac{h}{t} - 5.7 \sqrt{\frac{E}{f_y}} \right) \qquad (5.24)$$

In elastic design, this reduction in bending strength may be evaluated by using a reduced allowable bending stress, F'_b, that is related to the usual allowable bending stress, F_b, by the expression

$$F'_b = F_b \left[1.0 - 0.0005 \frac{A_w}{A_t} \left(\frac{h}{t} - 5.7 \sqrt{\frac{E}{f_y}} \right) \right] \qquad (5.25)$$

The web must also be proportioned to prevent buckling due to vertical forces. Figure 5.9 shows that the curvature which accompanies bending causes an unbalanced vertical component of the force in the flanges. Because most flanges are flat plates that have little resistance to such forces, the forces must be resisted by the web. If the web is too slender the flanges may buckle into the web and cause premature failure. Tests have shown that such a failure will not occur if the width-to-thickness ratio of the web does not exceed the approximate theoretical value

$$\frac{h}{t} = \frac{0.48\ E}{\sqrt{f_y\ (f_y + f_r)}} \qquad (5.26)$$

where f_r is the residual stress present at the juncture of the flange and the web. An average value of 16,500 psi has been measured for f_r. Thus, the maximum value may be expressed as

$$\frac{h}{t} = \frac{14,000,000}{\sqrt{f_y\ (f_y + 16,500)}} \qquad (5.27)$$

b. Girders in Shear

Under an increasing load, shear stresses develop in the web of a girder and, according to Equation 5.6, are approximately equal to V/ht, where h is the height of the web. Shear forces resisted in this manner will be referred to here as shear carried by "beam

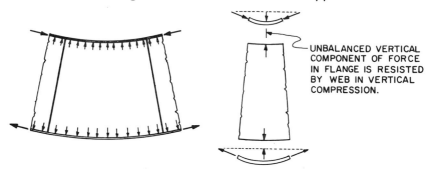

UNBALANCED VERTICAL
COMPONENT OF FORCE
IN FLANGE IS RESISTED
BY WEB IN VERTICAL
COMPRESSION.

**FIGURE 5.9 VERTICAL WEB COMPRESSION DUE
TO CURVATURE OF FLANGES**

action." The buckling behavior of a typical web panel due to beam shear is similar to that described in Chapter 4 for a flat plate — the web buckles perpendicular to the direction of the principal compressive stresses due to shear. However, like other plates, web plates of transversely stiffened girders can carry shear loads considerably greater than their buckling load. The nature of the post-buckling strength of a girder web is illustrated in Figure 5.10. After the web buckles, the girder acts in a manner similar to that of a Pratt truss; a part of each web panel acts as a diagonal tension member and the stiffeners act as vertical compression members.[5] Thus, both beam shear and "tension-field action" contribute to the shear strength of a transversely stiffened girder.

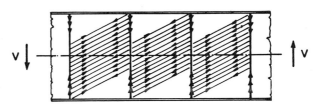

FIGURE 5.10 GIRDER SHEAR CARRIED BY TENSION-FIELD ACTION

Theoretical and experimental work have resulted in the following equations for the ultimate shear stress, f_{us}, of a transversely stiffened girder:

$$f_{us} = f_{crs} + \frac{\sqrt{3}}{2}\left(\frac{1 - f_{crs}/f_{ys}}{\sqrt{1 + (a/h)^2}} \right) \quad \text{when } f_{crs} \leq f_{ys} \text{ and } a/h \leq 3.0 \quad \textbf{(5.28)}$$

$$f_{us} = f_{crs} \quad \text{when } f_{crs} \geq f_{ys} \text{ or } a/h \geq 3.0 \quad \textbf{(5.29)}$$

where a is the stiffener spacing. The first term on the right-hand side of Equation 5.28 represents shear strength due to beam action, which is limited by shear buckling; the second term represents shear strength due to tension-field action, which is limited to yielding due to the combined stresses present in the web tension zone. As indicated above, shear strength due to tension-field action cannot be considered when the stiffeners are too widely spaced, $a/h > 3.0$, or when the shear buckling stress exceeds the yield stress in shear, $f_{crs} > f_{ys}$.

By substituting $f_y/\sqrt{3}$ for f_{ys} and the term C_v for f_{crs}/f_{ys}, Equations 5.28 and 5.29 may be simplified as

$$f_{us} = \frac{f_y}{\sqrt{3}}\left(C_v + \frac{1 - C_v}{1.15\sqrt{1 + (a/h)^2}} \right) \quad \begin{array}{l} \text{when } C_v \leq 1.0 \\ \text{and } a/h \leq 3.0 \end{array} \quad (5.30)$$

$$f_{us} = \frac{f_y \, C_v}{\sqrt{3}} \quad \begin{array}{l} \text{when } C_v \geq 1.0 \\ \text{or } a/h \geq 3.0 \end{array} \quad (5.31)$$

The term C_v may be expressed as

$$C_v = \frac{45 \times 10^6 \, k_s}{f_y \, (h/t)^2} \quad \text{when } C_v \leq 0.80 \quad (5.32)$$

If simply supported edge conditions are assumed, the coefficient k_s, which was plotted in Figure 4.6, may be expressed as

$$k_s = 4.00 + \frac{5.34}{(a/h)^2} \quad \text{when } a/h \leq 1.0 \quad (5.33)$$

$$k_s = 5.34 + \frac{4.00}{(a/h)^2} \quad \text{when } a/h \geq 1.0 \quad (5.34)$$

$$k_s = 5.34 \quad \text{when } a/h > 3.0 \quad (5.35)$$

Tests on girder webs have shown that the elastic equation for shear buckling is valid when $f_{crs} < 0.80 \, f_{ys}$, and that for larger calculated values of f_{crs}, the inelastic shear buckling stress, f'_{crs}, may be approximated for girder webs as

$$f'_{crs} = \sqrt{0.80 \, f_{ys} f_{cr}} \quad (5.36)$$

$$C_v = \frac{6000}{h/t}\sqrt{\frac{k_s}{f_y}} \quad \text{when } C_v > 0.80 \quad (5.37)$$

The compressive force, F, that must be carried by a stiffener when the ultimate shear force due to tension-field action is reached is

$$F = \left(\frac{1 - C_v}{2} \right)\left(\frac{a}{h} - \frac{(a/h)^2}{\sqrt{1 + (a/h)^2}} \right) f_y ht \quad (5.38)$$

where f_y is the yield stress of the web. The required total area of stiffeners at a panel point, A_{st}, may be expressed as

$$A_{st} = \frac{1 - C_v}{2} \left[\frac{a}{h} - \frac{(a/h)^2}{\sqrt{1 + (a/h)^2}} \right] YDht \qquad (5.39)$$

where Y is the ratio of the web yield stress to stiffener yield stress and D has the following value:

1.0 for stiffeners furnished in pairs.
1.8 for single-angle stiffeners.
2.4 for single-plate stiffeners.

A larger total area is required for single stiffeners than for pairs of stiffeners because single stiffeners are loaded eccentrically. No safety factor is needed with Equation 5.39 because of the form of the equation. If a safety factor is applied to the ultimate shear force, the stiffener will automatically have the same factor of safety against yielding. The connection between the web and the stiffener must withstand an ultimate shear force, v', per unit length of single stiffener or pair of stiffeners equal to

$$v' = 0.045 \, h \sqrt{\frac{f_y^3}{E}} \qquad (5.40)$$

Because the end panel of a stiffened girder must act as an anchor for the tension stress field and resist shear by beam action only, the end panel spacing must be reduced so that local buckling does not occur. This requirement will be met if the smaller end-panel dimension, a or h, is limited to $11,000t/\sqrt{f_v}$, where f_v is the shear stress in the end panel. If high values of moment and shear are present at the same location in a girder that is subject to tension field action, yielding may occur because of the combined stresses present in the web and consequently reduce both the bending strength and shear strength of the girder. A theoretical interaction curve that has been verified by tests is shown in Figure 5.11.[6] The figure shows that bending and shear may be considered separately except where high shear-stress and bending-stress ratios are simultaneously present. For example, as indicated by the dashed lines in the figure, if the shear stress is limited to 0.60 times the ultimate shear stress and the bending stress is limited to 0.60 times the yield stress, girder webs can be proportioned on the basis of (1) maximum allowable bending stress when the concurrent shear is not greater than 0.60 times the allowable shear stress, or (2) maximum allowable shear stress when the bending stress is not more than 0.75 times the maximum allowable.

c. Web Crippling

When loads are applied to a beam or girder through the flange plate, the resulting vertical compression stresses in the web can cause the web to buckle locally. Thus, most specifications include

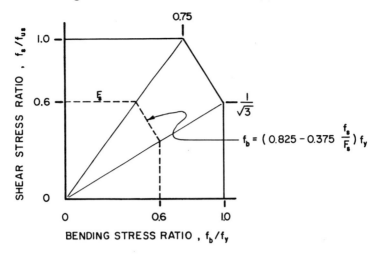

FIGURE 5.11   INTERACTION DIAGRAM FOR COMBINED BENDING AND
SHEAR IN GIRDERS SUBJECT TO TENSION-FIELD ACTION

provisions to prevent such "web crippling" by requiring a bearing
stiffener when the vertical compressive stress under concentrated
loads becomes large. A portion of the web is usually assumed to
act with the stiffener and the entire section is designed as a column.
Since transversely stiffened girder webs may be relatively thin, a
limitation must also be placed on the amount of load that can be
applied between stiffeners to prevent web crippling between stiffeners. Design rules for this condition are given in Reference 7.

5.5.2 *Longitudinally Stiffened Webs*

The buckling strength of webs of girders in bending can be
greatly increased by adding a longitudinal stiffener in the compression zone of the web. For girder webs in bending, a longitudinal stiffener has the greatest effect when placed a distance of
$0.20h$ from the compression flange. At this location, the buckling
strength of the web in bending is theoretically increased 5.4 times
that of an unstiffened web.[8]

A longitudinal stiffener also increases the buckling strength of
webs of girders in shear, but the increase is smaller than that
of girders in bending. For a stiffener at the $0.20h$ location, the
increase in buckling strength is about 1.6 times that of an unstiffened web. Therefore, since transverse stiffeners are generally
more effective in shear and longitudinal stiffeners are more effective in bending, girder webs — which are usually subjected to
combined bending and shear — are sometimes stiffened with a
combination of longitudinal and transverse stiffeners.

The ultimate strength of girders having longitudinal stiffeners is
presently being investigated.

5.6 Design of Bending Members for Buildings

The basic allowable bending and shear stresses for beams and girders in buildings corresponding to the requirements of the AISC specification[7] are given in Table 5.1. The allowable bending stress for compact sections, $0.66f_y$, is 10 percent greater than that for other sections, $0.60f_y$, because compact sections can reach a plastic bending moment at least 10 percent greater than their yield moment. Maximum width-to-thickness ratios for flanges and unstiffened webs were given in Table 4.3 for compact sections and in Table 4.1 for other sections.

The AISC also permits certain types of statically indeterminate structures to be proportioned according to the "plastic design" method.[1] This method is predicated upon the ability of the members to form a series of yield hinges at points of maximum moment before collapse. Members so designed must be able to support an ultimate load which, for simple and continuous beams, is 1.70 times their design load. This factor becomes 1.85 times the design load for continuous frames, or 1.40 times the dead load and live load acting in conjunction with 1.40 times the specified wind or earthquake forces.

For girders with transversely stiffened webs, the AISC specification gives design rules that are based on the previously discussed results of thin-web girder tests. The reduced allowable bending stress due to local buckling from bending given by Equation 5.25 is specified when $h/t > 31{,}000/\sqrt{f_y}$, and the maximum h/t due to vertical web buckling is that given by Equation 5.27. The web shear is limited to 0.60 of the ultimate shear stress given by Equations 5.30 and 5.31, and may not exceed the basic allowable shear stress of 0.40 f_y when Equation 5.31 governs. The required area of intermediate stiffeners is that given by Equation 5.39, and the design value for the shear force between stiffeners and the girder web is 0.60 times the value given by Equation 5.40. When the maximum shear stress in a panel is less than the allowable value derived from Equation 5.30, the required area of intermediate stiffeners can be reduced proportionately. Under combined bending and shear, the maximum bending stress is limited to the value shown by the dashed line in Figure 5.11.

In addition, for practical considerations the maximum depth of girders that do not require intermediate stiffeners is limited to 260 times the web thickness, and the aspect ratio of girders that do require intermediate stiffeners is limited to $\left(\dfrac{260}{h/t}\right)^2$. The minimum moment of inertia of a pair of stiffeners, or a single stiffener, about an axis in the plane of the web is $(h/50)^4$. The AISC also gives rules for the design of bearing stiffeners for girders.

Tables 5.2 through 5.10 give allowable shear stresses and required stiffener areas calculated according to the AISC specification for girders having specified minimum yield stresses of 36 to 100 ksi. Supplementary data for the girders are given in Table 5.11.

The AISC specification also includes rules for the design of composite beams in building construction. Composite beams consisting of steel beams and shear-connected concrete slabs can be designed by elastic theory with the steel bending stress limited to the usual values, $0.60f_y$ or $0.66f_y$. On the basis of ultimate strength considerations, the composite section may be assumed to resist both dead and live loads, even when temporary shores are not used. However, for unshored construction, the section modulus of the transformed section (referred to the tension flange) used in stress calculations must not exceed

$$S_{tr} = \left(1.35 + 0.35 \, \frac{M_l}{M_d} \right) S_s \qquad (5.41)$$

where M_l and M_d are the live-load and dead-load moments, respectively, and S_s is the section modulus of the steel beam referred to its tension flange. However, the steel beam alone must not exceed its basic allowable bending stress when supporting dead loads before the concrete has hardened. Equation 5.41 ensures that the maximum bending stress in the steel beam under service loading is well below yield stress.

The effective width of the concrete slab, when the slab projects from both sides of the beam, is limited to
1. Total effective width of ¼ the beam span.
2. Projecting width, each side, of 8 times the slab thickness.
3. Projecting width, each side, of ½ clear distance to adjacent beam.

For slabs projecting from only one side of the beam, the effective width is limited to
1. Projecting width of 1/12 the beam span.
2. Projecting width of 6 times the slab thickness.
3. Projecting width of ½ clear distance to adjacent beam.

As required by ultimate strength considerations, the total horizontal shear, V_h, to be resisted by the shear connectors between the point of maximum positive bending moment and a point of zero moment is the smaller of

$$V_h = 0.85f'_c A_c/2 \qquad (5.42)$$

$$V_h = A_s f_y/2 \qquad (5.43)$$

The number of shear connectors required can be determined by dividing V_h by the allowable shear loads given in Table 5.12, and may be spaced uniformly between maximum and zero moment points.

5.7 Design of Bending Members for Bridges

The basic allowable bending and shear stresses for beams and girders in bridges corresponding to the requirements of the AASHO[9] and AREA[10] specifications are given in Table 5.13. Maximum width-to-thickness ratios for flanges and untiffened webs were given in Table 4.2.

For girders having stiffened webs, neither AASHO nor AREA permits design to be based on tension-field action, but instead they give design rules that are intended to prevent local buckling of the web. Maximum web depth-to-thickness ratios for stiffened webs are given in Table 5.14. AASHO requires that, when the web is stressed to its maximum allowable bending stress, the intermediate stiffener spacing be no greater than $11,000t/\sqrt{f_v}$ and no greater than the web depth. Proportionately greater spacings are permitted when the web is not stressed to its maximum allowable bending stress. The first two stiffener spaces at the ends of simply supported girders must be one half the maximum permitted for intermediate stiffeners. AREA limits intermediate stiffener spacing to $10,500t/\sqrt{f_v}$ or 72 in., whichever is smaller. Each specification gives rules for required moment of inertia and size of intermediate stiffeners, and for the design of bearing stiffeners. Also, as indicated in Table 5.14, AASHO permits greater h/t ratios if in addition to the transverse stiffeners, a longitudinal stiffener having the required rigidity is placed a distance of 0.20h from the compression flange.

The AASHO specification also gives rules for the elastic design of composite beams that consist of steel beams and concrete slabs. The usual allowable bending stress of 0.55 f_y is used for the steel and an allowable bending stress of 0.40 f'_c for the maximum compressive bending stress in concrete. For unshored construction, the dead-load stresses must be calculated for the steel beam only and superimposed with live-load stresses for the composite section as illustrated in Figure 5.6c. The effect of creep must be considered if the composite section supports dead load. For such beams, bending stresses and horizontal shears from dead load are considered as the higher of those calculated by using the usual values of n, or those calculated by replacing n with 3n.

The total effective width of the concrete slab when the slab projects from both sides of the beam is limited to

1. One fourth the beam span.
2. Twelve times the slab thickness.
3. The distance center-to-center of beams.

If the slab projects from only one side of the beam, the total effective slab width is limited to

1. One twelfth the beam span.
2. Six times the slab thickness.
3. One half the distance center-to-center of adjacent beam.

The AASHO specification requires that shear connector spacings be selected to resist the elastic horizontal shear stresses, v_h, from Equation 5.22. Allowable shear values for various connectors are given in Table 5.15.

5.8   Design Examples

Example 5.1

Determine the maximum design value for bending moment and shear force for a 30WF99 beam with adequate lateral support, if the beam is furnished in (a) A36 steel and (b) USS TRI-TEN steel. The beam will be designed according to AISC specifications.

Solution:

a.   A36 Steel

$b_f/2t_f = 10.458/(2 \times 0.670) = 7.8 < 8.5$	**(Table 4.3)**
$d/t_w = 29.64/0.522 = 56.9 < 70.1$	**(Table 4.3)**

Therefore, beam is a compact section and

$F_b = 24,000$ psi	**(Table 5.1)**
$M = F_bS = 24,000 \times 269.1 =$ **6450 in. kips**	**(Equation 5.2)**
$h/t_w = 28.3/0.522 = 54.2 < 63.2$	**(Table 4.1)**
Therefore, $f_v = 14,500$ psi	**(Table 5.1)**
$V = f_vA_w = 14,500 \times 29.64 \times 0.522 =$ **224 kips**	**(Equation 5.6)**

b.   USS TRI-TEN Steel

$b_f/2t_f = 7.8 > 7.2$	**(Table 4.3)**

Therefore, beam is not a compact section.

$b_f/2t_f < 13.8$	**(Table 4.1)**
$d/t_w < 164$	**(Table 5.12)**
Therefore, $F_b = 30,000$ psi	**(Table 5.1)**
$M = F_bS = 30,000 \times 269.1 =$ **8070 in. kips**	**(Equation 5.2)**
$h/t_w < 55.4$	**(Table 4.1)**
Therefore, $f_v = 20,000$ psi	**(Table 5.1)**
$V = f_vA_w = 20,000 \times 29.64 \times 0.522 =$ **310 kips**	**(Equation 5.6)**

Example 5.2

The hybrid beam shown in the sketch at the right has been tentatively selected for a main longitudinal member for a special highway trailer. Determine design values for bending moment and shear that will provide a safety factor of 2.0 against flange yielding and shear yielding, respectively.

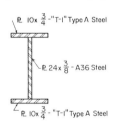

℞ 10x $\frac{3}{4}$ -"T-I" Type A Steel

℞ 24x $\frac{3}{8}$ - A36 Steel

℞ 10x $\frac{3}{4}$ - "T-I" Type A Steel

Solution:

Check width-to-thickness ratios:

Flange — $b/2t = 10/(2 \times 0.750) = 6.67 < 9.5$	**(Table 4.1)**
Web — $h/t = 24/0.375 = 64 < 70$	**(Table 4.3)**

$$M_{yf} = \frac{b_ft_f(d+h)^2f_{yf}}{4d} + \frac{t_wh^2}{4}f_{yw} - \frac{t_wd^2}{12}\left(\frac{f^3_{yw}}{f^2_{yf}}\right)$$ **(Equation 5.11)**

$$= \frac{10 \times .75(25.5+24)^2100}{4 \times 25.5} + \frac{0.375(24)^236}{4} - \frac{0.375(25.5)^2}{12}\left(\frac{36^3}{100^2}\right)$$

$$= 19,900 \text{ in. kips}$$

Design moment $= 19,900/2 =$ **9,950 in. kips**

$$V_p = A_wf_y/\sqrt{3}$$ **(Equation 5.7)**

$$= 24 \times 0.375 \times 36,000/1.73$$

$$= 187 \text{ kips}$$

Design shear $= 187/2 =$ **93.5 kips**

(Note: For this application, this member must also be checked for fatigue.)

Example 5.3

A plan view of the structural steel in a bay of a warehouse is shown at right. A 4-inch-thick concrete slab will cover the beams, and a composite design is desired to support the 250-psf live load. Determine the required stringer size and shear connector requirements if A36 steel and concrete with a 3000-psi compressive strength are used. The construction will be shored.

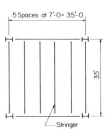

Solution:

Try a 21WF62 beam. By following AISC rules, the effective slab is as shown at the right. From statics or from the AISC manual, the section modulus referred to the bottom is $S_b = 172.4$ in.³.
The section modulus referred to the top is $S_t = 488.1$ in.³. Load per foot on stringer, $w = (250 + 48)\ 7 + 62 = 2148$ lb/ft.

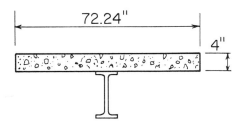

Bending moment, $M = wL^2/8 = 2148 \times 35^2 \times 12/8 = 3950$ in kips.
Maximum bending stress in steel, $f_s = M/S = 3950/172.4 = 22{,}900$ psi $<$ 24,000 psi
(Allowable stress is 24,000 psi because a check of width-to-thickness ratios shows that the beam is a compact section.)

Maximum bending stress in concrete, $f_c = \dfrac{3950}{488.1 \times 10} = 808$ psi

(Equation 5.14)

21WF62 beam is satisfactory.
Horizontal shear for shear connectors is smaller of the following values:

$V_h = 0.85\ f'_c A_c/2$ **(Equation 5.42)**

$\quad = 0.85 \times 3000 \times 72.24 \times 4/2 = 368$ kips

$V_h = A_s f_y/2$ **(Equation 5.43)**

$\quad = 18.23 \times 36{,}000/2 = 328$ kips

Therefore, $V_h = 328$ kips
From Table 5.12, if **¾-in.-diameter by 3-in.-long studs** are used, the number of studs required from midspan to end is $\dfrac{328}{11.5} = 29$.
If 2 studs are used at each location, the uniform spacing along the stringer is $\dfrac{210}{29} \times 2 = 14\frac{1}{2}$ **in.**

Example 5.4

A girder must support the load indicated in the sketch below. The compression flange has adequate lateral support. Design the girder in A36 steel according to the requirements of the AISC specification.

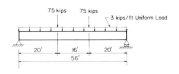

Solution:

The following diagrams for applied shear and bending moment may be obtained from statics:

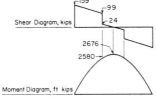

Shear Diagram, kips

Moment Diagram, ft kips

Trial sizes for the flange and web plates, selected by a preliminary analysis, are as follows:

Flange plate—20 in. by ⅞ in.

Web plate—80 in. by ¼ in.

Check width-to-thickness ratios:

$b_f/2t_f = 20/(2 \times 0.875) = 11.4 < 15.8$ **(Table 4.1)**

$h/t = 80/0.250 = 320 \leq 320$ **(Table 5.11)**

Section properties, determined from statics, are as follows:

$I = 67,900$ in.⁴

$S = 1660$ in.³

$h/t = 80/0.250 = 320 > 164$ **(Table 5.11)**

Therefore, calculate reduced allowable bending stress from Equation 5.25, with $F_b = 0.60 f_y$

$$F'_b = F_b \left[1.0 - 0.0005 \frac{A_w}{A_f} \left(\frac{h}{t} - \frac{24,000}{\sqrt{F_b}} \right) \right]$$

$$= 22,000 \left[1.0 - 0.0005 \frac{20.0}{17.5} \left(320 - \frac{24,000}{\sqrt{22,000}} \right) \right]$$

$$= 20,000 \text{ psi}$$

$f_b = M/S = 2676 \times 12/1660$ **(Equation 5.2)**

$$= 19,300 \text{ psi} < 20,000 \text{ psi}$$

Determine stiffener spacing for end panel:

$f_v = V/A_w = 159,000/20 = 7950$ psi   **(Equation 5.6)**

Maximum for smaller panel dimension is

$$\frac{11,000 \ t}{\sqrt{f_v}} = \frac{11,000 \times 0.250}{\sqrt{7950}} = 30.8 \text{ in.}$$

Select $a = 30$ in. for end panel.

Determine spacing for interior panel:

$$\frac{a}{h_{max}} = \left(\frac{260}{h/t} \right)^2 = \left(\frac{260}{320} \right)^2 = 0.66$$

$a_{max.} = 0.66h = 0.66 \times 80 = 52.8$ in.

Bearing stiffeners will be used at concentrated loads. Between concentrated load and end panel, try 5 spaces at 42 in.

$a/h = 42/80 = 0.525$

$F_v = 10,600$ psi $A_{st} = 0.099\ A_w$ **(Table 5.2)**

Maximum shear in this portion of girder is 151.5 kips at 30 in. from girder end.

$f_v = V/A_w = 151,500/20 = 7570$ psi $< 10,600$ psi

Between concentrated loads, try 4 spaces at 48 in.

$a/h = 48/80 = 0.60$

$F_v = 10,100$ psi $A_{st} = 0.112\ A_w$ **(Table 5.2)**

$f_v = V/A_w = 24,000/20 = 1200$ psi $< 10,100$ psi

Consider interaction of shear and moment. By inspection, the most significant combination occurs when $V = 99$ kips and $M = 2580$ ft kips.

$$\frac{f_v}{F_v} = \frac{4950}{10,600} = 0.47 < 0.60$$

Therefore, interaction does not reduce allowable stresses.
Determine size of intermediate stiffeners:
For the 42-in. spacing, $A_{st} = 0.099 \times 20 = 1.98$ in.^{2}
Try 2 plates 3¼ by 5/16, $A_{st} = 2.03$ in.^{2}

$b/t = 3.25/.3125 = 10.4 < 15.8$ **(Table 4.1)**

I required $= (h/50)^4 = (80/50)^4 = 6.55$ in.^{4}
I furnished $= 0.3125\ (6.50)^3/12 = 7.16$ in.$^4 > 6.55$ in.^{4}
In a similar manner, 2 plates 3¾ by 5/16 in. are satisfactory for the 48-in. spacing.
Design value for shear between each intermediate stiffener and web is

$$v' = 0.045h\ \sqrt{\frac{36,000^3}{29 \times 10^6}} = 57h \qquad \textbf{(Equation 5.40)}$$

$f_v = 0.60\ v'/2 =$

35 $h/2 = 35 \times 80/2 = 1400$ lb/in. Web crippling, checked by AISC specification, is satisfactory between stiffeners. Also from the specification, bearing stiffeners 9 in. by ⅝ in. are satisfactory. Resulting girder design is

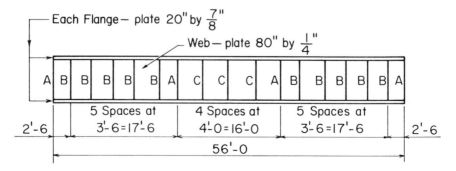

A stiffeners – 2 plates 9″ by $\frac{5}{8}$ ″

B stiffeners – 2 plates $3\frac{1}{4}$ ″ by $\frac{5}{16}$ ″

C stiffeners – 2 plates $3\frac{3}{4}$ ″ by $\frac{5}{16}$ ″

References (Chapter 5)

1. L. S. Beedle, **Plastic Design of Steel Frames,** John Wiley & Sons, New York City, 1958.

2. R. W. Frost and C. G. Schilling, "The Behavior of Hybrid Beams Subjected to Static Loads," **Journal of the Structural Division, Proceedings** ASCE, 90, No. ST3, June 1964.

3. "Tentative Recommendations for the Design and Construction of Composite Beams and Girders for Buildings," **Journal of the Structural Division, Proceedings** ASCE, 86, No. ST 12, December 1960.

4. K. Basler and B. Thurlimann, "Strength of Plate Girders in Bending," **Journal of the Structural Division, Proceedings** ASCE, 87, No. ST 6, August 1961.

5. K. Basler, "Strength of Plate Girders in Shear," **Journal of the Structural Division, Proceedings** ASCE, 87, No. ST 7, October 1961,

6. K. Basler, "Strength of Plate Girders Under Combined Bending and Shear," **Journal of the Structural Division, Proceedings** ASCE, 87, No. ST 7, October 1961.

7. American Institute of Steel Construction, "Specification for the Design, Fabrication and Erection of Structural Steel for Buildings," 1963.

8. F. Bleich, **Buckling Strength of Metal Structures,** McGraw-Hill Book Company, New York City, 1952.

9. American Association of State Highway Officials, "Standard Specifications for Highway Bridges," 1965.

10. American Railway Engineering Association, "Standard Specifications for Steel Railway Bridges," 1966.

Table 5.1

Basic Allowable Bending and Shear Stresses for Beams and Girders in Buildings

Specified Minimum Yield Stress, ksi	Allowable Bending Stresses, ksi		Allowable Shear Stresses, ksi
	Compact, Adequately Braced Beams With Axis of Symmetry in Plane of Loading	All Other Adequately Braced Beams and Girders	
	$0.66\ f_y$	$0.60\ f_y$	$0.40\ f_y$
36	24.0*	22.0*	14.5*
42	28.0*	25.0*	17.0*
46	30.5*	27.5*	18.5*
50	33.0*	30.0*	20.0*
60	39.6	36.0	24.0
70		42.0	28.0
80		48.0	32.0
90		54.0	36.0
100		60.0	40.0

* Value according to AISC specification.

Table 5.2

Allowable Shear Stresses* and Required Gross Areas* of Pairs of Intermediate Stiffeners for Building Girders Having Transversely Stiffened Webs—$f_y = 36$ ksi

Slenderness Ratios h/t: Web Depth to Web Thickness	Aspect Ratios a/h: Stiffener Spacing to Web Depth													Over 3
	0.5	0.6	0.7	0.8	0.9	1.0	1.2	1.4	1.6	1.8	2.0	2.5	3.0	
70	14.5	14.5	14.5	14.5	14.5	14.5	14.5	14.5	14.5	14.5	14.3	14.0	13.7	13.1
80	14.5	14.5	14.5	14.5	14.5	14.5	14.2	13.5	13.1	12.8	12.6	12.3	12.1	11.5
											0.7	*0.3*	*0.4*	
90	14.5	14.5	14.5	14.5	14.4	13.9	12.6	12.3	12.1	11.9	11.7	11.4	11.2	10.2
								0.6	*0.9*	*1.1*	*1.2*	*1.3*	*1.2*	
100	14.5	14.5	14.5	14.0	13.0	12.4	12.0	11.7	11.4	11.2	11.0	10.4	10.1	8.4
						0.5	*1.4*	*1.8*	*2.1*	*2.1*	*2.2*	*2.3*	*2.1*	
110	14.5	14.5	14.0	12.7	12.3	12.0	11.6	11.1	10.6	10.3	9.9	9.3	8.9	6.9
					1.0	*1.8*	*2.5*	*3.1*	*3.5*	*3.6*	*3.6*	*3.4*	*3.1*	
120	14.5	14.4	12.8	12.3	12.0	11.6	10.9	10.4	9.9	9.5	9.1	8.5	8.0	5.8
				1.1	*2.1*	*2.9*	*4.1*	*4.7*	*4.9*	*4.9*	*4.8*	*4.3*	*3.8*	
130	14.5	13.3	12.4	12.0	11.6	11.1	10.4	9.8	9.3	8.9	8.5	7.8	7.4	5.0
			0.9	*2.2*	*3.2*	*4.3*	*5.6*	*5.9*	*6.0*	*5.8*	*5.6*	*5.0*	*4.4*	
140	14.3	12.5	12.1	11.7	11.1	10.6	9.9	9.3	8.8	8.4	8.0	7.3	6.8	.43
		0.3	*1.9*	*3.2*	*4.8*	*5.9*	*6.7*	*6.9*	*6.8*	*6.6*	*6.3*	*5.5*	*4.9*	
150	13.4	12.3	11.9	11.3	10.8	10.3	9.5	8.9	8.4	8.0	7.6	6.9	6.4	3.7
		1.2	*2.8*	*4.7*	*6.1*	*7.1*	*7.6*	*7.7*	*7.5*	*7.2*	*6.8*	*6.0*	*5.2*	
160	12.6	12.1	11.6	11.0	10.4	10.0	9.2	8.6	8.1	7.7	7.3	6.6		3.2
	0.1	*2.1*	*4.1*	*6.0*	*7.2*	*8.0*	*8.4*	*8.3*	*8.1*	*7.7*	*7.3*	*6.3*		
170	12.4	12.0	11.3	10.7	10.2	9.7	9.0	8.3	7.8	7.4	7.0			2.9
	0.9	*2.8*	*5.3*	*7.0*	*8.1*	*8.7*	*9.0*	*8.9*	*8.5*	*8.1*	*7.7*			
180	12.3	11.7	11.0	10.5	10.0	9.5	8.8	8.1	7.6	7.2	6.8			2.6
	1.6	*4.0*	*6.4*	*7.9*	*8.8*	*9.4*	*9.6*	*9.3*	*8.9*	*8.5*	*8.0*			
200	12.0	11.3	10.7	10.1	9.6	9.2	8.4	7.8	7.3					2.1
	2.9	*6.0*	*8.0*	*9.2*	*10.0*	*10.4*	*10.4*	*10.0*	*9.5*					
220	11.6	10.9	10.4	9.8	9.4	8.9	8.2	7.5						1.7
	4.8	*7.5*	*9.2*	*10.2*	*10.8*	*11.1*	*11.0*	*10.6*						
240	11.3	10.7	10.1	9.6	9.2	8.7								1.4
	6.2	*8.6*	*10.1*	*11.0*	*11.5*	*11.7*								
260	11.1	10.5	10.0	9.5	9.0	8.6								1.2
	7.3	*9.5*	*10.8*	*11.6*	*12.0*	*12.1*								
280	10.9	10.3	9.8	9.3										
	8.2	*10.2*	*11.4*	*12.1*										
300	10.8	10.2	9.7											
	9.0	*10.8*	*11.8*											
320	10.7	10.1												
	9.5	*11.2*												

* Allowable shear stresses, ksi, are shown in regular print. Required stiffener areas as a percent of web area are shown in italics. For single-angle stiffeners, multiply required areas by 1.8; for single-plate stiffeners, multiply by 2.4. Girders so proportioned that the computed shear is less than that given in the right-hand column do not require intermediate stiffeners.

Table 5.3

Allowable Shear Stresses* and Required Gross Areas* of Pairs of Intermediate Stiffeners for Building Girders Having Transversely Stiffened Webs—f_y = 42 ksi

Slenderness Ratios h/t: Web Depth to Web Thickness	Aspect Ratios a/h: Stiffener Spacing to Web Depth													Over 3
	0.5	0.6	0.7	0.8	0.9	1.0	1.2	1.4	1.6	1.8	2.0	2.5	3.0	
70	17.0	17.0	17.0	17.0	17.0	17.0	17.0	16.7	16.1	15.7	15.5	15.0	14.8	14.2
80	17.0	17.0	17.0	17.0	17.0	16.4	15.3	14.6	14.4	14.2	14.0	13.6	13.4	12.4
								0.1	*0.5*	*0.7*	*0.8*	*0.9*	*0.9*	
90	17.0	17.0	17.0	16.8	15.5	14.7	14.2	13.8	13.5	13.3	13.1	12.6	12.2	10.4
					0.1	*1.0*	*1.5*	*1.8*	*1.9*	*1.9*	*1.9*	*1.8*		
100	17.0	17.0	16.6	15.1	14.4	14.1	13.6	13.2	12.6	12.2	11.8	11.1	10.6	8.4
				0.7	*1.5*	*2.3*	*2.7*	*3.2*	*3.4*	*3.4*	*3.2*	*2.9*		
110	17.0	17.0	15.1	14.4	14.0	13.6	12.9	12.2	11.6	11.1	10.7	10.0	9.5	6.9
			1.0	*2.0*	*2.7*	*3.9*	*4.5*	*4.7*	*4.7*	*4.6*	*4.2*	*3.8*		
120	17.0	15.5	14.4	14.0	13.6	13.0	12.1	11.4	10.8	10.4	9.9	9.2	8.6	5.8
		0.9	*2.1*	*3.2*	*4.5*	*5.5*	*5.9*	*5.9*	*5.8*	*5.6*	*5.0*	*4.4*		
130	16.6	14.6	14.1	13.6	13.0	12.4	11.5	10.8	10.2	9.7	9.3	8.5	7.9	5.0
		0.3	*2.0*	*3.3*	*4.9*	*6.0*	*6.8*	*6.9*	*6.8*	*6.6*	*6.3*	*5.6*	*4.9*	
140	15.5	14.3	13.9	13.2	12.5	11.9	11.1	10.4	9.8	9.3	8.8	8.0	7.4	4.3
		1.4	*2.9*	*4.9*	*6.3*	*7.2*	*7.7*	*7.9*	*7.6*	*7.3*	*6.9*	*6.0*	*5.3*	
150	14.6	14.1	13.5	12.7	12.1	11.5	10.7	10.0	9.4	8.9	8.4	7.6	7.0	3.7
	0.2	*2.2*	*4.3*	*6.2*	*7.4*	*8.1*	*8.5*	*8.5*	*8.2*	*7.8*	*7.4*	*6.4*	*5.6*	
160	14.4	13.9	13.1	12.4	11.8	11.2	10.4	9.7	9.1	8.5	8.1	7.2		3.2
	1.1	*3.1*	*5.6*	*7.3*	*8.3*	*8.9*	*9.2*	*9.0*	*8.7*	*8.2*	*7.8*	*6.7*		
170	14.3	13.6	12.8	12.1	11.5	11.0	10.3	9.4	8.8	8.3	7.8			2.9
	1.8	*4.4*	*6.7*	*8.1*	*9.1*	*9.6*	*9.7*	*9.5*	*9.1*	*8.6*	*8.1*			
180	14.1	13.3	12.5	11.9	11.3	10.8	9.9	9.2	8.6	8.0	7.6			2.6
	2.5	*5.5*	*7.6*	*8.9*	*9.8*	*10.1*	*10.2*	*9.9*	*9.4*	*8.9*	*8.3*			
200	13.6	12.8	12.1	11.5	11.0	10.4	9.6	8.9	8.2					2.1
	4.4	*7.2*	*9.0*	*10.1*	*10.7*	*11.0*	*10.9*	*10.5*	*9.9*					
220	13.3	12.5	11.9	11.3	10.7	10.2	9.3	8.6						1.7
	6.1	*8.5*	*10.0*	*10.9*	*11.4*	*11.6*	*11.4*	*10.9*						
240	13.0	12.3	11.6	11.1	10.5	10.0								1.4
	7.3	*9.5*	*10.8*	*11.6*	*12.0*	*12.1*								
260	12.7	12.1	11.5	10.9	10.4	9.9								1.2
	8.3	*10.2*	*11.4*	*12.1*	*12.4*	*12.5*								
280	12.6	11.9	11.3	10.8										
	9.0	*10.8*	*11.9*	*12.5*										

* Allowable shear stresses, ksi, are shown in regular print. Required stiffener areas as a percent of web area are shown in italics. For single-angle stiffeners, multiply required areas by 1.8; for single-plate stiffeners, multiply by 2.4. Girders so proportioned that the computed shear is less than that given in the right-hand column do not require intermediate stiffeners.

Table 5.4

Allowable Shear Stresses* and Required Gross Areas* of Pairs of Intermediate Stiffeners for Building Girders Having Transversely Stiffened Webs—$f_y = 46$ ksi

Slenderness Ratios h/t: Web Depth to Web Thickness	Aspect Ratios a/h: Stiffener Spacing to Web Depth													Over 3
	0.5	0.6	0.7	0.8	0.9	1.0	1.2	1.4	1.6	1.8	2.0	2.5	3.0	
60	18.5	18.5	18.5	18.5	18.5	18.5	18.5	18.5	18.5	18.5	18.5	18.3	18.0	17.3
70	18.5	18.5	18.5	18.5	18.5	18.5	18.3	17.5	16.9	16.5	16.2	15.8	15.3	14.9
												0.2	*0.3*	
80	18.5	18.5	18.5	18.5	18.3	17.2	16.1	15.7	15.4	15.1	14.9	14.5	14.2	13.0
						0.1	*0.7*	*1.0*	*1.2*	*1.3*	*1.3*	*1.2*		
90	18.5	18.5	18.5	17.6	16.3	15.8	15.3	14.8	14.5	14.2	13.8	13.1	12.6	10.4
						0.1	*1.6*	*2.0*	*2.2*	*2.3*	*2.5*	*2.5*	*2.3*	
100	18.5	18.5	17.4	16.0	15.6	15.2	14.6	13.9	13.3	12.8	12.4	11.6	11.0	8.4
				0.3	*1.3*	*2.1*	*2.9*	*3.6*	*4.0*	*4.0*	*4.0*	*3.7*	*3.3*	
110	18.5	17.8	16.0	15.5	15.1	14.6	13.6	12.9	12.3	11.7	11.3	10.5	9.9	6.9
			0.3	*1.6*	*2.6*	*3.6*	*4.8*	*5.3*	*5.4*	*5.3*	*5.2*	*4.6*	*4.1*	
120	18.5	16.3	15.6	15.1	14.5	13.8	12.9	12.1	11.5	10.9	10.5	9.6	9.0	5.8
			1.5	*2.7*	*4.2*	*5.4*	*6.2*	*6.5*	*6.5*	*6.3*	*6.0*	*5.3*	*4.7*	
130	17.4	15.8	15.3	14.6	13.9	13.2	12.3	11.5	10.9	10.3	9.9	9.0	8.3	5.0
		1.0	*2.5*	*4.3*	*5.8*	*6.7*	*7.4*	*7.5*	*7.3*	*7.0*	*6.7*	*5.9*	*5.1*	
140	16.2	15.5	14.9	14.1	13.4	12.8	11.8	11.1	10.4	9.8	9.4	8.4	7.8	4.3
		1.9	*3.8*	*5.8*	*7.0*	*7.8*	*8.3*	*8.2*	*8.0*	*7.6*	*7.2*	*6.3*	*5.5*	
150	15.9	15.3	14.5	13.7	13.0	12.4	11.5	10.7	10.0	9.4	9.0	8.0	7.4	3.7
	0.8	*2.8*	*5.3*	*7.0*	*8.0*	*8.7*	*9.0*	*8.9*	*8.5*	*8.1*	*7.7*	*6.7*	*5.8*	
160	15.7	14.9	14.1	13.4	12.7	12.1	11.2	10.4	9.7	9.1	8.6	7.7		3.2
	1.7	*4.1*	*6.4*	*7.9*	*8.9*	*9.4*	*9.6*	*9.4*	*9.0*	*8.5*	*8.0*	*6.9*		
170	15.5	14.6	13.8	13.1	12.4	11.8	10.9	10.1	9.4	8.9	8.4			2.9
	2.4	*5.3*	*7.4*	*8.7*	*9.6*	*10.0*	*10.1*	*9.8*	*9.3*	*8.8*	*8.3*			
180	15.2	14.3	13.5	12.8	12.2	11.6	10.7	9.9	9.2	8.6	8.1			2.6
	3.2	*6.3*	*8.2*	*9.4*	*10.1*	*10.5*	*10.5*	*10.1*	*9.6*	*9.1*	*8.5*			
200	14.7	13.9	13.1	12.5	11.9	11.3	10.4	9.6	8.9					2.1
	5.3	*7.9*	*9.5*	*10.5*	*11.0*	*11.3*	*11.2*	*10.7*	*10.1*					
220	14.3	13.6	12.9	12.2	11.6	11.1	10.1	9.3						1.7
	6.7	*9.0*	*10.4*	*11.3*	*11.7*	*11.9*	*11.6*	*11.1*						
240	14.0	13.3	12.6	12.0	11.4	10.9								1.4
	7.9	*9.9*	*11.2*	*11.9*	*12.2*	*12.3*								
260	13.8	13.1	12.5	11.8	11.3	10.7								1.2
	8.8	*10.6*	*11.7*	*12.3*	*12.6*	*12.7*								

* Allowable shear stresses, ksi, are shown in regular print. Required stiffener areas as a percent of web area are shown in italics. For single-angle stiffeners, multiply required areas by 1.8; for single-plate stiffeners, multiply by 2.4. Girders so proportioned that the computed shear is less than that given in the right-hand column do not require intermediate stiffeners.

Table 5.5

Allowable Shear Stresses* and Required Gross Areas* of Pairs of Intermediate Stiffeners for Building Girders Having Transversely Stiffened Webs—$f_y = 50$ ksi

Slenderness Ratios h/t: Web Depth to Web Thickness	\multicolumn{13}{c}{Aspect Ratios a/h: Stiffener Spacing to Web Depth}													Over 3
	0.5	0.6	0.7	0.8	0.9	1.0	1.2	1.4	1.6	1.8	2.0	2.5	3.0	
60	20.0	20.0	20.0	20.0	20.0	20.0	20.0	20.0	20.0	20.0	19.7	19.1	18.8	18.1
70	20.0	20.0	20.0	20.0	20.0	20.0	19.1	18.2	17.6	17.3	17.1	16.7	16.5	15.5
										0.2	*0.4*	*0.6*	*0.6*	
80	20.0	20.0	20.0	20.0	19.1	17.9	17.1	16.7	16.4	16.1	15.8	15.4	15.0	13.1
						0.6	*1.2*	*1.4*	*1.6*	*1.6*	*1.6*	*1.6*	*1.5*	
90	20.0	20.0	20.0	18.3	17.3	16.9	16.3	15.8	15.3	14.8	14.3	13.5	13.0	10.4
					0.4	*1.3*	*2.1*	*2.5*	*2.8*	*3.1*	*3.1*	*3.0*	*2.8*	
100	20.0	20.0	18.1	17.2	16.7	16.3	15.4	14.6	13.9	13.4	12.9	12.0	11.4	8.4
				0.9	*1.9*	*2.6*	*3.8*	*4.4*	*4.6*	*4.6*	*4.5*	*4.1*	*3.7*	
110	20.0	18.5	17.2	16.7	16.2	15.4	14.4	13.6	12.9	12.3	11.8	10.9	10.3	6.9
			0.9	*2.2*	*3.2*	*4.5*	*5.5*	*5.9*	*5.9*	*5.8*	*5.6*	*5.0*	*4.4*	
120	19.7	17.4	16.8	16.2	15.4	14.7	13.7	12.8	12.1	11.5	11.0	10.1	9.4	5.8
		0.4	*2.0*	*3.4*	*5.0*	*6.1*	*6.9*	*7.0*	*6.9*	*6.7*	*6.4*	*5.8*	*4.9*	
130	18.2	17.0	16.4	15.6	14.8	14.1	13.1	12.2	11.5	10.9	10.4	9.4	8.7	5.0
		1.5	*3.1*	*5.1*	*6.5*	*7.4*	*7.9*	*7.9*	*7.7*	*7.4*	*7.0*	*6.1*	*5.3*	
140	17.3	16.7	15.9	15.1	14.3	13.6	12.6	11.8	11.0	10.4	9.9	8.9	8.2	4.3
	0.5	*2.5*	*4.7*	*6.5*	*7.7*	*8.4*	*8.7*	*8.6*	*8.3*	*7.9*	*7.5*	*6.5*	*5.7*	
150	17.1	16.4	15.5	14.6	13.9	13.3	12.2	11.4	10.7	10.0	9.5	8.5	7.7	3.7
	1.4	*3.6*	*6.0*	*7.6*	*8.6*	*9.2*	*9.4*	*9.2*	*8.8*	*8.4*	*7.9*	*6.8*	*5.9*	
160	16.9	16.0	15.1	14.3	13.6	13.0	11.9	11.1	10.3	9.7	9.2	8.1		3.2
	2.2	*4.9*	*7.1*	*8.5*	*9.4*	*9.8*	*9.9*	*9.7*	*9.2*	*8.7*	*8.2*	*7.1*		
170	16.7	15.6	14.8	14.0	13.3	12.7	11.7	10.8	10.1	9.5	8.9			2.9
	2.9	*6.0*	*8.0*	*9.2*	*10.0*	*10.4*	*10.4*	*10.0*	*9.6*	*9.0*	*8.5*			
180	16.3	15.4	14.5	13.8	13.1	12.5	11.5	10.6	9.9	9.2	8.7			2.6
	4.1	*7.0*	*8.8*	*10.0*	*10.5*	*10.9*	*10.8*	*10.4*	*9.8*	*9.3*	*8.7*			
200	15.8	14.9	14.1	13.4	12.8	12.2	11.1	10.3	9.5					2.1
	5.9	*8.4*	*9.9*	*10.8*	*11.4*	*11.6*	*11.4*	*10.9*	*10.3*					
220	15.4	14.6	13.8	13.2	12.5	11.9	10.9	10.0						1.7
	7.3	*9.5*	*10.8*	*11.6*	*12.0*	*12.1*	*11.8*	*11.3*						
240	15.1	14.3	13.6	13.0	12.3	11.7								1.4
	8.3	*10.3*	*11.5*	*12.1*	*12.4*	*12.5*								

* Allowable shear stresses, ksi, are shown in regular print. Required stiffener areas as a percent of web area are shown in italics. For single-angle stiffeners, multiply required areas by 1.8; for single-plate stiffeners, multiply by 2.4. Girders so proportioned that the computed shear is less than that given in the right-hand column do not require intermediate stiffeners.

Table 5.6

Allowable Shear Stresses* and Required Gross Areas* of Pairs of Intermediate Stiffeners for Building Girders Having Transversely Stiffened Webs—$f_y = 60$ ksi

Slenderness Ratios h/t: Web Depth to Web Thickness	Aspect Ratios a/h: Stiffener Spacing to Web Depth													
	0.5	0.6	0.7	0.8	0.9	1.0	1.2	1.4	1.6	1.8	2.0	2.5	3.0	Over 3
50	24.0	24.0	24.0	24.0	24.0	24.0	24.0	24.0	24.0	24.0	24.0	24.0	24.0	23.5
60	24.0	24.0	24.0	24.0	24.0	24.0	24.0	23.0	22.3	21.7	21.3	20.7	20.5	19.6
													0.1	
70	24.0	24.0	24.0	24.0	23.6	22.2	20.7	20.3	19.9	19.5	19.3	18.7	18.4	16.8
								0.6	*1.0*	*1.2*	*1.3*	*1.3*	*1.2*	
80	24.0	24.0	24.0	22.3	20.7	20.2	19.6	19.0	18.6	18.0	17.5	16.6	15.9	13.0
					0.1	*0.9*	*1.8*	*2.2*	*2.4*	*2.6*	*2.7*	*2.7*	*2.5*	
90	24.0	24.0	21.8	20.5	19.9	19.4	18.5	17.5	16.7	16.1	15.5	14.5	13.8	10.3
				0.7	*1.7*	*2.5*	*3.5*	*4.1*	*4.4*	*4.4*	*4.4*	*4.0*	*3.6*	
100	24.0	22.1	20.4	19.8	19.3	18.4	17.2	16.2	15.4	14.7	14.1	13.0	12.2	8.3
			0.8	*2.1*	*3.1*	*4.4*	*5.4*	*5.8*	*5.9*	*5.7*	*5.5*	*4.9*	*4.4*	
110	23.3	20.6	19.9	19.2	18.2	17.4	16.2	15.2	14.4	13.7	13.1	11.9	11.1	6.9
		0.5	*2.1*	*3.5*	*5.1*	*6.2*	*6.9*	*7.1*	*7.0*	*6.7*	*6.4*	*5.6*	*4.9*	
120	21.3	20.2	19.4	18.4	17.5	16.7	15.4	14.4	13.6	12.9	12.3	11.1	10.2	5.8
		1.7	*3.3*	*5.4*	*6.7*	*7.5*	*8.0*	*8.0*	*7.8*	*7.4*	*7.1*	*6.2*	*5.4*	
130	20.5	19.8	18.7	17.7	16.9	16.1	14.9	13.9	13.0	12.3	11.6	10.4	9.6	4.9
	0.7	*2.7*	*5.1*	*6.8*	*7.9*	*8.6*	*8.9*	*8.8*	*8.4*	*8.0*	*7.6*	*6.6*	*5.7*	
140	20.2	19.3	18.2	17.2	16.4	15.6	14.4	13.4	12.5	11.8	11.2	9.9	9.0	4.2
	1.6	*4.1*	*6.4*	*7.9*	*8.9*	*9.4*	*9.6*	*9.4*	*8.9*	*8.5*	*8.0*	*6.9*	*6.0*	
150	19.9	18.8	17.8	16.8	16.0	15.3	14.0	13.0	12.1	11.4	10.8	9.5	8.6	3.7
	2.5	*5.4*	*7.5*	*8.8*	*9.6*	*10.1*	*10.1*	*9.8*	*9.4*	*8.8*	*8.3*	*7.2*	*6.2*	
160	19.6	18.4	17.4	16.5	15.7	15.0	13.7	12.7	11.8	11.1	10.4	9.2		3.2
	3.6	*6.5*	*8.4*	*9.6*	*10.3*	*10.6*	*10.6*	*10.2*	*9.7*	*9.1*	*8.6*	*7.4*		
170	19.2	18.1	17.1	16.2	15.4	14.7	13.5	12.5	11.6	10.8	10.2			2.9
	4.7	*7.4*	*9.2*	*10.2*	*10.8*	*11.1*	*11.0*	*10.5*	*10.0*	*9.4*	*8.8*			
180	18.9	17.8	16.8	16.0	15.2	14.5	13.3	12.2	11.4	10.6	9.9			2.6
	5.7	*8.2*	*9.8*	*10.7*	*11.2*	*11.5*	*11.3*	*10.8*	*10.2*	*9.6*	*9.0*			
200	18.3	17.3	16.5	15.6	14.9	14.2	13.0	11.9	11.0					2.1
	7.2	*9.4*	*10.8*	*11.5*	*11.9*	*12.1*	*11.8*	*11.2*	*10.6*					

* Allowable shear stresses, ksi, are shown in regular print. Required stiffener areas as a percent of web area are shown in italics. For single-angle stiffeners, multiply required areas by 1.8; for single-plate stiffeners, multiply by 2.4. Girders so proportioned that the computed shear is less than that given in the right-hand column do not require intermediate stiffeners.

Table 5.7

Allowable Shear Stresses* and Required Gross Area* of Pairs of Intermediate Stiffeners for Building Girders Having Transversely Stiffened Webs—$f_y = 70$ ksi

Slenderness Ratios h/t: Web Depth to Web Thickness	Aspect Ratios a/h: Stiffener Spacing to Web Depth													Over 3
	0.5	0.6	0.7	0.8	0.9	1.0	1.2	1.4	1.6	1.8	2.0	2.5	3.0	
50	28.0	28.0	28.0	28.0	28.0	28.0	28.0	28.0	28.0	28.0	27.7	26.9	26.4	25.4
60	28.0	28.0	28.0	28.0	28.0	28.0	26.1	24.9	24.1	23.8	23.5	23.0	22.6	21.2
									0.1	*0.3*	*0.5*	*0.7*	*0.7*	
70	28.0	28.0	28.0	27.6	25.5	24.1	23.4	22.8	22.3	21.9	21.5	20.7	20.0	17.0
						0.1	*1.1*	*1.6*	*1.8*	*1.9*	*1.9*	*1.9*	*1.9*	
80	28.0	28.0	26.5	24.2	23.6	23.0	22.2	21.1	20.2	19.5	18.8	17.7	16.9	13.0
				0.1	*1.2*	*2.0*	*2.7*	*3.4*	*3.7*	*3.8*	*3.8*	*3.6*	*3.2*	
90	28.0	26.5	24.0	23.3	22.7	21.8	20.4	19.3	18.3	17.5	16.9	15.6	14.7	10.3
			0.4	*1.7*	*2.7*	*3.8*	*4.9*	*5.4*	*5.5*	*5.4*	*5.2*	*4.7*	*4.2*	
100	27.7	24.1	23.4	22.6	21.5	20.5	19.1	17.9	17.0	16.1	15.5	14.1	13.2	8.3
		0.2	*1.9*	*3.1*	*4.8*	*5.9*	*6.6*	*6.9*	*6.8*	*6.5*	*6.3*	*5.5*	*4.8*	
110	25.1	23.6	22.8	21.5	20.5	19.5	18.1	16.9	16.0	15.1	14.4	13.0	12.1	6.9
		1.5	*3.1*	*5.2*	*6.5*	*7.4*	*7.9*	*7.9*	*7.7*	*7.4*	*7.0*	*6.1*	*5.3*	
120	24.0	23.1	21.9	20.7	19.7	18.8	17.4	16.2	15.2	14.3	13.6	12.2	11.2	5.8
	0.7	*2.6*	*5.0*	*6.7*	*7.9*	*8.5*	*8.9*	*8.7*	*8.4*	*8.0*	*7.6*	*6.6*	*5.7*	
130	23.6	22.5	21.2	20.1	19.1	18.2	16.8	15.6	14.6	13.7	13.0	11.6	10.5	4.9
	1.7	*4.1*	*6.5*	*8.0*	*8.9*	*9.4*	*9.6*	*9.4*	*9.0*	*8.5*	*8.0*	*6.9*	*6.0*	
140	23.2	21.9	20.7	19.6	18.6	17.8	16.3	15.1	14.1	13.2	12.5	11.0	10.0	4.2
	2.5	*5.6*	*7.6*	*8.9*	*9.7*	*10.2*	*10.2*	*9.9*	*9.4*	*8.9*	*8.4*	*7.2*	*6.2*	
150	22.7	21.4	20.2	19.2	18.2	17.4	16.0	14.8	13.7	12.9	12.1	10.6	9.6	3.7
	3.8	*6.7*	*8.6*	*9.7*	*10.4*	*10.7*	*10.7*	*10.3*	*9.8*	*9.2*	*8.6*	*7.4*	*6.4*	
160	22.3	21.0	19.9	18.9	17.9	17.1	15.7	14.5	13.4	12.5	11.8	10.3		3.2
	5.0	*7.7*	*9.3*	*10.4*	*10.9*	*11.2*	*11.1*	*10.6*	*10.1*	*9.5*	*8.9*	*7.6*		
170	21.9	20.6	19.6	18.6	17.7	16.8	15.4	14.2	13.2	12.3	11.5			2.9
	6.0	*8.5*	*10.0*	*10.9*	*11.4*	*11.6*	*11.4*	*10.9*	*10.3*	*9.7*	*9.1*			
180	21.5	20.4	19.3	18.4	17.5	16.6	15.2	14.0	13.0	12.1	11.3			2.6
	6.9	*9.1*	*10.5*	*11.3*	*11.8*	*11.9*	*11.7*	*11.1*	*10.5*	*9.8*	*9.2*			

* Allowable shear stresses, ksi, are shown in regular print. Required stiffener areas as a percent of web area are shown in italics. For single-angle stiffeners, multiply required areas by 1.8; for single-plate stiffeners, multiply by 2.4. Girders so proportioned that the computed shear is less than that given in the right-hand column do not require intermediate stiffeners.

Table 5.8

Allowable Shear Stresses* and Required Gross Area* of Pairs of Intermediate Stiffeners for Building Girders Having Transversely Stiffened Webs—$f_y = 80$ ksi

Slenderness Ratios h/t: Web Depth to Web Thickness	Aspect Ratios a/h: Stiffener Spacing to Web Depth													
	0.5	0.6	0.7	0.8	0.9	1.0	1.2	1.4	1.6	1.8	2.0	2.5	3.0	Over 3.0
50	32.0	32.0	32.0	32.0	32.0	32.0	32.0	31.9	30.9	30.1	29.6	28.7	28.2	27.1
60	32.0	32.0	32.0	32.0	31.9	29.9	27.9	27.1	26.6	26.2	25.8	25.1	24.7	22.6
								0.5	*0.9*	*1.1*	*1.2*	*1.2*	*1.2*	
70	32.0	32.0	32.0	29.5	27.5	26.9	26.0	25.3	24.6	23.8	23.1	21.8	20.9	17.0
				0.2	*1.1*	*1.9*	*2.3*	*2.5*	*2.8*	*2.9*	*2.8*	*2.6*		
80	32.0	31.9	28.3	27.1	26.3	25.7	24.2	22.9	21.8	20.9	20.2	18.8	17.8	13.0
			1.0	*2.0*	*2.8*	*4.0*	*4.6*	*4.8*	*4.8*	*4.7*	*4.2*	*3.8*		
90	32.0	28.3	27.0	26.2	25.1	23.9	22.3	21.0	19.9	19.0	18.2	16.7	15.7	10.3
			1.3	*2.6*	*3.9*	*5.1*	*6.1*	*6.4*	*6.3*	*6.2*	*5.9*	*5.2*	*4.6*	
100	29.6	27.1	26.2	25.0	23.7	22.6	21.0	19.7	18.6	17.6	16.8	15.2	14.1	8.3
		1.2	*2.7*	*4.6*	*6.0*	*7.0*	*7.6*	*7.6*	*7.4*	*7.1*	*6.8*	*5.9*	*5.2*	
110	27.5	26.5	25.2	23.9	22.7	21.6	20.0	18.7	17.5	16.6	15.8	14.1	13.0	6.9
	0.4	*2.4*	*4.6*	*6.4*	*7.6*	*8.3*	*8.7*	*8.6*	*8.3*	*7.9*	*7.4*	*6.5*	*5.6*	
120	27.0	25.8	24.4	23.1	21.9	20.9	19.3	17.9	16.8	15.8	15.0	13.3	12.1	5.8
	1.5	*3.8*	*6.2*	*7.8*	*8.7*	*9.3*	*9.5*	*9.3*	*8.9*	*8.4*	*7.9*	*6.9*	*6.0*	
130	26.6	25.1	23.7	22.4	21.3	20.3	18.7	17.4	16.2	15.2	14.3	12.7	11.5	4.9
	2.5	*5.4*	*7.5*	*8.8*	*9.6*	*10.1*	*10.1*	*9.8*	*9.4*	*8.8*	*8.3*	*7.2*	*6.2*	
140	26.0	24.4	23.1	21.9	20.9	19.9	18.3	16.9	15.7	14.7	13.8	12.2	10.9	4.2
	3.8	*6.7*	*8.5*	*9.7*	*10.4*	*10.7*	*10.7*	*10.3*	*9.8*	*9.2*	*8.6*	*7.4*	*6.4*	
150	25.4	24.0	22.7	21.5	20.5	19.5	17.9	16.5	15.3	14.3	13.4	11.7	10.5	3.7
	5.1	*7.7*	*9.4*	*10.4*	*11.0*	*11.2*	*11.1*	*10.6*	*10.1*	*9.5*	*8.9*	*7.6*	*6.6*	
160	25.0	23.6	22.3	21.2	20.2	19.2	17.6	16.2	15.0	14.0	13.1	11.4		3.2
	6.1	*8.5*	*10.0*	*10.9*	*11.4*	*11.6*	*11.4*	*10.9*	*10.3*	*9.7*	*9.1*	*7.8*		

* Allowable shear stresses, ksi, are shown in regular print. Required stiffener areas as a percent of web area are shown in italics. For single-angle stiffeners, multiply required areas by 1.8; for single-plate stiffeners, multiply by 2.4. Girders so proportioned that the computed shear is less than that given in the right-hand column do not require intermediate stiffeners.

Table 5.9

Allowable Shear Stresses* and Required Gross Area* of Pairs of Intermediate Stiffeners for Building Girders Having Transversely Stiffened Webs—$f_y = 90$ ksi

Slenderness Ratios h/t: Web Depth to Web Thickness	Aspect Ratios a/h: Stiffener Spacing to Web Depth													
	0.5	0.6	0.7	0.8	0.9	1.0	1.2	1.4	1.6	1.8	2.0	2.5	3.0	Over 3.0
50	36.0	36.0	36.0	36.0	36.0	36.0	35.5	33.8	32.7	31.9	31.4	30.7	30.3	28.8
												0.2	*0.3*	
60	36.0	36.0	36.0	36.0	33.8	31.7	30.4	29.7	29.1	28.5	28.1	27.2	26.7	23.1
						0.7	*1.2*	*1.5*	*1.6*	*1.7*	*1.7*	*1.5*		
70	36.0	36.0	34.3	31.3	30.4	29.6	28.6	27.3	26.2	25.2	24.4	22.9	21.9	17.0
				1.0	*1.9*	*2.6*	*3.2*	*3.6*	*3.7*	*3.7*	*3.5*	*3.2*		
80	36.0	33.8	30.8	29.9	29.1	27.9	26.1	24.6	23.4	22.4	21.5	19.9	18.8	13.0
			0.5	*1.8*	*2.8*	*4.0*	*5.1*	*5.5*	*5.6*	*5.5*	*5.3*	*4.8*	*4.2*	
90	34.9	30.9	29.9	28.8	27.3	26.1	24.3	22.8	21.5	20.5	19.6	17.8	16.6	10.3
		0.5	*2.1*	*3.6*	*5.2*	*6.2*	*6.9*	*7.1*	*7.0*	*6.7*	*6.4*	*5.6*	*4.9*	
100	31.4	30.1	28.9	27.3	26.0	24.7	22.9	21.4	20.1	19.1	18.1	16.4	15.1	8.3
		1.9	*3.8*	*5.7*	*7.0*	*7.8*	*8.3*	*8.2*	*8.0*	*7.6*	*7.2*	*6.3*	*5.5*	
110	30.6	29.4	27.7	26.2	24.9	23.8	22.0	20.4	19.1	18.0	17.1	15.3	14.0	6.9
	1.2	*3.2*	*5.7*	*7.4*	*8.4*	*9.0*	*9.2*	*9.1*	*8.7*	*8.2*	*7.8*	*6.7*	*5.9*	
120	30.0	28.4	26.8	25.4	24.2	23.0	21.2	19.7	18.4	17.3	16.3	14.4	13.1	5.8
	2.2	*5.0*	*7.2*	*8.6*	*9.4*	*9.9*	*10.0*	*9.7*	*9.2*	*8.7*	*8.2*	*7.1*	*6.2*	
130	29.4	27.6	26.1	24.8	23.6	22.5	20.7	19.1	17.8	16.7	15.7	13.8	12.4	4.9
	3.5	*6.4*	*8.3*	*9.5*	*10.2*	*10.6*	*10.6*	*10.2*	*9.7*	*9.1*	*8.6*	*7.4*	*6.4*	
140	28.7	27.0	25.6	24.3	23.1	22.0	20.2	18.6	17.3	16.2	15.2	13.3	11.9	4.2
	4.9	*7.6*	*9.3*	*10.3*	*10.9*	*11.2*	*11.0*	*10.6*	*10.0*	*9.4*	*8.8*	*7.6*	*6.6*	

* Allowable shear stresses, ksi, are shown in regular print. Required stiffener areas as a percent of web area are shown in italics. For single-angle stiffeners, multiply required areas by 1.8; for single-plate stiffeners, multiply by 2.4. Girders so proportioned that the computed shear is less than that given in the right-hand column do not require intermediate stiffeners.

Table 5.10

Allowable Shear Stresses* and Required Gross Areas* of Pairs of Intermediate Stiffeners for Building Girders Having Transversely Stiffened Webs—$f_y = 100$ ksi

Slenderness Ratios h/t: Web Depth to Web Thickness	Aspect Ratios a/h: Stiffener Spacing to Web Depth													
	0.5	0.6	0.7	0.8	0.9	1.0	1.2	1.4	1.6	1.8	2.0	2.5	3.0	Over 3
40	40.0	40.0	40.0	40.0	40.0	40.0	40.0	40.0	40.0	40.0	40.0	40.0	39.5	37.9
50	40.0	40.0	40.0	40.0	40.0	40.0	37.4	35.7	34.5	34.1	33.7	32.9	32.4	30.3
										0.3	*0.5*	*0.6*	*0.7*	
60	40.0	40.0	40.0	38.4	35.6	34.2	33.1	32.2	31.4	30.8	30.2	28.7	27.7	23.1
					0.5	*1.4*	*1.8*	*2.1*	*2.1*	*2.2*	*2.3*	*2.1*		
70	40.0	40.0	36.2	34.1	33.2	32.3	30.7	29.1	27.8	26.7	25.8	24.0	22.8	17.0
			0.7	*1.8*	*2.5*	*3.5*	*4.2*	*4.5*	*4.5*	*4.4*	*4.0*	*3.6*		
80	40.0	35.6	33.8	32.8	31.5	30.0	28.0	26.4	25.0	23.9	22.9	21.0	19.7	13.0
		1.3	*2.5*	*3.8*	*5.0*	*6.0*	*6.3*	*6.3*	*6.1*	*5.9*	*5.2*	*4.6*		
90	36.7	33.9	32.7	31.1	29.6	28.2	26.2	24.5	23.1	21.9	20.9	19.0	17.6	10.3
		1.2	*2.8*	*4.7*	*6.1*	*7.0*	*7.6*	*7.7*	*7.5*	*7.2*	*6.8*	*6.0*	*5.2*	
100	34.3	33.0	31.3	29.7	28.2	26.9	24.9	23.2	21.7	20.5	19.5	17.5	16.0	8.3
	0.6	*2.6*	*4.9*	*6.7*	*7.8*	*8.5*	*8.8*	*8.7*	*8.4*	*8.0*	*7.5*	*6.5*	*5.7*	
110	33.6	32.0	30.2	28.6	27.2	25.9	23.9	22.2	20.7	19.5	18.4	16.4	14.9	6.9
	1.8	*4.4*	*6.7*	*8.1*	*9.0*	*9.6*	*9.7*	*9.5*	*9.0*	*8.6*	*8.1*	*7.0*	*6.0*	
120	33.0	31.0	29.3	27.8	26.4	25.2	23.2	21.4	20.0	18.7	17.6	15.6	14.0	5.8
	2.9	*6.0*	*8.0*	*9.2*	*10.0*	*10.4*	*10.4*	*10.0*	*9.5*	*9.0*	*8.5*	*7.3*	*6.3*	
130	32.1	30.2	28.6	27.1	25.8	24.6	22.6	20.9	19.4	18.1	17.0	14.9	13.4	4.9
	4.5	*7.3*	*9.0*	*10.1*	*10.7*	*11.0*	*10.9*	*10.5*	*9.9*	*9.3*	*8.8*	*7.5*	*6.5*	

* Allowable shear stresses, ksi, are shown in regular print. Required stiffener areas as a percent of web area are shown in italics. For single-angle stiffeners, multiply required areas by 1.8; for single-plate stiffeners, multiply by 2.4. Girders so proportioned that the computed shear is less than that given in the right-hand column do not require intermediate stiffeners.

Table. 5.11

Supplementary Data for Beams and Girders in Buildings

Specified Maximum Yield Stress, psi	Maximum Web Depth-to-Thickness Ratio, h/t $\dfrac{14{,}000{,}000}{\sqrt{f_y(f_y+16{,}500)}}$	Reduce Allowable Bending Stress When h/t Exceeds: $\dfrac{31{,}000}{\sqrt{f_y}}$	Maximum Design Shear Between Web and Intermediate Stiffeners,* lb/in. $h\sqrt{\left(\dfrac{f_y}{3400}\right)^3}$
36,000	320**	164**	35h**
42,000	282**	151**	43h**
46,000	260**	145**	50h**
50,000	243**	139**	56h**
60,000	207	127	74h
70,000	180	117	93h
80,000	159	110	114h
90,000	143	103	136h
100,000	130	98	160h

* Where intermediate stiffeners are furnished in pairs, the design shear for each stiffener is one half of the tabulated value. The value of h is expressed in inches.

** Value according to AISC specification.

Table 5.12

Allowable Horizontal Shear Load for Connectors in Composite Beams in Buildings*

Connector	Allowable Shear, kips, for Indicated Concrete Compressive Strength (f'_c), psi		
	$f'_c = 3000$	$f'_c = 3500$	$f'_c = 4000$
Hooked or Headed Stud			
½-in. diam. by 2 in.	5.1	5.5	5.9
⅝-in. diam. by 2½ in.	8.0	8.6	9.2
¾-in. diam. by 3 in.	11.5	12.5	13.3
⅞-in. diam. by 3½ in.	15.6	16.8	18.0
Rolled Channel**			
3 in. deep by 4.1 lb	4.3w	4.7w	5.0w
4 in. deep by 5.4 lb	4.6w	5.0w	5.3w
5 in. deep by 6.7 lb	4.9w	5.3w	5.6w
Spiral Bar*			
½-in. diam.	11.9	12.4	12.8
⅝-in. diam.	14.8	15.4	15.9
¾-in. diam.	17.8	18.5	19.1

* Values are based on the requirements of AISC and are applicable only to concrete made with ASTM C33 aggregates. Values must be used in conjunction with Equations 5.42 and 5.43 only.

** w is channel length, inches.

*** Loads for spiral bars are kips per pitch.

Table 5.13

Basic Allowable Bending and Shear Stresses for Beams and Girders in Bridges

Specified Minimum Yield Stress, ksi	Allowable Bending Stress for Adequately Braced Members, ksi $0.55 f_y$*	Allowable Shear Stress, ksi $0.33 f_y$
36	20.0[+0]	12.0[+]
42	23.0[+]	14.0[+]
46	25.0[+]	15.0[+]
50	27.0[+0]	16.0[+0]
60	33.0	20.0
70	38.5	23.3
80	44.0	26.7
90	49.5	30.0
100	55.0	33.3

* Allowable stresses may differ slightly from this value but are given as listed in the indicated specifications.

+ AASHO specification.

0 AREA specification.

Table 5.14

Maximum Web Depth-to-Thickness Ratios for Bridge Girders Having Stiffened Webs

Specified Minimum Yield Stress, psi	Webs Having Only Transverse Stiffeners* $\dfrac{31{,}000}{\sqrt{f_y}}$	Webs Having Transverse and Longitudinal Stiffeners** $\dfrac{62{,}000}{\sqrt{f_y}}$
36,000	165[+]	330[+]
42,000	150[+]	300[+]
46,000	145[+]	290[+]
50,000	140[+]	280[+]
60,000	127	253
70,000	117	234
80,000	110	219
90,000	103	207
100,000	98	196

* Values are based on the requirements of AASHO. If the maximum compressive bending stress, f_b, is less than the allowable bending stress, the h/t ratio may be increased to $23{,}000/\sqrt{f_b}$, but must not exceed 170. f_y and f_b are in psi.

** The values are based on the requirements of AASHO. If the maximum compressive bending stress is less than the allowable bending stress, the h/t ratio may be increased to $46{,}000/\sqrt{f_b}$, but must not exceed 340. f_y and f_b are in psi.

\+ Value according to AASHO specification.

Table 5.15

Allowable Horizontal Shear Load for Connectors in Composite Beams in Bridges*

Connector	Allowable Shear, kips, for Indicated Concrete Compressive Strength (f'_c), psi		
	$f'_c = 3000$	$f'_c = 3500$	$f'_c = 4000$
Welded Stud			
¾-in. diam. by 4 in.	3.38	3.66	3.92
⅞-in. diam. by 4 in.	4.61	4.98	5.33
Rolled Channel**			
3 in. deep by 4.1 lb	3.09w	3.28w	3.51w
4 in. deep by 5.4 lb	3.36w	3.56w	3.81w
5 in. deep by 6.7 lb	3.65w	3.87w	4.15w
Spiral Bar***			
½-in. diam.	4.69	4.92	5.09
⅝-in. diam.	5.91	6.15	6.36
¾-in. diam.	7.08	7.25	7.64

* The values are based on the requirements of AASHO and include a safety factor of 3.0.

** w is channel length, inches.

*** Loads for spiral bars are kips per pitch.

CHAPTER 6

Additional Considerations for Bending Members

6.1 Introduction

The topics treated in this chapter include biaxial bending, shear center, and lateral buckling. These additional considerations for bending members require a modification of the simple bending theory discussed in the previous chapter. Torsion, which sometimes occurs in bending members, will be discussed in Chapter 7.

6.2 Biaxial Bending

Through the centroid of any cross section, there is an axis about which the moment of intertia is a maximum and another about which the moment of inertia is a minimum. These two orthogonal axes are known as the "principal centroidal axes" or, simply, as the principal axes."[1] Members loaded so that bending occurs simultaneously about both principal axes are in "biaxial bending."

If the loads are perpendicular to one principal axis, simple bending occurs about that axis in accordance with the fundamental relationships for bending discussed in Chapter 5.* If loads are simultaneously applied perpendicular to both principal axes, elastic stresses and deflections may be calculated separately for bending about each axis and superimposed. If an applied load is not perpendicular to either principal axis, it may be resolved into two components that are perpendicular to the principal axes.

Thus, the total elastic bending stress, f_b, at any point in the cross section of a member subjected to biaxial bending is

---

*In this discussion it is assumed that the loads also pass through the shear center so that torsion does not occur. See Section 6.3.

$$f_b = \frac{M_1}{I_1} m + \frac{M_2}{I_2} n \qquad \text{(6.1)}$$

and the total resultant bending deflection, Δ, is

$$\Delta = \sqrt{(\Delta_1)^2 + (\Delta_2)^2} \qquad \text{(6.2)}$$

The subscripts 1 and 2 refer to the principal axes; I_1 and I_2 are the maximum and minimum moments of inertia, respectively. The bending moments M_1 and M_2 are caused by loads perpendicular to Axis 1 and 2, respectively.* The distance m is measured perpendicular from Axis 1, and n is measured perpendicular from Axis 2.* Equations for the total elastic shear stress and deflection at the point may be written in a similar manner.

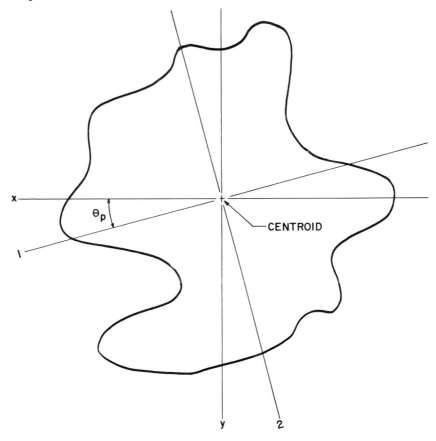

FIGURE 6.1 ORIENTATION OF PRINCIPAL AXES

*Positive coordinates are shown in Figure 6.1. M_1 is considered positive when it causes tensile stress at points with positive m coordinates. M_2 is considered positive when it causes tensile stress at points with positive n coordinates.

For the general shape shown in Figure 6.1, the moment of inertias about the principal axes are

$$I_1 = \frac{I_x + I_y}{2} + \sqrt{\left(\frac{I_x - I_y}{2}\right)^2 + I^2_{xy}} \qquad (6.3)$$

$$I_2 = \frac{I_x + I_y}{2} - \sqrt{\left(\frac{I_x - I_y}{2}\right)^2 + I^2_{xy}} \qquad (6.4)$$

where I_x and I_y are the moments of inertia about any two orthogonal axes, x and y, through the centroid, and I_{xy} is the product of inertia of the cross section referred to the x and y axis. Then angle, θ_p, between Axis 1 and the x axis may be calculated from

$$\tan 2\theta_p = \frac{2I_{xy}}{I_y - I_x} \qquad (6.5)$$

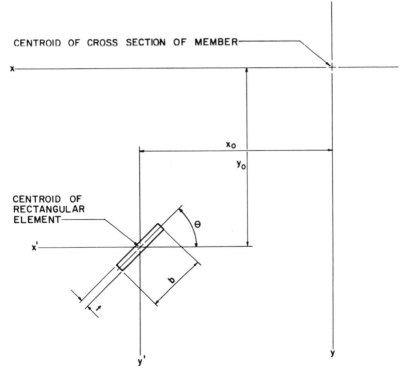

$$I_{xy} = I_{x'y'} + Ax_oy_o$$

$$I_{x'y'} = \frac{b^3t - t^3b}{12} \sin \theta \cos \theta$$

FIGURE 6.2 PRODUCT OF INERTIA FOR RECTANGULAR ELEMENT

A general relationship for the product of inertia of a rectangular element is shown in Figure 6.2. The product of inertia for an entire cross section is the sum of the products of inertia of the various elements of the cross section.

If a member contains at least one axis of symmetry, the product of inertia is zero (with respect to that axis), and from Equations 6.3 and 6.4, the axis of symmetry is a principal axis. Thus, as illustrated in Figure 6.3, the principal axes of wide flange or I shapes and channels are conincident with the usual x and y centroidal axes, and Equations 6.1 and 6.2 become

$$f_b = \frac{M_x y}{I_x} + \frac{M_y x}{I_y} \tag{6.6}$$

$$\Delta = \sqrt{(\Delta_x)^2 + (\Delta_y)^2} \tag{6.7}$$

For shapes that do not contain an axis of symmetry, such as the zee and unequal leg angle shapes shown in Figure 6.3, the principal axes are inclined to the usual x and y centroidal axes.

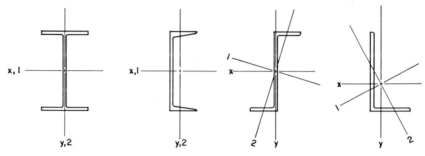

FIGURE 6.3 PRINCIPAL AXES FOR STRUCTURAL SHAPES

The following general expression for the total bending stress at any point in the cross section of a member is equivalent to Equation 6.1 but is written for any orthogonal axes, x and y, rather than specifically for the principal axes:

$$f_b = \left[\frac{M_x - M_y \frac{I_{xy}}{I_y}}{I_x - \frac{I^2_{xy}}{I_y}} \right] y + \left[\frac{M_y - M_x \frac{I_{xy}}{I_x}}{I_y - \frac{I^2_{xy}}{I_x}} \right] x \tag{6.8}$$

M_x and M_y are the bending moments caused by loads perpendicular to the x and y axis, respectively, and the distances x and y are measured perpendicular to the axes.* For nonsymmetric sections,

---

*Positive coordinates are shown in Figure 6.1. M_x is considered positive when it causes tensile stress at points with positive y coordinates. M_y is considered positive when it causes tensile stress at points with positive x coordinates.

it is often more convenient to use Equation 6.8 than to resolve the bending moments into components about the principal axes and use Equation 6.1.

When f_b equals zero, Equation 6.8 may be written as

$$x = \left[\frac{M_x - M_y\frac{I_{xy}}{I_y}}{-M_y + M_x\frac{I_{xy}}{I_x}}\right]\frac{I_y}{I_x}y = \left[\frac{1 - \frac{M_y}{M_x}\frac{I_{xy}}{I_y}}{-\frac{M_y}{M_x} + \frac{I_{xy}}{I_x}}\right]\frac{I_y}{I_x}y \qquad \textbf{(6.9)}$$

Since the bending stress is zero only on the neutral axis, values of x and y that satisfy Equation 6.9 give the location of a point on the neutral axis. A line passing through this point and the centroid is the neutral axis. Thus, for a cross section in biaxial bending, the location of the neutral axis depends on the relative value of the applied moments as well as on the sectional properties.

The resultant bending deflection of the member, Equation 6.2, is perpendicular to the neutral axis. For the special loading when the moments have the relative value

$$\frac{M_y}{M_x} = \frac{I_{xy}}{I_x} \qquad \textbf{(6.10)}$$

the member will deflect parallel to the y axis, and from Equation 6.6, the total bending stress is simply

$$f_b = \frac{M_x y}{I_x} \qquad \textbf{(6.11)}$$

6.3   The Shear Center

If the external forces on a bending member are not directed through the "shear center" of the cross section, both twisting and bending will result. This behavior is important primarily for members with open-type cross sections. Therefore, the location of the shear center will be considered below for only such cross sections. The behavior of members subjected to twisting (torsion) is considered in Chapter 7.

As discussed in Chapter 5, the internal shear stress present due to transverse loads on bending members is VQ/It, and the shear force per unit length, or "shear flow," is VQ/I. In these expressions, I is the moment of inertia about the neutral axis of bending calculated for the same loading that causes the shear force V, Q is the statical moment of the cross-sectional area beyond the point where the shear stress is calculated taken about that neutral axis, and t is the thickness of the element on which the shear stress is calculated. The shear flow acts parallel to the sides of the element.

For an open-type cross section, the VQ/I expression can be used to obtain the shear flow in each element, where I is referred to any arbitrary centroidal axis; the static resultant of the shear flows in the elements gives the line through which the shear force V must act so that the arbitrarily selected centroidal axis will be a neutral axis. The intersection of two shear flow resultants, calculated for the shear flows referred to any two orthogonal centroidal axes, is the "shear center" of the cross section. An illustration of this procedure for determining the shear center of a cross section comprising rectangular elements is given in Example 6.4, and the location of the shear center for several cross sections is shown in Figure 6.4. In addition, the following general observations may be made regarding the location of the shear center.

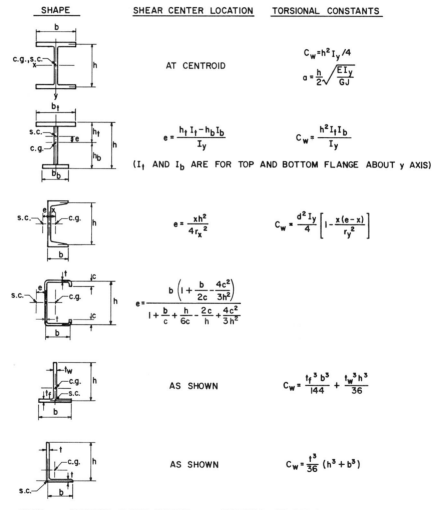

NOTE: s.c. DENOTES SHEAR CENTER; c.g. DENOTES CENTROID.

FIGURE 6.4 SHEAR-CENTER LOCATION AND
TORSIONAL CONSTANTS FOR SEVERAL SHAPES

If a cross section contains an axis of symmetry, its shear center lies on that axis. If the cross section is symmetrical about two axes, the shear center is coincident with the centroid. If the cross section comprises only two rectangular elements, the shear center is at the juncture of the elements.

Note that the shear center has no significance for a beam in pure bending, since a resultant shearing force does not exist on any cross section.

6.4 Lateral Buckling

If the compression region of a bending member does not have adequate lateral support, the member may deflect laterally in a torsional mode before the compressive bending stress reaches the yield stress. This mode of failure is known as "lateral torsional buckling," or simply "lateral buckling." The tendency to twist is resisted by a combination of St. Venant torsion and warping torsion.*

In resisting lateral buckling by warping torsion, the compression flange acts as a column susceptible to buckling in the lateral direction. In closed sections, such as box girders or tubes, torsional stiffness is generally very large and lateral buckling is not important. However, since the torsional stiffness of open sections, such as rolled shapes and plate girders, is generally not large, lateral buckling must be considered when designing such sections.

The following equation[2] gives the theoretical elastic lateral buckling stress, f_c, for beams with an I-shaped profile symmetrical about both axes, and subject to strong axis bending:

$$f_c = \frac{C_1 \pi \sqrt{EI_y GJ}}{S_x(KL)} \left[\sqrt{1 + \frac{\pi^2 C_w E}{JG(KL)^2}(C_2^2 + 1)} \pm \left(\frac{C_2 \pi}{KL} \right) \sqrt{\frac{C_w E}{JG}} \right] \quad (6.12)$$

In the equation, J is a torsional constant,* C_w is a warping constant,* and KL is the effective length for column buckling in the weak plane of bending. The coefficient C_1 accounts for the beneficial effect of the moment gradient; that is, the compressive bending stress may vary along the length of the flange. The coefficient C_2 pertains to the tipping or stabilizing effect that occurs if the loads are applied at the top flange or bottom flange of the beam. The last term in the brackets of the equation should be subtracted if the load is applied through the top flange, and added if the load is applied through the bottom flange. C_2 is zero if the load is applied at the centroid of the beam or if the beam is loaded by end couples. Values of C_1 and C_2 for several conditions are given in Figure 6.5.

Because of the complexity of the theoretical expressions for lateral buckling stress that take into account the simultaneous resistance to lateral buckling afforded by St. Venant torsion and warping torsion, conservative simplified expressions have been developed for design use that consider the effects separately. For example, the AISC specification[3] gives the following rules for

---

*See Chapter 7.

LOAD AND SUPPORT CONDITIONS*	END RESTRAINT ABOUT y AXIS	COEFFICIENTS FOR EQUATION 6.12		
		K	C_1	C_2
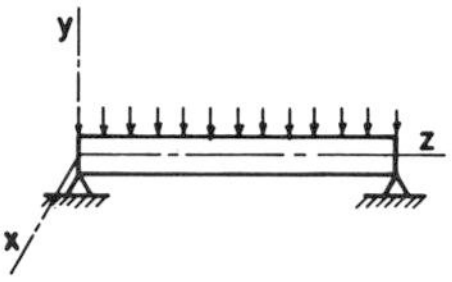	NONE	1.00	1.13	0.45
	FULL	0.50	0.97	0.29
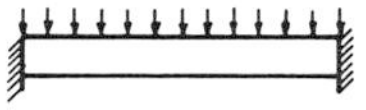	NONE	1.00	1.30	1.55
	FULL	0.50	0.86	0.82
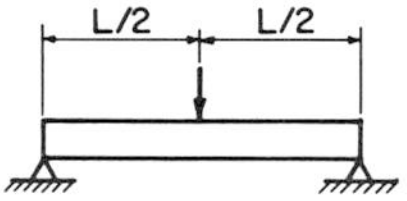	NONE	1.00	1.35	0.55
	FULL	0.50	1.04	0.84
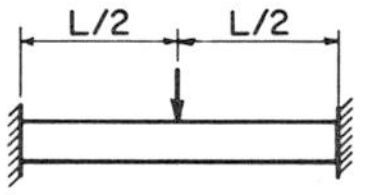	NONE	1.00	1.70	1.42
	FULL	0.50	1.04	0.84
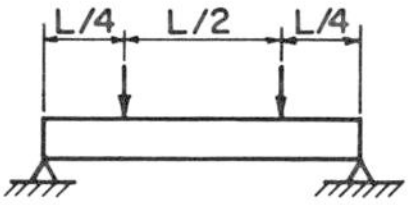	NONE	1.00	1.04	0.42
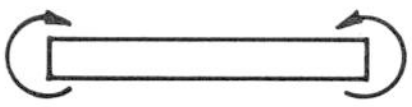	NONE	1.00	1.00	0

*ALL BEAMS ARE RESTRAINED AT ENDS AGAINST ROTATION ABOUT THE z AXIS AND DISPLACEMENT IN THE x AND y DIRECTIONS.

FIGURE 6.5 COEFFICIENTS FOR CALCULATING LATERAL BUCKLING STRESS

determining the maximum allowable compressive stress in members other than compact sections.

"Compression on extreme fibers of rolled shapes, plate girders and built-up members having an axis of symmetry in the plane of their web (other than box-type beams and girders), the larger value computed by Equations 6.13* and 6.14, but not more than 0.60 F_y

$$F_b = \left[1.0 - \frac{(L/r)^2}{2C_c{}^2 C_b} \right] 0.60\, f_y \qquad (6.13)$$

$$F_b = \frac{12,000,000}{Ld/A_f} \text{ (psi)} \qquad (6.14)$$

*Equation numbers refer to those used in this manual.

where L is the unbraced length of the compression flange; r is the radius of gyration of a tee section comprising the compression flange plus one sixth of the web area, about an axis in the plane of the web; A_f is the area of the compression flange; C_c is defined by Equation 3.13 and C_b, which can conservatively be taken as unity, is equal to

$$C_b = 1.75 - 1.05 \left(\frac{M_1}{M_2} \right) + 0.30 \left(\frac{M_1}{M_2} \right)^2 \text{ , but not more than 2.30,}$$

where M_1 is the smaller and M_2 the larger bending moment at the ends of the unbraced length, taken about the strong axis of the member, and where M_1/M_2, the ratio of end moments, is positive when M_1 and M_2 have the same sign (single curvature bending) and negative when they are of opposite signs, (reverse curvature bending). When the bending moment at any point within an unbraced length is larger than that at both ends of this length the ratio M_1/M_2 shall be taken as unity."

For compact sections designed for a maximum bending stress of 0.66 f_y, the specification requires that the distance in inches between lateral support points must not exceed 2400 $b_f/\sqrt{f_y}$ nor 20,000,000 A_f/df_y, where f_y is in psi and other dimensions are in inches.

Equation 6.13 concerns the resistance to lateral buckling when St. Venant torsion is neglected and is equivalent to the basic column formula given in Chapter 3 divided by a safety factor of 1.67. The section resisting lateral buckling is assumed to consist of the compression flange and a portion of the web. The coefficient C_b is equivalent to the coefficient C_1 of Equation 6.12. The AISC specification also states that when L/r is less than 40, the allowable stress reduction given by Equation 6.13 is inconsequential and may be neglected. However, for steels having yield stresses greater than about 70,000 psi, equation 6.13 should not be neglected unless L/r is less than 20. Equation 6.14 includes the resistance to lateral buckling afforded by St. Venant torsion as well as lateral bending resistance and can be derived from Equation 6.12 by neglecting warping torsion and making other simplifying assumptions. Generally, Equation 6.14 controls the design of shallow heavy members, such as most rolled beams, and Equation 6.13 controls the design of deep built-up girders.

For rolled channels, the AISC specification permits allowable stresses to be calculated by Equation 6.14. The effect of eccentricity should be considered in the stress analysis if the loads are not applied through the shear center.

Bridge design specifications are usually concerned with deep girders and, therefore, give equations for the allowable compression stress that are based on resistance to warping torsion. For example, the AASHO specifications[4] give the following formula that is similar in form to Equation 6.13 but takes no account of the beneficial effect of moment gradient:

$$F_b = \left[1.0 - \frac{(L/r)^2 f_y}{4\pi^2 E} \right] 0.55 f_y \tag{6.15}$$

150   *Additional Considerations for Bending Members*

6.5   Design Examples

Example 6.1

A 30-foot-long simply supported beam supports a concentrated oblique load at each third point as illustrated in the sketch at the right. Select an A36 steel WF beam according to the AISC specifications. Also determine location of the neutral axis and deflection at midspan.

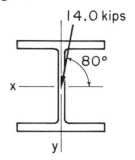

Solution:

Resolve load into components:

$P_x = 14.0\sin 80° = 14.0 \times 0.9848 = 13.79$ kips
$P_y = 14.0\cos 80° = 14.0 \times 0.1736 = 2.43$ kips

Calculate bending moments at midspan:

About x axis—$M_x = PL/3 = 13.79 \times 120 = 1655$ in. kips

Assume beam weight of 90 lb/ft

$M = wL^2/8 = 90 \times 30 \times 360/8 = 121$ in. kips
Total moment $= 1655 + 121 = 1776$ in. kips

About y axis—$M_y = PL/3 = 2.43 \times 120 = 292$ in. kips

Try a 14WF 84 beam.

$S_x = 130.9$ in.³ $S_y = 37.5$ in.³ $I_x = 928.4$ in.⁴ $I_y = 225.5$ in.⁴

From Equation 6.6

$$f_b = \frac{M_x}{S_x} + \frac{M_y}{S_y}$$

$$= \pm\frac{1776}{130.9} \pm \frac{292}{37.5}$$

$$f_b = \pm 13.57 \pm 7.79$$

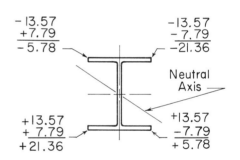

Total bending stress at each corner is as shown in sketch at right. Maximum stress is 21.36 ksi. A check by Equations 6.13 and 6.14 shows that the beam which is laterally unsupported over its 30 ft length has an allowable bending stress of 21.93 ksi for bending about the x axis. For bending about the weak axis the allowable bending stress for this beam may be taken as 22.0 ksi, because there is no tendency for the beam to buckle in a direction perpendicular to its weak axis. The combined effects of the bending stresses that limit beam selection may be conservatively considered by the following interaction equation:

$$\frac{f_{bx}}{F_{bx}} + \frac{f_{by}}{F_{by}} \leq 1.0$$

$$\frac{13.57}{21.93} + \frac{7.79}{22.0} = 0.973 < 1.0$$

Therefore, select a 14WF84 beam.

Location of neutral axis:

$$f_b = \frac{M_x y}{I_x} + \frac{M_y x}{I_y} \qquad \text{(Equation 6.6)}$$

$f_b = 0$ on neutral axis. Arbitrarily select $x = 10$ and solve for y.

$$0 = \frac{1776}{928.4} y + \frac{292}{225.5} 10$$

$$y = -6.77 \text{ in.}$$

Therefore, under this loading the neutral axis at midspan is a line that has a slope of $-6.77/10$ or -0.677 and passes through the origin. See previous sketch.

Deflection:

From beam weight—$\Delta_y = \dfrac{5}{384} \dfrac{wL^4}{EI} = \dfrac{5 \times 90 \times 30 \times 360^3}{384 \times 29 \times 10^6 \times 928.4} = 0.061$ in.

From vertical load—$\Delta_y = \dfrac{23}{648} \dfrac{PL^3}{EI} = \dfrac{23 \times 13,790 \times 360^3}{648 \times 29 \times 10^6 \times 928.4} = 0.848$ in.

Total $\Delta_y = 0.061 + 0.848 = 0.909$ in.

From horizontal load—$\Delta_x = \dfrac{23 \times 2,430 \times 360^3}{648 \times 29 \times 10^6 \times 225.5} = 0.615$ in.

$\Delta = \sqrt{(\Delta_x)^2 + (\Delta_y)^2} = \sqrt{(0.615)^2 + (0.909)^2} = 1.10$ in.   **(Equation 6.7)**

Direction of deflection is as shown:

$\Delta x = 0.615$ ———Neutral Axis

$\Delta x = 1.10$ $\Delta y = 0.909$

Example 6.2

A 10-foot-long simply supported zee beam supports a vertical load at each third point. The section is of A36 steel and has the dimensions and properties shown in the sketch at the right. Determine the design load on the section for an allowable stress of 22 ksi. (Check of lateral buckling shows that allowable stress of 22 ksi is acceptable.)

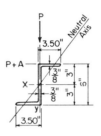

Solution:

Determine I_{xy}: (See Figure 6.2)

$I_x = 25.3$ in.^{4} $I_y = 9.1$ in.^{4}
$S_x = 8.4$ in.^{3} $S_y = 2.8$ in.^{3}

Web—$I_{xy} = 0$
Top Flange—$I_{xy} = I_{x'y'} + A x_o y_o$
$= 0 + 3.125 \times .375 \times (-1.750) \times (-2.812) = 5.77$ in.^{4}
Bottom Flange—$I_{xy} = 0 + 3.125 \times .375 \times 1.750 \times 2.812 = 5.77$ in.^{4}
I_{xy} of Section $= 11.54$ in.^{4}
Locate neutral axis

$$x = \left[\dfrac{M_x - M_y \dfrac{I_{xy}}{I_y}}{-M_y + M_x \dfrac{I_{xy}}{I_x}}\right] \dfrac{I_y}{I_x} y \qquad \text{(Equation 6.9)}$$

Since $M_y = 0$, and arbitrarily assuming $y = 10$,

$$x = \dfrac{I_y}{I_{xy}} y = \dfrac{9.1}{11.54} \times 10 = 7.89$$

Slope of neutral axis $= 7.89/10 = 0.789$ (see sketch above)
Point A, $x = 0.1875$ and $y = -3.00$, is farthest point from neutral axis and, therefore, is highest stressed point. Allowable stress is 22 ksi.
From Equation 6.8

$$f_b = \left[\cfrac{M_x - \cfrac{I^2_{xy}}{I_y}}{I_x}\right] y - \left[\cfrac{M_x \cfrac{I_{xy}}{I_x}}{I_y - \cfrac{I^2_{xy}}{I_x}}\right] x$$

$$= \frac{M_x}{I_x I_y - I^2_{xy}} (I_y y - I_{xy} x)$$

$$-22 = \frac{M_x}{25.3 \times 9.1 - (11.54)^2} (-9.1 \times 3.00 - 11.54 \times 0.1875)$$

$M_x = 72.47$ in. kips

Moment from beam weight $= wL^2/8 = 15.7 \times 10 \times 120/8 = 2.36$ in. kips

Moment from load $= PL/3 = 40P$

$$P = \frac{72.47 - 2.36}{40} = \underline{175 \text{ kips}}$$

Example 6.3

Determine the maximum allowable vertical load for the zee beam of Example 6.2 if a horizontal restraint at each third point causes the beam to deflect in a vertical plane. Determine the magnitude of the horizontal restraint.

Solution:

$$f_b = \frac{M_x y}{I_x} \qquad\qquad \textbf{(Equation 6.11)}$$

$$22 = \frac{3M_x}{25.3} \qquad\qquad M_x = 184.8 \text{ in. kips}$$

$$P = \frac{184.8 - 2.36}{40} = \textbf{4.56 kips} \quad \text{Allowable vertical load at third point}$$

From Equation 6.10, when $M_y = \dfrac{P_H L}{3}$ and $M_x = \dfrac{PL}{3}$:

$$P_H = \frac{P I_{xy}}{I_x}$$

$$= \frac{4.56 \times 11.54}{25.3} = \textbf{2.08 kips} \quad \text{Required horizontal restraint at third point}$$

Example 6.4

Determine the shear center of the ½-inch-thick formed section shown below. The location of the center of gravity determined from statics, is shown in the sketch. The x and y axes shown are arbitrarily selected centroidal axes.

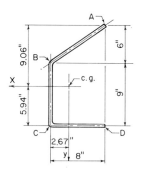

Solution:

1. Write general equations. To facilitate solution of this problem, general equations will be written for the shear flow and total shear in a narrow rectangle such as that shown at the right. The value of V_y/I_x and V_x/I_y is regarded as unity. If bending occurs so that the x axis is the neutral axis, the shear flow at point 2, V_2, is $V_1 + V_yQ/I_x$.

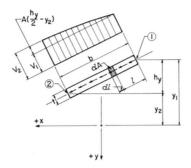

$$V_2 = V_1 - Ay_2 + Ah_y/2$$

where V_1 is the shear flow at Point 1, and A is the area of the rectangle. The total shear between 1 and 2, V_{1-2}, is $V_1b + {}_2\int^1 vdA$.

$$v = \frac{VQ}{It} = \frac{V\,A_1\bar{y}}{I\ t}\ ;\ \frac{V}{I} = 1,\ A_1 = lt,\ \text{and}\ \bar{y} = -(y_1 + \frac{lhy}{2b}). \text{ Therefore}$$

$$v = \frac{lt}{t}(-y_1 - \frac{lhy}{2b}) = -(y_1 l + \frac{hyl^2}{2b})$$

$$dA = tdl$$

Integrating and summarizing terms results in the equation

$$V_{1-2} = (V_1 + V_2 + \frac{Ah_y}{6})\ \frac{b}{2}$$

The distance h_y may be $+$ or $-$ according to the relationship

$$h_y = y_2 - y_1$$

Similarly, if bending occurs so that the y axis is the neutral axis, the following relationships are obtained:

$$V_2 = V_1 - Ax_2 + Ah_x/2$$

$$V_{1-2} = (V_1 + V_2 + \frac{Ah_x}{6})\ \frac{b}{2}$$

$$h_x = x_2 - x_1$$

2. Consider shear resultant referred to the x axis.
2.a Calculate shear force in each element of the formed section. Refer to equations developed above.

$$y_A = -9.056 \text{ in.}$$

$$y_B = -3.056 \text{ in.}$$

$$y_C = y_D = +5.944 \text{ in.}$$

In AB, $h_y = -3.056 - (-9.056) = +6.00$ in.

In BC, $h_y = +5.944 - (-3.056) = +9.00$ in.

In CD, $h_y = +5.944 - 5.944 = 0$

 $V_A = 0$

 $V_B = 0 - (5.0)(-3.056) + (5.0)(6.00/2) = 30.28$

 $V_C = 30.28 - (4.5)(5.944) + (4.5)(9.00/2) = 23.78$

 $V_{AB} = (0 + 30.28 + 5.0 \times 6.0/6)\,10.0/2 = 176.4$

 $V_{BC} = (30.28 + 23.78 + 4.5 \times 9.0/6)\,9.0/2 = 273.6$

 $V_{CD} = (23.78 + 0 + 0)\,8.0/2 = 95.12$

2.b Locate resultant of shear forces.

Adding the x and y components of each shear force,

 $V_x = 0.80 \times 176.4 + 0 - 95.12 = 46.00$

 $V_y = 0.60 \times 176.4 + 273.6 + 0 = 379.4$

Taking moments about point B and not considering V_x,

 $379.49x^* = 95.12 \times 9.0$

  $x^* = 2.26$ in.

Therefore, the resultant must pass through $x^* = 2.26$ in. and $y^* = 0$

Taking moments about point B and not considering V_y,

 $46.00\,y^* = -95.12 \times 9.0$

  $y^* = -18.61$ in.

Therefore, the resultant must pass through $x^* = 0$ and $y^* = -18.61$ in.

Resultant may now be plotted. See concluding sketch.
3. Consider shear resultant referred to the y axis.
3.a Calculate shear forces.

 $X_A = X_D = -5.333$

 $X_B = X_C = 2.667$

In AB, $h_x = 2.667 - (-5.333) = 8.00$

In BC, $h_x = 2.667 - (2.667) = 0$

In CD, $h_x = -5.333 - (2.667) = -8.00$

 $V_A = 0$

 $V_B = 0 - (5.0)(2.667) + (5.0)(8.0/2) = 6.67$

 $V_C = 6.67 - (4.5)(2.667) + 0 = -5.33$

 $V_{AB} = (0 - 6.67 + 5.0 \times 8.0/6)\,10.0/2 = 66.68$

 $V_{BC} = (6.67 - 5.33 + 0)\,9.0/2 = 6.03$

 $V_{CD} = (-5.33 - 0 - 4.0 \times 8.00/6)\,8.0/2 = -42.65$

3.b. Locate resultant of shear forces.

 $V_x = 0.80 \times 66.68 + 0 + 42.65 = 96.01$

 $V_y = 0.60 \times 66.68 + 6.03 + 0 = 46.00$

 $96.00y^* = 42.65 \times 9.00$

  $y^* = 4.00$

 $-46.00x^* = 42.65 \times 9.00$

  $x^* = -8.34$

Plot resultant on sketch.

---

*Asterisked dimensions are measured from point B.

4. Locate shear center.

As shown in the concluding sketch below, the intersection of the two resultants is the shear center of the section.

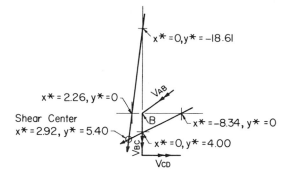

* Asterisked dimensions are measured from point B.

References (Chapter 6)

1. F. B. Seely and J. O. Smith, **Advanced Strength of Materials,** John Wiley & Sons, New York City, 1952.

2. Column Research Council, "Guide to Design Criteria for Metal Compression Members," 2nd Ed. 1966, John Wiley & Sons, publisher.

3. American Institute of Steel Construction, "Specification for the Design, Fabrication, and Erection of Structural Steel for Buildings," 1963.

4. American Association of State Highway Officials, "Standard Specifications for Highway Bridges," 1965.

CHAPTER 7

Torsion

7.1 Introduction

A torsional moment applied to opposite ends of a member causes each cross section of the member to rotate. As illustrated in Figure 7.1, if the member is a round bar or tube, each cross section rotates in its own plane without warping, and the resistance to torsion is provided by the shear stresses, which are proportional to the distance from the centroid. However, if a member with a non-circular cross section is subjected to the same torsional moment, the cross sections not only rotate but also deform nonuniformly in the longitudinal directions so that plane transverse sections do not remain plane after twisting. This latter deformation, known as "warping," is illustrated in Fig. 7.2 for a rectangular bar. If the warping is not restrained, resistance to torsion is due to a distribution of shear stress known as "St. Venant torsion." If warping **is** restrained, additional direct shear stresses due to bending of the component parts of the section are superposed on the St. Venant shear stresses and add effectively to the torsional resistance. Bending of the component parts also induces longitudinal direct stresses that may require consideration in design.

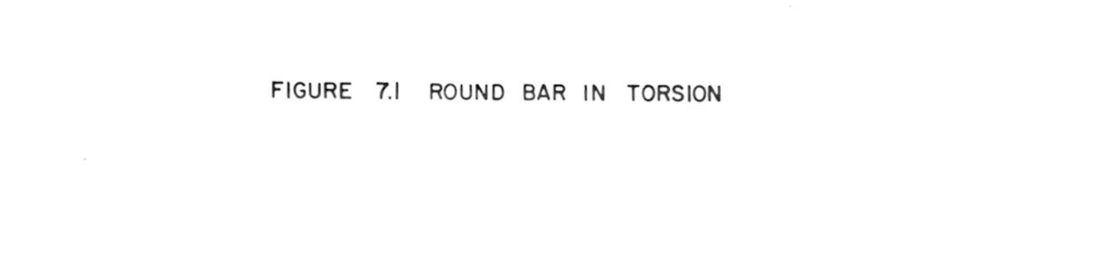

TWIST OF MEMBER

ROTATION OF
CROSS SECTION

DIRECTION OF
SHEAR STRESSES

DISTRIBUTION OF
SHEAR STRESSES

FIGURE 7.1 ROUND BAR IN TORSION

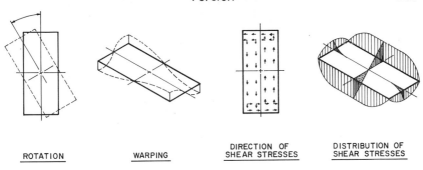

ROTATION   WARPING   DIRECTION OF SHEAR STRESSES   DISTRIBUTION OF SHEAR STRESSES

FIGURE 7.2 RECTANGULAR BAR IN TORSION

Most structural members resist torsion through a combination of St. Venant torsion and warping torsion. However, for closed cross sections—such as tubular members or box girders—and to a lesser extent for relatively compact open sections—such as rolled channels, zees, or angles—St. Venant torsion generally dominates. For structural members with large open cross sections, such as many wide-flange beams and fabricated plate girders, warping torsion generally dominates. St. Venant torsion for several shapes will be considered in the section below, and warping torsion will be considered in the following section. It is often convenient and always conservative to base designs on the dominant type of torsion for the particular section and neglect the effect of the other type of torsion.

7.2 St. Venant Torsion

If a unit length of round bar or tube is under a constant torsional moment, T, the end cross sections rotate with respect to each other through an angle

$$\theta_t = \frac{T}{GI_p} \qquad (7.1)$$

where θ_t is the angle of twist per unit of length and I_p is the polar moment of inertia. As illustrated in Figure 7.1, the torsional shear stress in a member with a round cross section varies linearly with the distance from the center, and the maximum value for a bar of radius R is

$$f_s = \frac{TR}{I_p} \qquad (7.2)$$

For a round bar,

$$I_p = R^4 \pi / 2 \qquad (7.3)$$

For a round tube,

$$I_p = (R^4_o - R^4_i)\, \pi / 2 \qquad (7.4)$$

where R_o and R_i are the outside and inside radius respectively. For a thin-wall tube with a wall thickness, t, and mean radius, R, I_p is approximately

$$I_p = 2\pi R^3 t \qquad (7.5)$$

As illustrated in Figure 7.3, the shear stresses in a closed rectangular section subject to torsion are parallel to the sides of the section. The shear flow has a uniform value along both sides, and when the moments at the corners are summed, the shear stresses along sides 1 and 2, respectively, are

$$f_{s1} = \frac{T}{2bht_1} \qquad (7.6)$$

$$f_{s2} = \frac{T}{2bht_2} \qquad (7.7)$$

The unit angle of twist for all noncircular cross sections is

$$\theta_t = \frac{T}{GJ} \qquad (7.8)$$

where J is a torsional constant. For the closed rectangular section, J is

$$J = \frac{2t_1 t_2 b^2 h^2}{bt_1 + ht_2} \qquad (7.9)$$

For a square tube with constant wall thickness, f_s and J become

$$f_s = \frac{T}{2b^2 t} \qquad (7.10)$$

$$J = tb^3 \qquad (7.11)$$

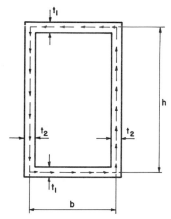

FIGURE 7.3 SHEAR STRESSES IN RECTANGULAR SECTION IN TORSION

The distribution of St. Venant shear stress in a rectangular bar is illustrated in Figure 7.2. Except near the free edges, the stress is nearly constant along the long sides and its maximum value equals

$$f_s = \frac{T\gamma t}{J} \tag{7.12}$$

The torsional constant for a rectangular bar is

$$J = \frac{bt^3}{3} - 2\psi t^4 \tag{7.13}$$

The terms γ and ψ are nondimensional numerical factors that depend on the b/t ratio and are listed in Table 7.1. As b/t approaches 4.0, f_s and J approach

$$f_s = \frac{Tt}{J} \tag{7.14}$$

$$J = \frac{bt^3}{3} - 0.21t^4 \tag{7.15}$$

Furthermore, for a thin rectangle, J is approximately

$$J = \frac{bt^3}{3} \tag{7.16}$$

The flow of shear stresses in several open-type structural shapes is illustrated in Figure 7.4. As suggested by an examination of the figure, each of the shapes behaves as a series of rectangular elements, the behavior of each element being similar to that of the rectangular bar shown in Figure 7.3. Shear stresses near the unsupported edges that act perpendicular to the long dimensions of the elements are small and may be neglected. The torsional constant of an open-type section can be approximately determined by adding the torsional constants of the individual elements of the

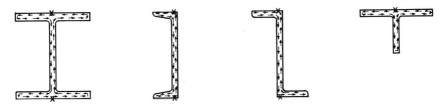

NOTE: X INDICATES LOCATION OF MAXIMUM SHEAR STRESS (EXCEPT IN FILLET)

FIGURE 7.4   SHEAR   STRESSES   IN   OPEN   STRUCTURAL   SHAPES   IN   TORSION

section, using Equation 7.16. However, an extensive numerical analysis,[1] which included the effect of increased torsional stiffness due to the extra material in the transition fillets at the juncture of elements, has resulted in the torsional constants listed in Table 7.2 for most hot-rolled structural shapes.

If the stress concentration at the juncture of individual elements is neglected, the maximum torsional shear stress in the wide-flange and tee shapes shown in Figure 7.4 occurs at the center of the

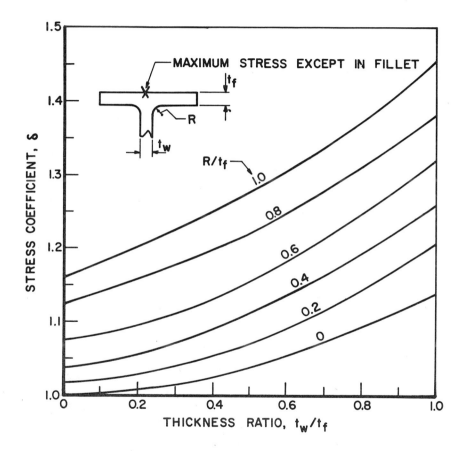

FIGURE 7.5 STRESS COEFFICIENTS FOR TEE OR WF SECTIONS WITH PARALLEL FLANGES

outer edge of the flange.* For the channel and zee shapes shown in the figure, the maximum shear stress occurs in the outer edge of the flange near its juncture with the web.* This maximum shear

---

* The flange is assumed to be thicker than the web.

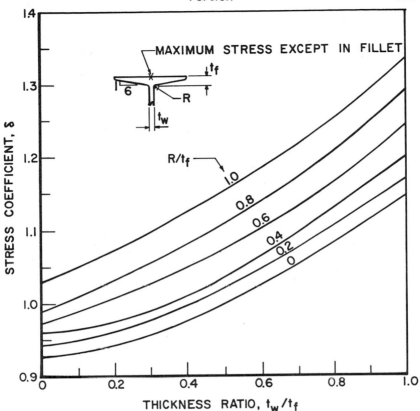

FIGURE 7.6 STRESS COEFFICIENTS FOR TEE OR I SECTIONS WITH SLOPING INNER FLANGES

stress in the shapes may be calculated from the equation, similar to Equation 7.12

$$f_s = \frac{T\delta t_f}{J} \qquad (7.17)$$

where δ is a numerical factor that includes the effect of the stress increase due to the increased thickness on the outer edge of the flange at the juncture point, and J is the torsional constant for the entire cross section. Figures 7.5 and 7.6 give curves for δ as a function of the geometry of the cross section for beam sections or tee sections having either parallel flanges or sloping inner flange surfaces.**

***

** In Table 7.2, sections designed as WF and B generally have parallel flanges. The inner flange surfaces of I, M, and C sections generally have a slope of 16⅔ percent except the 18C which has a slope of 3½ percent.

7.3 Warping Torsion

Figure 7.7 illustrates the behavior of a cantilevered wide-flange beam with a torsional moment applied to its free end. At the free end there is no warping restraint indicated. However, in introducing torsion by a framing connection a stiffener should be provided to maintain the shape of the cross section. Preferably, the torque should be introduced into the flanges. At the fixed end, warping is restrained, the St. Venant stresses are zero, and the shear stresses that arise from the lateral bending of the flange provide the torsional

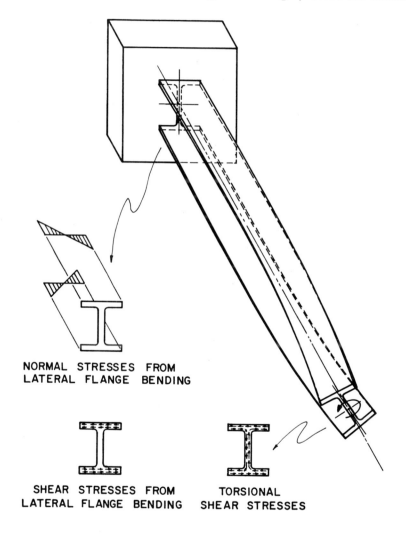

NORMAL STRESSES FROM
LATERAL FLANGE BENDING

SHEAR STRESSES FROM   TORSIONAL
LATERAL FLANGE BENDING   SHEAR STRESSES

WARPING TORSION   ST. VENANT TORSION

FIGURE 7.7 TORSIONAL BEHAVIOR OF WIDE-FLANGE BEAM

resistance. Cross sections at any other location are subject to a combination of St. Venant torsion and warping torsion.

The lateral flange bending moment due to warping torsion for a beam subjected to a torsional moment can be conservatively calculated by resolving the applied torsional moment into an applied force couple that acts through the centers of the flanges. This method is illustrated in Figure 7.8 for the cantilevered beam shown in Figure 7.7 and can be adapted in similar manner for other loading conditions. This approximation should only be applied to very short members since it becomes over conservative for long members. Lateral flange bending stresses can be calculated by the flexure formula, $f = \dfrac{Mc}{I}$, and the shear stress from lateral flange bending can be calculated from the beam shear formula, $f_s = VQ/It$. In applying these relationships, I and Q are referred to the y axis of the beam and are for one flange.

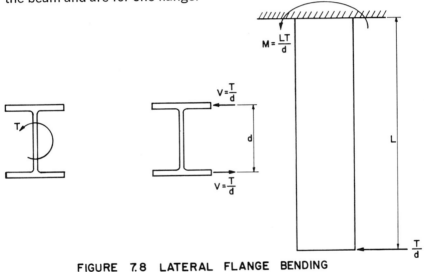

FIGURE 7.8 LATERAL FLANGE BENDING

For any given loading and support conditions, a mathematically exact value for the maximum lateral flange bending moment can be obtained from the general differential equation written for equilibrium requirements.[2] Solutions for six sets of conditions are given in Figures 7.9 and 7.10. The solutions are in terms of hyperbolic functions, which can be found in mathematics handbooks, and the torsional flange bending constant "a" given by

$$a = \sqrt{\frac{EC_w}{JG}} = \frac{d}{2}\sqrt{\frac{EI_y}{JG}} \qquad (7.18)$$

where C_w is a torsional warping constant.* Values of "a" are tabu-

* Equations for C_w for various cross sections are given in Reference 3 where the symbol T replaces C_w.

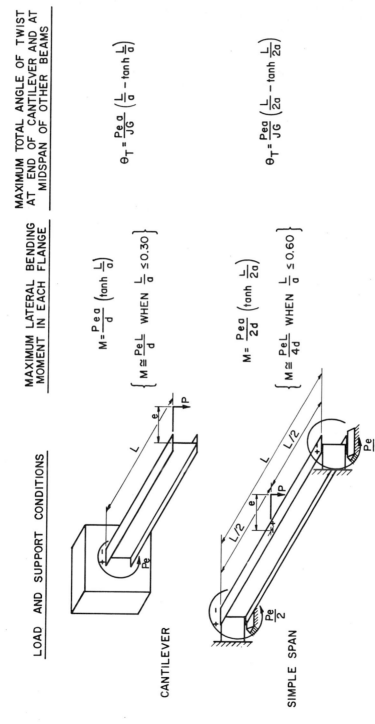

LOAD AND SUPPORT CONDITIONS	MAXIMUM LATERAL BENDING MOMENT IN EACH FLANGE	MAXIMUM TOTAL ANGLE OF TWIST AT END OF CANTILEVER AND AT MIDSPAN OF OTHER BEAMS
CANTILEVER	$M = \dfrac{Pea}{d}\left(\tanh\dfrac{L}{a}\right)$ $\left\{M \cong \dfrac{PeL}{d} \text{ WHEN } \dfrac{L}{a} \leq 0.30\right\}$	$\theta_T = \dfrac{Pea}{JG}\left(\dfrac{L}{a} - \tanh\dfrac{L}{a}\right)$
SIMPLE SPAN	$M = \dfrac{Pea}{2d}\left(\tanh\dfrac{L}{2a}\right)$ $\left\{M \cong \dfrac{PeL}{4d} \text{ WHEN } \dfrac{L}{a} \leq 0.60\right\}$	$\theta_T = \dfrac{Pea}{JG}\left(\dfrac{L}{2a} - \tanh\dfrac{L}{2a}\right)$

FIGURE 7.9 MAXIMUM LATERAL BENDING MOMENT AND TOTAL ANGLE OF TWIST FOR BEAMS IN TORSION FROM CONCENTRATED LOADS

(Continued on Page 165)

LOAD AND SUPPORT CONDITIONS	MAXIMUM LATERAL BENDING MOMENT IN EACH FLANGE	MAXIMUM TOTAL ANGLE OF TWIST AT END OF CANTILEVER AND AT MIDSPAN OF OTHER BEAMS

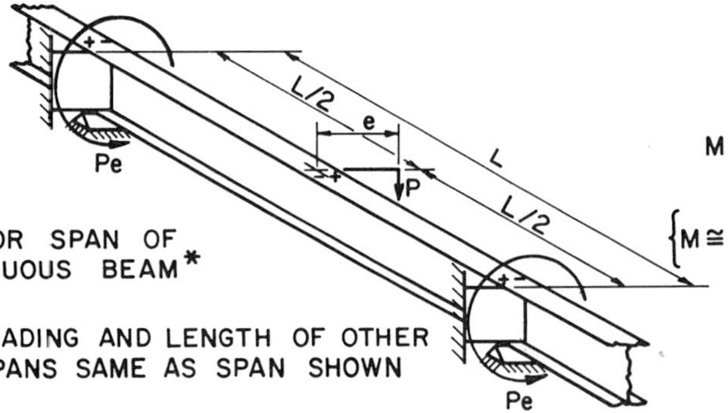

$$M = \frac{Pea}{2d}\left(\tanh \frac{L}{4a}\right)$$

$$\left\{ M \cong \frac{PeL}{8d} \text{ WHEN } \frac{L}{a} \leq 1.20 \right\}$$

$$\theta_T = \frac{2Pea}{JG}\left(\frac{L}{4a} - \tanh \frac{L}{4a}\right)$$

INTERIOR SPAN OF CONTINUOUS BEAM*

*LOADING AND LENGTH OF OTHER SPANS SAME AS SPAN SHOWN

FIGURE 7.9 MAXIMUM LATERAL BENDING MOMENT AND TOTAL ANGLE OF TWIST FOR BEAMS IN TORSION FROM CONCENTRATED LOADS

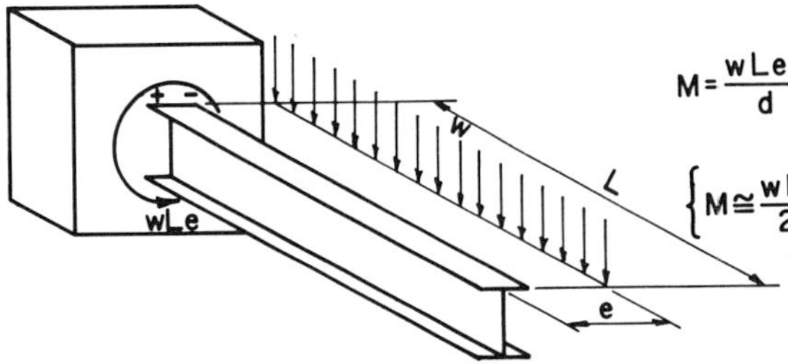

$$M = \frac{wLea}{d}\left(\tanh \frac{L}{a} + \frac{1}{\frac{L}{a}\cosh \frac{L}{a}} - \frac{a}{L}\right)$$

$$\left\{ M \cong \frac{wL^2 e}{2d} \text{ WHEN } \frac{L}{a} \leq 0.30 \right\}$$

$$\theta_T = \frac{wLea}{JG}\left(\frac{L}{2a} - \tanh \frac{L}{a} + \frac{1}{\frac{L}{a}\cosh \frac{L}{a}} - \frac{a}{L}\right)$$

CANTILEVER

FIGURE 7.10 MAXIMUM LATERAL BENDING MOMENT AND TOTAL ANGLE OF TWIST FOR BEAMS IN TORSION FROM UNIFORM LOADS

(Continued on Page 166)

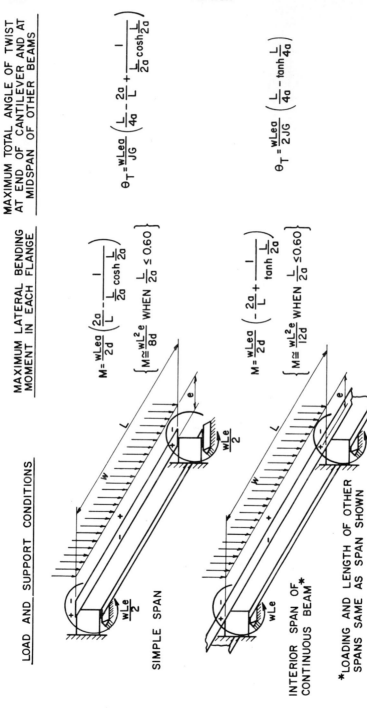

LOAD AND SUPPORT CONDITIONS	MAXIMUM LATERAL BENDING MOMENT IN EACH FLANGE	MAXIMUM TOTAL ANGLE OF TWIST AT END OF CANTILEVER AND AT MIDSPAN OF OTHER BEAMS
SIMPLE SPAN	$M = \dfrac{wL e a}{2d}\left(\dfrac{2a}{L} - \dfrac{1}{\frac{L}{2a}\cosh\frac{L}{2a}}\right)$ $\left\{M \cong \dfrac{wL^2 e}{8d}\ \text{WHEN}\ \dfrac{L}{2a} \leq 0.60\right\}$	$\theta_T = \dfrac{wL e a}{JG}\left(\dfrac{L}{4a} - \dfrac{2a}{L} + \dfrac{1}{\frac{L}{2a}\cosh\frac{L}{2a}}\right)$
INTERIOR SPAN OF CONTINUOUS BEAM*	$M = \dfrac{wL e a}{2d}\left(-\dfrac{2a}{L} + \dfrac{1}{\tanh\frac{L}{2a}}\right)$ $\left\{M \cong \dfrac{wL^2 e}{12d}\ \text{WHEN}\ \dfrac{L}{2a} \leq 0.60\right\}$	$\theta_T = \dfrac{wL e a}{2JG}\left(\dfrac{L}{4a} - \tanh\dfrac{L}{4a}\right)$

*LOADING AND LENGTH OF OTHER SPANS SAME AS SPAN SHOWN

FIGURE 7.10 MAXIMUM LATERAL BENDING MOMENT AND TOTAL ANGLE OF TWIST FOR BEAMS IN TORSION FROM UNIFORM LOADS

lated in Table 7.2 for most rolled beam sections. Equations for the maximum total angle of twist are also given in the figures.

The approximate values for maximum lateral flange bending moment given by the bracketed equations in Figures 7.9 and 7.10 for certain values of L/a are those obtained by the simple method outlined above for the cantilever beam. The approximate values are conservative and are within 5 percent of the mathematically exact values when L/a does not exceed the value indicated in the figure.

In Figures 7.9 and 7.10, the maximum lateral bending moment occurs at the end support for the cantilever beams and at midspan for the simply supported beams; the maximum occurs simultaneously at the supports and at midspan for the continuous span. Compression and tension bending stresses in the top flange at these locations are indicated by − and +, respectively.

7.4 Design Examples

Example 7.1

The section of Example 6.4 is subjected to the loading shown in the sketch at the right. The load is applied at the end of a long cantilever. Determine the torsional shear stress and angle of twist per unit length near the loaded end of the beam.

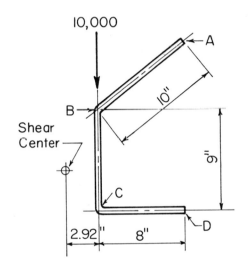

Solution:

Under the stated conditions, the effect of any warping restraint may be neglected. The torsional constant J may be determined by adding the J values of each rectangular element of the section. Since the b/t for each rectangular element is greater than 4.0, the J for each rectangle is given by Equation 7.16.

$$J_{AB} = 10(0.5)^3/3 = 0.417 \text{ in.}^4$$

$$J_{BC} = 9(0.5)^3/3 = 0.375 \text{ in.}^4$$

$$J_{CD} = 8(0.5^3/3 = 0.333 \text{ in.}^4$$

For the entire section, $J = 0.417 + 0.375 + 0.333 = 1.125 \text{ in.}^4$

Torsional moment, $T = 10,000 \times 2.92 = 29,200$ in.-lb

$$f_s = \frac{Tt}{J} = \frac{29,200 \times 0.50}{1.125} = 13,000 \text{ psi.} \qquad \text{(Equation 7.14)}$$

(The stress is uniform over the section because t is constant.)

$$\theta_t = \frac{T}{GJ} = \frac{29,200}{11 \times 10^6 \times 1.125} = 0.00236 \text{ radians/in.} \qquad \text{(Equation 7.8)}$$

Example 7.2

Determine the maximum torsional moment that can be applied to the following three sections: (a) 8WF31 rolled shape, (b) 8-in. outside-diameter round tube with ⅜-in.-thick wall, and (c) 7-in. square (outside width) tube with ⅜-in.-thick wall. The allowable shear stress is 14,500 psi and warping restraint may be neglected.

Solution:

(a) 8WF31 $A = 9.12$ in.²

  $J = 0.534$ in.⁴   **(Table 7.2)**

  $\overset{*}{R}/t_f = 0.40/0.433 = 0.924$

  $t_w/t_f = 0.288/0.433 = 0.665$ $\delta = 1.3$ **(Figure 7.5)**

  $T = \dfrac{f_s J}{\delta t_f} = \dfrac{14{,}500 \times 0.534}{1.3 \times 0.433} = 13{,}800$ in.-lb   **(Equation 7.17)**

(b) 8-in. round tube $A = 8.94$ in.²

  $I_p = 2\pi R^3 t = 2 \times 3.14(3.81)^3 \times 0.375 = 130$ in.⁴ **(Equation 7.5)**

  $T = \dfrac{f_s I_p}{R} = \dfrac{14{,}500 \times 130}{3.81} = 495{,}000$ in.-lb   **(Equation 7.2)**

(c) 7-in-square tube $A = 9.33$ in.²

  $J = tb^3 = 0.375 \times (6.625)^3 = 109$ in.⁴   **(Equation 7.11)**

  $T = 2f_s b^2 t = 2 \times 14{,}500 \times (6.625)^2 \times 0.375$

  $T = 477{,}000$ in.-lb   **(Equation 7.10)**

(Note: This example illustrates the advantage of closed sections over open sections in St. Venant torsion. However, warping restraint could significantly increase the value of T for the WF beam.)

Example 7.3

A continuous WF spandrel beam is attached to exterior column faces as shown below. The beam supports a wall load of 1 kip/ft that has a 2-inch eccentricity. Determine the beam size for A36 steel.

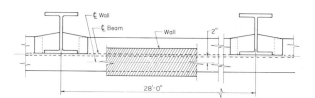

Solution:

A preliminary investigation suggests a 12WF58 trial section. Wall load plus beam weight = 1.06 kip/ft. Properties of the section are:

  $S_x = 78.1$ in.³ $I_y = 107.4$ in.⁴

  $b = 10.01$ in. $t_f = 0.641$ in.

  $d = 12.19 - 0.641 = 11.55$ in.

From Table 7.2:

  $J = 2.10$ in.⁴ $a = 66.49$ in.

  $\dfrac{L}{4a} = \dfrac{28 \times 12}{4 \times 66.49} = 1.263$ $\dfrac{L}{2a} = 2.527$

---

*Values of R are given in U.S. Steel's "Hot Rolled Shapes and Plate," (Publication ADUSS 27-3400).

From mathematical tables:

$$\tanh \frac{L}{4a} = 0.8519 \qquad\qquad \tanh \frac{L}{2a} = 0.9873$$

Lateral bending moment in each flange:

$$M = \frac{wLea}{2d}\left(-\frac{2a}{L} + \frac{1}{\tanh \frac{L}{2a}}\right) \qquad \textbf{(See Figure 7.10)}$$

$$= \frac{1.06 \times 28 \times 2 \times 66.49}{2 \times 11.55}\left(-\frac{1}{2.527} + \frac{1}{0.9873}\right)$$

$$= 105 \text{ in. kips}$$

Bending stress from lateral bending moment:

$$f = \frac{Mc}{I_y} = \frac{105 \times 10.01/2}{107.4/2} = 9.79 \text{ ksi}$$

Beam bending moment:

$$M = \frac{wL^2}{12} = \frac{1.06 \times 28 \times 28 \times 12}{12} = 831 \text{ in. kips}$$

Beam bending stress:

$$f = \frac{M}{S} = \frac{831}{78.1} = 10.64 \text{ ksi}$$

Maximum total bending stress is 20.4 ksi at support. See sketch.

20.4 ksi < 22.0 ksi O.K.

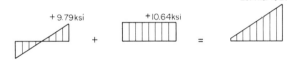

+9.79 ksi   +10.64 ksi

−9.79 ksi

Therefore, 12WF58 beam is satisfactory.

Total angle of twist is

$$\theta_t = \frac{wLea}{2JG}\left(\frac{L}{4a} - \tanh \frac{L}{4a}\right) \qquad \textbf{(See Figure 7.10)}$$

$$= \frac{1060 \times 28 \times 2 \times 66.49}{2 \times 2.10 \times 11 \times 10^6}(1.263 - 0.852)$$

$$\theta_t = \textbf{0.0351 radians or 2 degrees.}$$

Effect of rotation on wall should be considered.

References (Chapter 7)

1. I. A. El Darwish and B. G. Johnston, "Torsion of Structural Shapes," **Journal of the Structural Division, Proceedings** ASCE, **91**, No. ST1, 1965.

2. I. Lyse and B. G. Johnston, "Structural Beams in Torsion," **Transactions** ASCE, **101**, 1936.

3. F. Bleich, **Buckling Strength of Metal Structures**, McGraw-Hill Book Company, New York City, 1952.

Table 7.1

Factors for Determining the Torsion Constant and Maximum Torsional Shear Stress in Rectangular Bars

Width-to-Thickness Ratio, b/t	Factors for Equations 7.12 and 7.13	
	2ψ	γ
1.00	0.1928	0.6753
1.10	0.1973	0.7198
1.20	0.2006	0.7578
1.30	0.2031	0.7935
1.40	0.2050	0.8222
1.50	0.2064	0.8976
1.60	0.2074	0.8695
1.80	0.2086	0.9044
2.00	0.2093	0.9300
2.50	0.2099	0.9681
3.00	0.2101	0.9855
4.00	0.2101	0.9970
∞	0.2101	1.0000

Table 7.2

Torsion Constants for Structural Shapes

Shape	J, in.⁴	a, in.	Shape	J, in.⁴	a, in.
36WF 300	64.71	122.89	18WF 114	9.21	74.25
36WF 280	53.02	129.82	18WF 105	7.22	79.35
36WF 260	42.08	138.13	18WF 96	5.54	85.34
36WF 245	35.06	145.22	18WF 85	5.56	59.30
36WF 230	29.03	152.84	18WF 77	4.22	64.00
36WF 194	22.49	112.85	18WF 70	3.17	69.16
36WF 182	18.60	118.88	18WF 64	2.45	74.25
36WF 170	15.19	125.69	18WF 60	2.19	65.59
36WF 160	12.54	132.12	18WF 55	1.68	70.52
36WF 150	10.22	139.25	18WF 50	1.26	76.29
36WF 135	7.11	151.14	18WF 45	0.899	83.36
33WF 240	36.90	125.94	16WF 96	6.22	71.84
33WF 220	28.45	135.16	16WF 88	4.77	77.14
33WF 200	21.32	146.23	16WF 78	4.87	52.74
33WF 152	12.47	118.52	16WF 71	3.70	56.82
33WF 141	9.80	126.21	16WF 64	2.74	61.60
33WF 130	7.46	135.06	16WF 58	2.05	66.62
33WF 118	5.39	145.51	16WF 50	1.53	60.11
30WF 210	28.80	116.14	16WF 45	1.12	65.49
30WF 190	21.40	126.00	16WF 40	0.799	71.93
30WF 172	15.90	136.62	16WF 36	0.553	78.55
30WF 132	9.82	102.49	14WF 730	1447.54	25.51
30WF 124	8.08	107.97	14WF 665	1124.24	26.61
30WF 116	6.50	114.04	14WF 605	868.73	27.85
30WF 108	5.09	120.71	14WF 550	669.72	29.23
30WF 99	3.84	128.82	14WF 500	514.06	30.79
27WF 177	20.26	106.54	14WF 455	395.74	32.48
27WF 160	15.07	115.56	14WF 426	330.27	33.73
27WF 145	11.36	124.99	14WF 398	272.28	35.19
27WF 114	7.43	95.31	14WF 370	222.00	36.84
27WF 102	5.32	104.37	14WF 342	177.75	38.78
27WF 94	4.10	111.73	14WF 320	136.91	40.99
27WF 84	2.83	122.15	14WF 314	139.75	41.05
24WF 160	16.47	103.95	14WF 287	107.94	43.72
24WF 145	12.19	112.89	14WF 264	85.31	46.36
24WF 130	8.67	123.79	14WF 246	69.71	48.81
24WF 120	8.27	104.41	14WF 237	62.58	50.19
24WF 110	6.45	111.93	14WF 228	56.16	51.62
24WF 100	4.87	120.95	14WF 219	49.91	53.25
24WF 94	5.27	83.12	14WF 211	44.79	54.79
24WF 84	3.75	91.17	14WF 202	39.61	56.63
24WF 76	2.73	99.17	14WF 193	34.69	58.69
24WF 68	1.88	108.60	14WF 184	30.34	60.87
21WF 142	13.87	86.58	14WF 176	26.50	63.17
21WF 127	10.08	94.61	14WF 167	22.77	65.87
21WF 112	6.94	104.87	14WF 158	19.52	68.78
21WF 96	6.59	66.31	14WF 150	16.73	71.82
21WF 82	4.15	75.10	14WF 142	14.22	75.16
21WF 73	3.06	76.87	14WF 136	13.46	71.64
21WF 68	2.48	81.40	14WF 127	11.09	75.74
21WF 62	1.86	87.83	14WF 119	9.20	79.93
21WF 55	1.26	96.64	14WF 111	7.48	84.83

Table 7.2 (Continued)

Shape	J, in.⁴	a, in.	Shape	J, in.⁴	a, in.
14WF 103	6.02	90.41	8WF 28	0.533	38.98
14WF 95	4.74	96.94	8WF 24	0.343	44.20
14WF 87	3.68	104.56	8WF 20	0.248	36.62
14WF 84	4.41	77.24	8WF 17	0.149	41.56
14WF 78	3.52	82.43	6WF 25	0.463	28.96
14WF 74	3.86	63.58	6WF 20	0.243	34.81
14WF 68	3.01	68.26	6WF 15.5	0.113	42.79
14WF 61	2.19	74.85	5WF 18.5	0.295	20.79
14WF 53	1.93	58.42	5WF 16	0.192	23.37
14WF 48	1.44	63.53	24B 61.0	1.808	80.87
14WF 43	1.05	69.59	24B 55.0	1.300	87.31
14WF 38	0.806	60.58	21B 49.0	1.114	76.72
14WF 34	0.575	66.46	21B 44.0	0.784	83.51
14WF 30	0.383	73.42	18B 40.0	0.818	67.51
12WF 190	48.89	35.39	18B 35.0	0.519	75.92
12WF 161	30.59	39.83	16B 31.0	0.472	61.45
12WF 133	17.64	46.02	16B 26.0	0.267	70.47
12WF 120	12.93	50.02	14B 26.0	0.362	51.90
12WF 106	9.10	55.13	14B 22.0	0.213	59.13
12WF 99	7.43	58.32	12B 22.0	0.292	37.85
12WF 92	6.01	61.92	12B 19.0	0.183	42.60
12WF 85	4.80	66.06	12B 16.5	0.112	47.27
12WF 79	3.85	70.33	12B 14.0	0.070	53.43
12WF 72	2.94	76.04	10B 19.0	0.232	33.79
12WF 65	2.19	82.90	10B 17.0	0.155	37.22
12WF 58	2.10	66.49	10B 15.0	0.104	40.72
12WF 53	1.59	72.04	10B 11.5	0.049	50.03
12WF 50	1.79	52.26	8B 15.0	0.136	31.01
12WF 45	1.32	56.95	8B 13.0	0.087	34.34
12WF 40	0.956	62.54	8B 10.0	0.042	42.59
12WF 36	0.835	50.23	6B 16.0	0.222	20.79
12WF 31	0.540	56.72	6B 12.0	0.090	26.19
12WF 27	0.357	63.45	6B 8.5	0.033	34.38
10WF 112	15.01	32.34	8X8M 34.3	0.682	43.60
10WF 100	10.85	35.18	6X6M 25.0	0.522	23.04
10WF 89	7.74	38.47	6X6M 20.0	0.265	29.73
10WF 77	5.11	43.08	5X5M 18.9	0.314	18.15
10WF 72	4.17	45.57	4X4M 13.0	0.172	12.98
10WF 66	3.27	48.80	24I 120.0	12.96	47.23
10WF 60	2.49	52.71	24I 105.9	10.38	50.89
10WF 54	1.84	57.51	24I 100.0	7.63	46.96
10WF 49	1.38	62.54	24I 90.0	6.05	51.14
10WF 45	1.50	45.65	24I 79.9	4.89	55.19
10WF 39	0.971	51.57	20I 95.0	8.46	37.59
10WF 33	0.580	59.60	20I 85.0	6.63	40.96
10WF 29	0.583	39.99	20I 75.0	4.71	39.15
10WF 25	0.376	45.18	20I 65.4	3.59	43.18
10WF 21	0.212	52.10	18I 70.0	4.15	33.89
8WF 67	5.05	27.23	18I 54.7	2.36	41.81
8WF 58	3.32	30.42	15I 50.0	2.12	31.84
8WF 48	1.96	35.14	15I 42.9	1.54	35.71
8WF 40	1.12	41.02	12I 50.0	2.82	21.78
8WF 35	0.768	45.72	12I 40.8	1.75	25.70
8WF 31	0.534	50.75	12I 35.0	1.08	28.09

Table 7.2 (Continued)

Shape	J, in.⁴	a, in.	Shape	J, in.⁴	a,* in.
12I 31.8	0.90	29.99	18[58.0	2.81	
10I 35.0	1.29	19.66	18[51.9	2.03	
10I 25.4	0.601	25.96	18[45.8	1.46	
8I 23.0	0.550	17.27	18[42.7	1.24	
8I 18.4	0.334	20.59	15[50.0	2.66	
7I 20.0	0.451	13.96	15[40.0	1.46	
7I 15.3	0.240	17.88	15[33.9	1.01	
6I 17.25	0.374	11.27	12[30.0	0.864	
6I 12.5	0.167	14.91	12[25.0	0.540	
5I 14.75	0.323	8.90	12[20.7	0.368	
5I 10.0	0.113	12.30	10[30.0	1.22	
4I 9.5	0.120	8.22	10[25.0	0.690	
4I 7.7	0.072	9.75	10[20.0	0.370	
3I 7.5	0.091	5.62	10[15.3	0.210	
3I 5.7	0.044	7.13	9[20.0	0.429	
			9[15.0	0.209	
			9[13.4	0.167	
			8[18.75	0.187	
			8[13.75	0.436	
			8[11.5	0.131	
			7[14.75	0.268	
			7[12.25	0.161	
			7[9.8	0.100	
			6[13.0	0.241	
			6[10.5	0.130	
			6[8.2	0.075	
			5[9.0	0.109	
			5[6.7	0.055	
			4[7.25	0.082	
			4[5.4	0.039	
			3[6.0	0.073	
			3[5.0	0.043	
			3[4.1	0.027	
			6X3½Z 21.1	0.539	
			6X3½Z 15.7	0.228	
			5X3¼Z 17.9	0.460	
			5X3¼Z 16.4	0.324	
			5X3¼Z 14.0	0.205	
			5X3¼Z 11.6	0.119	
			4X3 Z 15.9	0.411	
			4X3 Z 12.5	0.184	
			4X3 Z 10.3	0.107	
			4X3 Z 8.2	0.055	
			3X2¾Z 12.6	0.330	
			3X2¾Z 9.8	0.147	
			3X2¾Z 6.7	0.046	

---

* This term has no significance for shapes where it is not shown.

CHAPTER 8

Members Under Combined Axial and Bending Loads

8.1 Axial Compression and Bending

8.1.1 *Behavior of Beam Columns*

Initially straight members that are subjected to a combination of axial compression and bending are known as beam columns. The bending may be caused by lateral loading, applied end moments, or eccentric application of the axial load. The general behavior of such a member is illustrated by the load-deflection curve shown in Figure 8.1 for an eccentrically loaded column.[1] In this discussion, the member is considered to be supported laterally to prevent buckling in a plane other than the plane of the applied moment. As the load increases, the summation of bending stresses and compression stresses increases until the yield load, P_y is reached that causes the outer fiber to yield at midlength. The relationship between load and midlength deflection is not linear, even within this range of elastic stresses because of the amplification factor discussed in Chapter 3.

As the load increases above P_y, yielding progresses through the cross section and, since the yielded portion contributes little to stiffness, the stiffness of the member is reduced. Since each successive transverse deflection increment results in additional yielding and a further reduction in stiffness, the load increment required to produce each successive deflection increment becomes progressively smaller and is reduced to zero at ultimate load. As the transverse deflection is further increased, the axial load that can be supported decreases. Thus, the member fails through instability caused by excessive bending in the plane of applied moments. In

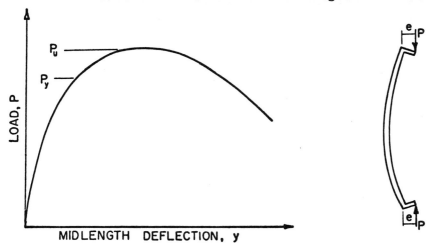

FIGURE 8.1   LOAD-DEFLECTION   CURVE   FOR ECCENTRICALLY   LOADED   COLUMN

a very short member, the ultimate load is the load that causes full plastification of the cross section. Also, if a beam column is subjected to bending about its strong axis and is not adequately supported in the lateral direction, it may fail prematurely through lateral-torsional buckling.

Residual stresses, which cause premature yielding and a corresponding reduction in stiffness, may reduce both the initial yield and the ultimate load of beam columns. Similarly, an initial crookedness, which increases the bending moment caused by any given load, reduces both the initial yield and ultimate load. The design loading for a beam column can be based on the loading that causes initial yielding or on the ultimate load. The determination of each will be considered in the following sections.

8.1.2 *Determination of Yield Load*

a. "Direct" Method for Laterally Supported Members[2]

As explained in Chapter 3, if an axially loaded column has an initial curvature with an initial ordinate, y_o, at midlength, the total midheight ordinate, y, after a load, P, has been applied is

$$y = y_o\left[\frac{1}{1 - P/P_e}\right] \qquad (8.1)$$

where P_e is the Euler load for buckling in the plane of initial curvature. The bracketed term is the amplification factor. The moment at midlength caused by the deflection, y, is Py or $Py_o \left[\dfrac{1}{1 - P/P_e} \right]$. If an initial moment, M_o, is present at midlength, such as that caused by an applied transverse load or applied end moments, the maximum total moment at midlength is

$$M = M_o + \frac{Py_o}{1 - P/P_e} \qquad (8.2)$$

where y_o is the midlength deflection caused by M_o plus any initial out-of-straightness at midlength. Although the above equation is derived for an initial curvature that has the form of a sine wave, the total moment calculated from the equation will be within 2 percent of the exact moment for all common cases where the maximum moment occurs at or near the center.[3]

Equation 8.2 can be rewritten as

$$M = M_o \left[\frac{1 + \psi P/P_e}{1 - P/P_e} \right] \qquad (8.3)$$

where ψ is defined by the equation

$$\psi = \frac{P_e y_o}{M_o} - 1 = \frac{\pi^2 y_o EI}{M_o L^2} - 1 \qquad (8.4)$$

The maximum stress, f_m, due to compression and bending is

$$f_m = \frac{P}{A} + \frac{Mc}{I} = \frac{P}{A} + \left[\frac{1 + \psi P/P_e}{1 - P/P_e} \right] \frac{M_o c}{I} \qquad (8.5)$$

The value of P that causes f_m to equal f_y is the initial yield load of the member.

The term ψ may be readily determined for a given loading condition by substituting values of y_o and M_o for the initial loading condition into Equation 8.4. For a uniformly distributed transverse load of total magnitude, W, the following value is obtained:

$$\psi = \frac{\pi^2 \left(\dfrac{5}{384} \right) WL^3}{\left(\dfrac{WL}{8} \right) L^2} - 1 = 0.0281$$

From Equation 8.5, the combination of axial load, P', and uniformly distributed transverse load, W', that will cause initial yielding is

$$f_y = \frac{P'}{A} + \left[\frac{1 + 0.0281 \, P'/P_e}{1 - P'/P_e} \right] \left(\frac{1}{8} \right) \left(\frac{L}{r} \right) \left(\frac{c}{r} \right) \left(\frac{W'}{A} \right) \qquad (8.6)$$

The term c/r is equal to the distance to the outer fiber divided by the radius of gyration. For wide-flange shapes, c/r equals approximately 2.00 for bending about the weak axis and 1.17 for bending about the strong axis. For applications where the ratio W'/P' is known, the ratio can be termed k_1 and W' can be replaced by k_1P'. For practical columns assumed to be straight, a value of 0.01 should be added to the actual value of k_1 to allow for initial out-of-straightness and the effects of residual stresses. The value of 0.01 allows for an initial curvature of L/800, which is greater than that allowed by specifications; thus, the additional amount compensates for the effect of residual stresses.

Table 8.1 gives values of P'/A calculated for various combinations of f_y, L/r, and k_1c/r, and can be used directly for a beam column under a uniformly distributed transverse load. For other loading conditions, P'/A can be obtained from the table for an equivalent k_1c/r defined as [2]

$$\left(\frac{k_1c}{r}\right)_{eq.} = \left(\frac{W}{P}k_mk_\psi + k_e + 0.01\right)\frac{c}{r} \tag{8.7}$$

The term k_m is the ratio of the maximum moment caused by the actual transverse load to that caused by a uniform transverse load with the same total load magnitude. Thus,

$$k_m = \frac{8M_o}{WL} \tag{8.8}$$

The term k_ψ accounts for the initial deflection caused by the actual transverse load and is defined as

$$k_\psi = \frac{1 + \psi P/P_e}{1 + 0.281\ P/P_e} \cong 1 + \psi P/P_e \tag{8.9}$$

Values of k_m and ψ are listed in Figure 8.2 for various loading conditions. The term k_e accounts for eccentric application of load and is approximated as the smaller of the following two expressions:

$$k_e = \left(\frac{3.2e_1 + 4.8e_2}{L}\right)(1 + 0.23\ P/P_e) \tag{8.10}$$

$$k_e = \frac{3.2e_2}{L}(1 + 0.23\ P/P_e) \tag{8.11}$$

The terms e_1 and e_2 are end eccentricities where $e_1 < e_2$.

b. Interaction Equations

The AISC specification[4] gives interaction equations for combined stresses in beam columns that approximate those calculated by the method discussed above. The equations have been written to include the possible effects of lateral buckling. When the computed axial stress, f_a, is less than 15 percent of the allowable axial stress for columns, F_a, a simplified equation is given that neglects the bending caused by the axial load; for larger axial stresses an amplification factor is included. The requirements of the specification are as follows:

LOADING	EQUIVALENT LOAD FACTOR, K_m	DEFLECTION COEFFICIENT, ψ
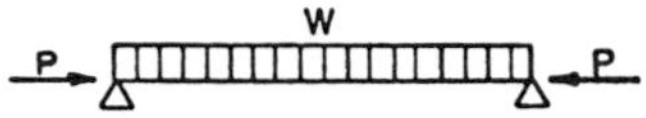	1.000	+0.028
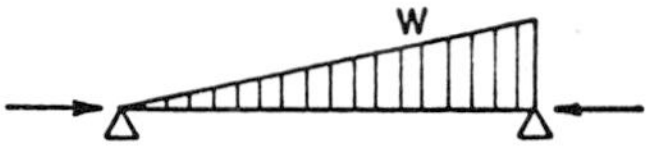	1.026	+0.003
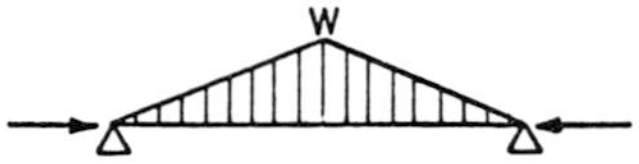	1.333	−0.013
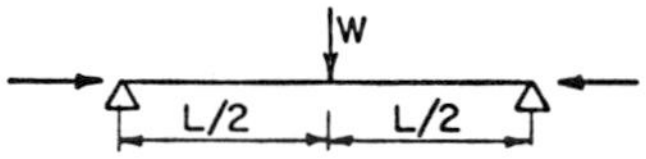	2.000	−0.178
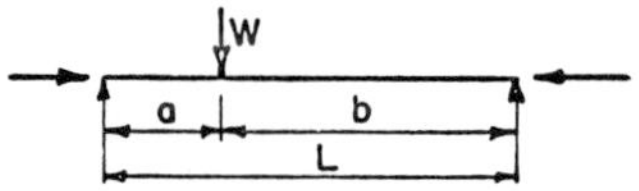	$\dfrac{8ab}{L^2}$	$\left(\dfrac{\pi^2 ab}{3L^2}-1\right)$
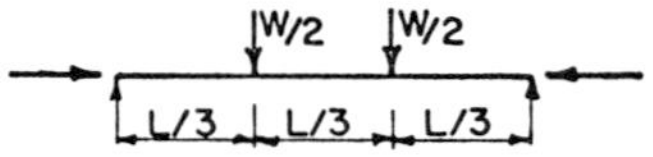	1.333	+0.051
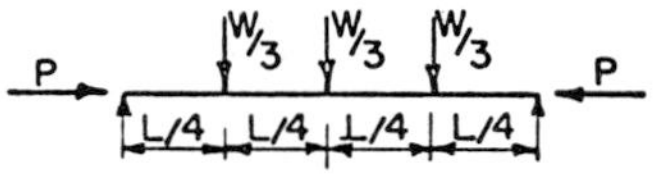	1.333	−0.023

FIGURE 8.2   LOAD AND DEFLECTION PARAMETERS FOR BEAM COLUMNS

$$\frac{f_a}{F_a}+\frac{f_b}{F_b}\leq 1.0 \qquad \text{when } f_a/F_a \leq 0.15 \qquad \textbf{(8.12)}$$

$$\frac{f_a}{F_a}+\frac{C_m f_b}{\left(1-\dfrac{f_a}{F'_e}\right)F_b}\leq 1.0 \qquad \text{when } f_a/F_a > 0.15 \qquad \textbf{(8.13)}$$

and, in addition, at points braced in the plane of bending,

$$\frac{f_a}{0.60f_y}+\frac{f_b}{F_b}\leq 1.0 \qquad\qquad \textbf{(8.14)}$$

where

F_a = axial stress that would be permitted if axial force alone
existed.

F_b = compressive bending stress that would be permitted if bending moment alone existed

$$F'_e = \frac{149,000,000 \text{ psi}}{(KL_b/r_b)^2}$$ (In the expression for F'_e, L_b is the actual unbraced length in the plane of bending and r_b is the corresponding radius of gyration. K is the effective length factor in the plane of bending. As is true for F_a, F_b, and $0.6\ f_y$, F'_e may be increased one third in accordance with provisions for wind or seismic loadings.)

f_a = computed axial stress.

f_b = computed compressive bending stress at the point under consideration.

C_m = a coefficient the value of which shall be taken as follows:

1. For compression members in frames subject to joint translation (sidesway), $C_m = 0.85$.

2. For restrained compression members in frames braced against joint translation and not subject to transverse loading between their supports in the plane of bending.

   $C_m = 0.6 + 0.4\dfrac{M_1}{M_2}$, but not less than 0.4, where M_1/M_2

   is the ratio of the smaller to larger moments at the ends of that portion of the member, unbraced in the plane of bending under consideration. M_1/M_2 is positive when the member is bent in single curvature and negative when it is bent in reverse curvature.

3. For compression members in frames braced against joint translation in the plane of loading and subjected to transverse loading between their supports, the value of C_m may be determined by rational analysis. However, in place of such analysis, the following values may be used: (a) for members with restrained ends, $C_m = 0.85$, and (b) for members with unrestrained ends, $C_m = 1.0$."

A detailed explanation of the above requirements is given in the commentary that accompanies the specification.

8.1.3 *Determination of Ultimate Load*

Interaction equations have been determined that relate the ultimate moment and ultimate axial load for wide-flange beam columns bent about their strong axis by applied end moments. The equations were determined for a wide-flange member with a shape factor of 1.10 and are conservative for members with higher shape factors. The members are assumed to be originally straight and free of accidental eccentricities, but the effect of residual stresses from cooling after hot rolling is included. The equations are given in

Part 2 of the AISC specifications, and may be used in plastic design of A36 steel members.

A complete description of the procedure used to obtain the relationships is given in Reference 5. The procedure could also be applied to higher strength steels. Briefly, for a given member and for given values of f_y, P, M, and L, the end slope of the member was determined from calculated deflections obtained by a numerical integration of curvature along the member. The curvature at each point was obtained from a moment curvature diagram that included the effects of residual stresses. Thus, the effects of the amount of yielding that had occurred at each cross section was considered. The calculations were repeated for successively higher values of M while P was held constant. Finally, a maximum end moment was determined that caused the end slope to increase without an increase in moment. This combination of moment and load represented corresponding values of ultimate load, P_u, and ultimate moment, M_u. The procedure was repeated for successively higher values of P so that an interaction curve relating P_u/P_y to M_u/M_p could be plotted. By repeating this general procedure for various values of L/r, a family of interaction curves was obtained. The interaction equations were obtained by curve fitting.

8.2 Axial Tension and Bending

8.2.1 *Structural Members*

If a member has an initial curvature with an initial ordinate, y_o, at midheight, the total midlength ordinate, y, after an applied axial tension load, P, is

$$y = y_o \left(\frac{1}{1 + P/P_e} \right) \tag{8.15}$$

In contrast with the behavior of beam columns, the deflection **decreases** under a tensile load, and the bracketed term in the above equation may be termed a "reduction factor." The moment at midlength caused by deflection y is Py or $Py_o \left(\dfrac{P}{1 + P/P_e} \right)$. If an initial moment, M_o, is present at midheight, such as that caused by an applied transverse load, the maximum total moment at midlength is

$$M = M_o - \frac{Py_o}{1 + P/P_e} \tag{8.16}$$

Thus, the axial load decreases the bending moment in the member. Of course, the total stress in the member is simply

$$f = \frac{P}{A} + \frac{M}{S} \tag{8.17}$$

If an initially straight member is subjected to an axial tension load that is eccentric at either end by an amount e, the maximum stress occurs at the ends and is

$$f = \frac{P}{A} + \frac{Pe}{S} \tag{8.18}$$

The stress at other points along the length of the member is less because the member deflects toward the line of action of the tensile forces and thus, the bending moment, which is equal to P times the distance from the line of action to the deflected member, becomes smaller.

The ultimate failure of members subject to axial tension and bending would usually be by excessive yielding after plastification of the full cross section at the location of maximum combined stress. However, if bending stresses are predominant, the member could fail through lateral instability.

For the design of members subject to axial tension and bending, the AISC specification[4] requires that the computed stresses meet the requirements of Equation 8.14, where f_b and F_b are the computed and the allowable tensile bending stresses, respectively. For compact sections ($F_b = 0.66\ f_y$), the safety factor against general provides a safety factor of 1.67 against yielding of the outer fiber. For compact sections ($F_b = 0.66\ f_y$), the safety factor against general yielding would be at least 1.67 for sections having a shape factor of 1.10 or greater. To prevent lateral buckling, the AISC also requires that the computed compressive bending stress alone must not exceed the values given by Equations 6.13 and 6.14.

8.2.2 *Plates*

If a uniformly distributed lateral load is applied to a plate with end supports that do not translate in the plane of the plate, both bending stress and axial tensile stress or membrane stress develop in the plate. Examples of such plates or sheets include rectangular panels between stiffeners on the sides of bins or railroad hopper cars. The behavior of such a panel is illustrated in Figure 8.3 and is discussed below. In Figure 8.3 (a) and (b), the edges are assumed to have zero slope at the supports initially; that is, the edges of the panel are either flexurally fixed or the panel is an interior span of a sheet that is continuous over several spans.

As a uniform lateral load is applied to a panel, both membrane tension and bending moments develop. The sheet sags slightly but remains elastic until yielding occurs within narrow zones along the lines of support (interior and exterior stiffeners) where the bending moment is greatest. Figure 8.3(a). With a further loading increase, the sheet remains elastic except within the local plastic zones near the supports until general yielding starts at midspan at a much higher load, Figure 8.3(b). Before midspan yielding, the panel sheet generally remains structurally useful, although some permanent sag occurs. After midspan yielding, the sheet can theoretically carry still greater loads until it sags enough to exhaust its ductility.

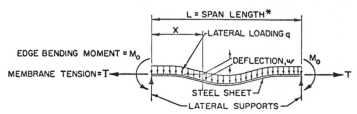

(a) SHEET WITH FIXED EDGES (ELASTIC RANGE)

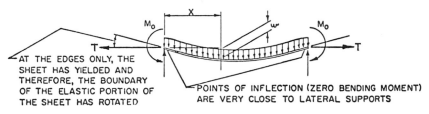

(b) SHEET WITH FIXED EDGES (INELASTIC RANGE)

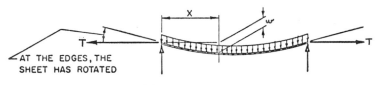

(c) SHEET WITH SIMPLE SUPPORTS

*SHORTEST RECTANGULAR PANEL DIMENSION

LONGITUDINAL DIRECTION (TYP)

**FIGURE 8.3   CROSS SECTIONS THROUGH LATERALLY
LOADED SHEETS WITH MEMBRANE TENSIONS**

Thus, as verified by tests,[6] initial yielding at midspan is a reasonable design criteria for sheets with either simple supports, Figure 8.3(c), or fixed supports. In sheets with fixed ends, the localized yielding at the ends is neglected. An appropriate procedure for calculating the bending and membrane stresses is given in Table 8.2.[7] If the sheet is supported by elastic members that can move in the plane of the sheet, any in-plane movement reduces the membrane stresses but increases the lateral deflection. If this condition is present, and initial value of the in-plane deflection, w_e, can be assumed for calculation of the membrane tension, T. The actual value of w_e caused by T acting on the support can then be calculated. The procedure can be repeated until consistent values of T and w_e are obtained. The framework supporting the sheet must be designed to withstand the membrane-tension force.

8.3 Design Examples

Example 8.1

A 30-foot-long wide-flange member is subjected to an axial compression load and a uniform load that causes bending about its weak axis as shown in the sketch at the right. Using Table 8.1, select an A36 steel shape that will provide a safety factor of 1.67, and check according to AISC specifications.

0.30 kips/ft

600 kips   600 kips

Solution:

a. Using Table 8.1

Total lateral load, $W = 0.30 \times 30 = 9$ kips.

$k_1 = W/P + 0.01 = 9/600 + 0.01 = 0.025$.

$c/r \cong 2.00$

$k_1 c/r = 0.025 \times 2.00 = 0.050$

Assume that a 14WF column section with $r_y = 4.0$ will be required.

$L/r = 30 \times 12/4.0 = 90$

From Table 8.1, for $f_y = 36$ ksi, average axial stress at initial yield is 17.10 ksi. Allowable axial stress is $17.10/1.67 = 10.2$ ksi.

Required $A = 600/10.2 = 58.8$ in.^{2}

Try 14WF202: $A = 59.39$ in.^{2} $r_y = 4.06$ in. $S = 124.4$ in.^{3}

$$c/r = \frac{15.75}{2 \times 4.06} = 1.94$$

$k_1 c/r = 0.025 \times 1.94 = 0.0485$

$L/r = 360/4.06 = 88.7$, $k = 1.0$ for simple supports   **(Figure 3.9)**

Interpolating from Table 8.1, $f = 17.6$ ksi.

Allowable axial stress is $17.6/1.67 = 10.5$ ksi

$P/A = 600/59.39 = 10.1$ ksi < 10.5 ksi

Therefore, select **14WF202**.

b. Check according to AISC specifications

$f_a = 600/59.39 = 10.1$ ksi

$F_a = 14.4$ ksi   **(Table 3.2)**

$$f_b = \frac{wL^2}{8S} = \frac{0.30 \times 30 \times 360}{8 \times 124.4} = 3.26 \text{ ksi}$$

$F_b = 24.0$ ksi (compact section)

$C_m = 1.0$

$$F'_e = \frac{149{,}000}{(KL/r)^2} = \frac{149{,}000}{(1 \times 88.7)^2} = 18.9 \text{ ksi}$$

$$\frac{f_a}{F_a} + \frac{C_m f_b}{\left(1 - \dfrac{f_a}{F'_e}\right) F_b} \leq 1.0 \qquad \textbf{(Equation 8.13)}$$

$$\frac{10.1}{14.4} + \frac{1.0 \times 3.26}{\left(1 - \dfrac{10.1}{18.9}\right) 24.0} = 0.99 < 1.0$$

14WF202 meets specification requirements.

Example 8.2

A column in a building frame is subjected to axial and eccentric loads as shown in the sketch at the right. The member is laterally supported at the A, B, and C levels. Select an A36 steel WF section in accordance with the requirements of the AISC specification.

Solution:

From a preliminary analysis it is determined that ¼ of the eccentric moment at B is distributed to end B of column segment BC, and ½ of the eccentric moment at C is distributed to end C of BC. Column load between B and C is 80 + 180 = 260 kips

M_{BC} = ¼ × 180 × 32 = +1440 in. kips

For a tentative selection of an 18WF96, eccentricity at C is 9.1 + 3.0 = 12.1 in.

M_{CB} = ½ × 40 × 12.1 = −242 in. kips

Properties of 18WF96 are as follows:

A = 28.22 in.² S_x = 184.4 in.³ r_x = 7.70 in.

r_y = 2.71 in. d/A_f = 1.86 in.⁻¹

f_a = 260/28.22 = 9.21 ksi

f_b = 1440/184.4 = 7.81 ksi

L/r_y = 288/2.71 = 106; k = 1.0; F_a = 12.2 ksi   (Table 3.2)

L/r_x = 288/7.70 = 37.4; k = 1.0; F'_e = $\dfrac{149{,}000}{(1 \times 37.4)^2}$ = 106.5

C_m = 0.60 + 0.40 M_1/M_2 = 0.60 − 0.40 × 242/1440 = 0.533

Max unsupported length for a compact section is

2400 $b_f/\sqrt{f_y}$ = 2400 × 11.75/$\sqrt{36000}$ = 148.6 in. > 288 in.

Thus, F_b is smaller of Equations 6.13 and 6.14 but no more than 0.60 f_y.

A check of these equations shows that F_b = 0.60 f_y = 22.0 ksi

$$\frac{f_a}{F_a} + \frac{C_m f_b}{\left(1 - \dfrac{f_a}{F'_e}\right) F_b} = \frac{9.21}{12.2} + \frac{0.533 \times 7.81}{\left(1 - \dfrac{9.21}{106.5}\right) 22} = 0.962 < 1.00$$

Therefore, 18WF96 section is satisfactory.

Example 8.3

A simply supported member supports concentrated transverse loads at its third points and an axial tension load acting through the centroid as shown in the sketch below.

Lateral support is provided at the load and reaction points and midway between the points. Select a rolled beam of USS "T-1" steel, using the requirements of the AISC specification where applicable.

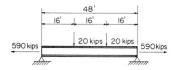

Solution:

Try an 18WF55 beam: $A = 16.19$ in.^{2} $I_x = 889.9$ in.^{4}
$S_x = 98.2$ in.^{3} $r_x = 7.41$ in.
$d/A_f = 3.82$ in.$^{-1}$

The maximum positive moment caused by the transverse loads alone is a constant value between the 20-kip loads. The negative moment caused by the axial tension load will be smaller at the 20-kip loads than at midspan because the initial deflection is smaller at the loads.
Therefore, the maximum total moment occurs at the 20-kip load.

$M_o = 20 \times 16 \times 12 = 3840$ in. kips

Deflection at 20 kips load, $y_o = \dfrac{5PL^3}{162EI} = \dfrac{5 \times 20{,}000 \times (48)^3 \times 1728}{162 \times 29 \times 10^6 \times 889.9} = 4.57$ in.

$L/r = 48 \times 12/7.41 = 77.7 \ (k = 1.0)$

$P_e = 47.3 \times 16.19 = 769$ kips **(Table 3.1)**

$M = M_o - \dfrac{Py_o}{1 + P/P_e} = 3840 - \dfrac{590 \times 4.57}{1 + 590/769} = 2310$ in. kips **(Equation 8.16)**

$f_a = P/A = 590/16.19 = 36.4$ ksi
$f_b = M/S = 2310/98.2 = 23.5$ ksi

$\dfrac{f_a}{0.60\,f_y} + \dfrac{f_b}{F_b} = \dfrac{36.4}{60.0} + \dfrac{23.5}{60.0} = \dfrac{59.9}{60.0} = 0.998 < 1.0$ **(Equation 8.14)***

Maximum compressive bending stress is limited by Equations 6.13 and 6.14. Equation 6.14 controls.

$\dfrac{12{,}000 \text{ ksi}}{8 \times 12 \times 3.82} = 32.7$ ksi > 23.5 ksi

Therefore, 18WF55 section is satisfactory.

Example 8.4

The sides of a rectangular bin or hopper car are subjected to a lateral pressure of 20 psi. Vertical stiffeners are spaced at 32-in. For a thickness of 12 ga. (0.1046 in.) ,determine the grade of USS EX-TEN Steel required to provide a safety factor of 1.50 against outer fiber yielding at midspan. Also determine the midspan deflection under this loading.

Solution:

The simple support membrane analysis given in Table 8.2 may be used with the following values: $w_{oo} = 0$, $w_1 = 0$, $t = 0.1046$ in., and $L = 32$ in.

1. $D = \dfrac{Et^3}{12\,(1 - u^2)} = \dfrac{29 \times 10^6 \times (0.1046)^3}{12 \times 0.91} = 3039$ in-lb

2. $w_o = \dfrac{5qL^4}{384D} + w_{oo} + \dfrac{2}{\pi}\sqrt{Lw_1} = \dfrac{5 \times 20 \times (32)^4}{384 \times 3039} + 0 + 0 = 89.9$ in.

---

* F_b was taken as 0.60 f_y since requirements for a compact section in "T-1" steel have not been determined.

3. $[1 + \alpha]^2 \left[\alpha + \frac{12L}{\pi^2 t^2} \left(w_1 + \frac{\pi^2 w_{oo}^2}{4L} \right) \right] = \frac{3w_o^2}{t^2}$

$(1 + \alpha)^2 \alpha = 3 \left(\frac{89.9}{0.1046} \right)^2$

$\alpha = 130$

4. $p = \sqrt{\frac{\pi^2 \alpha}{4}} = \sqrt{\frac{\pi^2 \times 130}{4}} = 17.9$

5. $T = \frac{4Dp^2}{L^2} = \frac{4 \times 3039 \times 320}{32 \times 32} = 3790 \text{ lb/in.}$

6. $M_c = \frac{qL^2}{8} \left[\frac{1 - \text{sech } p}{p^2/2} \right] = \frac{20 \times 32 \times 32}{8} \left[\frac{1 - 0}{0.5 \times 320} \right] = 16.0 \text{ in-lb/in.}$

7. $f_a = \frac{T}{t} = \frac{3790}{0.1046} = 36,230 \text{ psi}$

8. $f_b = \pm \frac{6M_c}{t^2} = \frac{6 \times 16.0}{(0.1046)^2} = 8770 \text{ psi}$

9. $f_t = f_a + f_b = 36,230 + 8,770 = 45,000 \text{ psi}$

   $1.5 \times 45,000 = 67,500 \text{ psi.}$ **Therefore, use EX-TEN 70 sheets.**

10. $\Delta = \frac{w_o}{1 + \alpha} = \frac{89.9}{131} =$ **0.686 in. midspan deflection.**

Design requirements for framework:

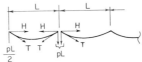

End post must be designed for force H and force $\frac{pL}{2}$. H is approximately equal to T, since the angle between H and T is small. Intermediate stiffeners need only be designed for force pL, since H components are self-balancing. Longitudinal members between stiffeners, or between stiffener and end post, must be designed for force H.

References (Chapter 8)

1. American Society of Civil Engineers, "Commentary on Plastic Design in Steel," 1960.

2. I. A. El Darwish and B. G. Johnston, "Strength of Steel Beam-Columns for Steel Yield Points Between 33 ksi and 100 ksi Including Effects of End-Restraint, Biplanar Bending, and Residual Stress," Office of Research Administration, University of Michigan, Ann Arbor, Michigan, 1964.

3. Column Research Council, "Guide to Design Criteria for Metal Compression Members," 2nd. Ed., 1966, John Wiley & Sons, publisher.

4. American Institute of Steel Construction, "Specification for the Design, Fabrication, and Erection of Structural Steel for Buildings," 1963.

5. T. V. Galambos and R. L. Ketter, "Columns Under Combined Bending and Thrust," **Journal of the Engineering Mechanics Division, Proceedings** ASCE, **85,** No. EM2, April 1959.

6. J. F. McDermott, "Theoretical and Experimental Study of Steel Panels in Which Membrane Tension is Developed," Paper No. 65-MET-15, ASME, 1965.

7. S. Timoshenko and S. Woinowski-Krieger, **Theory of Plates and Shells,** McGraw-Hill Book Company, New York City, 1959.

Table 8.1
Average Axial Stress, ksi, at Initial Yield in Beam Columns

$$f_y = 36 \text{ ksi}$$

Values of $\dfrac{k_i e}{r}$

Slenderness Ratio, L/r	.01	.02	.03	.04	.05	.06	.07	.08	.09	.10	.11	.12	.13	.14	.15
10	35.55	35.11	34.68	34.27	33.86	33.46	33.07	32.69	32.32	31.96	31.60	31.26	30.92	30.59	30.26
20	35.08	34.20	33.37	32.58	31.83	31.11	30.43	29.78	29.15	28.56	27.98	27.43	26.90	26.40	25.91
30	34.54	33.21	31.99	30.86	29.82	28.84	27.94	27.09	26.30	25.56	24.85	24.19	23.57	22.97	22.41
40	33.90	32.07	30.47	29.04	27.75	26.59	25.53	24.57	23.68	22.85	22.09	21.38	20.72	20.10	19.52
50	33.07	30.71	28.75	27.08	25.62	24.34	23.20	22.17	21.25	20.40	19.63	18.92	18.26	17.66	17.09
60	31.95	29.06	26.81	24.98	23.44	22.11	20.95	19.93	19.02	18.19	17.45	16.77	16.14	15.57	15.03
70	30.38	27.06	24.66	22.78	21.24	19.95	18.83	17.85	16.99	16.21	15.51	14.88	14.30	13.77	13.29
80	28.22	24.75	22.38	20.57	19.11	17.90	16.86	15.96	15.16	14.45	13.82	13.24	12.72	12.24	11.79
90	25.49	22.25	20.07	18.42	17.10	16.00	15.07	14.25	13.54	12.90	12.33	11.81	11.34	10.91	10.52
100	22.52	19.75	17.86	16.42	15.26	14.29	13.46	12.74	12.11	11.54	11.04	10.58	10.16	9.77	9.42
110	19.65	17.43	15.84	14.61	13.61	12.77	12.04	11.41	10.85	10.36	9.91	9.50	9.13	8.79	8.48
120	17.11	15.35	14.04	13.01	12.15	11.43	10.80	10.25	9.76	9.32	8.93	8.57	8.24	7.94	7.66
130	14.94	13.54	12.47	11.60	10.87	10.25	9.71	9.23	8.80	8.42	8.07	7.75	7.46	7.20	6.95
140	13.10	11.99	11.11	10.38	9.76	9.23	8.76	8.34	7.97	7.63	7.32	7.04	6.79	6.55	6.33
150	11.56	10.67	9.93	9.32	8.79	8.33	7.93	7.56	7.24	6.94	6.67	6.42	6.19	5.98	5.78
160	10.27	9.53	8.92	8.40	7.95	7.55	7.20	6.88	6.59	6.33	6.09	5.87	5.67	5.48	5.31
170	9.17	8.56	8.05	7.60	7.21	6.87	6.56	6.28	6.03	5.80	5.59	5.39	5.21	5.04	4.88
180	8.23	7.72	7.29	6.91	6.57	6.27	6.00	5.75	5.53	5.33	5.14	4.96	4.80	4.65	4.51
190	7.43	7.00	6.62	6.30	6.00	5.74	5.50	5.29	5.09	4.91	4.74	4.58	4.44	4.30	4.17
200	6.73	6.37	6.05	5.76	5.51	5.27	5.06	4.87	4.70	4.53	4.38	4.24	4.11	3.99	3.87

	.16	.17	.18	.19	.20	.21	.22	.23	.24	.25	.26	.27	.28	.29	.30
10	29.95	29.63	29.33	29.03	28.74	28.45	28.17	27.90	27.63	27.36	27.10	26.85	26.60	26.36	26.11
20	25.44	24.99	24.55	24.13	23.72	23.33	22.95	22.58	22.23	21.88	21.55	21.22	20.91	20.61	20.31
30	21.88	21.37	20.88	20.42	19.98	19.56	19.16	18.77	18.40	18.04	17.70	17.37	17.05	16.75	16.45
40	18.97	18.46	17.97	17.51	17.07	16.66	16.27	15.89	15.54	15.19	14.87	14.56	14.26	13.97	13.70
50	16.56	16.07	15.60	15.16	14.75	14.36	14.00	13.65	13.32	13.00	12.70	12.42	12.15	11.89	11.64
60	14.54	14.08	13.65	13.25	12.87	12.51	12.18	11.86	11.56	11.27	11.00	10.75	10.50	10.27	10.04
70	12.83	12.41	12.02	11.66	11.31	10.99	10.69	10.40	10.13	9.88	9.63	9.40	9.18	8.98	8.78
80	11.39	11.01	10.65	10.33	10.02	9.73	9.46	9.20	8.96	8.73	8.51	8.31	8.11	7.93	7.75
90	10.15	9.81	9.50	9.20	8.93	8.67	8.43	8.20	7.98	7.78	7.58	7.40	7.23	7.06	6.90
100	9.10	8.79	8.51	8.25	8.00	7.77	7.56	7.35	7.16	6.98	6.80	6.64	6.48	6.33	6.19
110	8.19	7.92	7.67	7.43	7.21	7.01	6.81	6.63	6.46	6.29	6.14	5.99	5.85	5.72	5.59
120	7.40	7.16	6.94	6.73	6.53	6.35	6.18	6.01	5.86	5.71	5.57	5.44	5.31	5.19	5.08
130	6.72	6.51	6.31	6.12	5.94	5.78	5.62	5.48	5.34	5.21	5.08	4.96	4.85	4.74	4.64
140	6.12	5.93	5.75	5.59	5.43	5.28	5.14	5.01	4.88	4.77	4.65	4.55	4.44	4.35	4.25
150	5.60	5.43	5.27	5.12	4.98	4.85	4.72	4.60	4.49	4.38	4.28	4.18	4.09	4.00	3.91
160	5.14	4.99	4.84	4.71	4.58	4.46	4.35	4.24	4.14	4.04	3.95	3.86	3.78	3.69	3.62
170	4.74	4.60	4.47	4.35	4.23	4.12	4.02	3.92	3.83	3.74	3.66	3.58	3.50	3.42	3.35
180	4.37	4.25	4.13	4.02	3.92	3.82	3.73	3.64	3.55	3.47	3.39	3.32	3.25	3.18	3.12
190	4.05	3.94	3.83	3.73	3.64	3.55	3.46	3.38	3.31	3.23	3.16	3.09	3.03	2.97	2.91
200	3.76	3.66	3.57	3.47	3.39	3.31	3.23	3.15	3.08	3.02	2.95	2.89	2.83	2.78	2.72

Table 8.1 (Continued)

Average Axial Stress, ksi, at Initial Yield in Beam Columns

$$f_y = 42 \text{ ksi}$$

Values of $\dfrac{k_l c}{r}$

Slenderness Ratio, L/r	.01	.02	.03	.04	.05	.06	.07	.08	.09	.10	.11	.12	.13	.14	.15
10	41.47	40.96	40.46	39.97	39.50	39.03	38.58	38.13	37.70	37.28	36.86	36.46	36.06	35.68	35.30
20	40.91	39.88	38.91	37.98	37.10	36.26	35.46	34.70	33.97	33.27	32.60	31.95	31.34	30.74	30.17
30	40.27	38.69	37.24	35.91	34.68	33.54	32.48	31.49	30.56	29.69	28.87	28.10	27.37	26.68	26.02
40	39.45	37.27	35.35	33.66	32.15	30.79	29.55	28.42	27.39	26.43	25.54	24.72	23.95	23.24	22.56
50	38.36	35.51	33.17	31.20	29.49	28.00	26.68	25.50	24.43	23.46	22.57	21.75	21.00	20.30	19.65
60	36.80	33.30	30.65	28.52	26.74	25.23	23.90	22.74	21.70	20.77	19.92	19.15	18.44	17.79	17.19
70	34.50	30.59	27.85	25.72	23.99	22.53	21.28	20.19	19.22	18.36	17.58	16.88	16.23	15.64	15.09
80	31.33	27.49	24.89	22.92	21.33	20.01	18.87	17.89	17.02	16.24	15.54	14.91	14.33	13.80	13.32
90	27.57	24.26	21.99	20.27	18.87	17.71	16.71	15.84	15.07	14.39	13.77	13.21	12.70	12.24	11.80
100	23.82	21.19	19.31	17.85	16.66	15.66	14.80	14.04	13.38	12.78	12.24	11.75	11.30	10.89	10.51
110	20.48	18.45	16.93	15.72	14.72	13.87	13.13	12.48	11.91	11.39	10.92	10.49	10.10	9.74	9.41
120	17.66	16.09	14.87	13.88	13.04	12.32	11.69	11.14	10.64	10.19	9.78	9.41	9.07	8.75	8.46
130	15.32	14.09	13.11	12.29	11.59	10.98	10.45	9.97	9.54	9.15	8.80	8.47	8.17	7.90	7.64
140	13.38	12.41	11.61	10.93	10.34	9.83	9.37	8.96	8.59	8.25	7.94	7.66	7.40	7.16	6.93
150	11.77	10.99	10.33	9.77	9.27	8.83	8.44	8.09	7.77	7.47	7.20	6.95	6.72	6.51	6.31
160	10.42	9.79	9.24	8.77	8.35	7.97	7.64	7.33	7.05	6.79	6.56	6.34	6.13	5.94	5.77
170	9.29	8.77	8.31	7.91	7.55	7.23	6.93	6.67	6.42	6.20	5.99	5.80	5.61	5.45	5.29
180	8.33	7.89	7.51	7.16	6.85	6.57	6.32	6.09	5.87	5.67	5.49	5.32	5.16	5.01	4.87
190	7.51	7.14	6.81	6.51	6.25	6.00	5.78	5.58	5.39	5.21	5.05	4.90	4.75	4.62	4.49
200	6.80	6.49	6.20	5.95	5.72	5.50	5.31	5.13	4.96	4.80	4.66	4.52	4.39	4.27	4.16

	.16	.17	.18	.19	.20	.21	.22	.23	.24	.25	.26	.27	.28	.29	.30
10	34.93	34.56	34.21	33.86	33.52	33.18	32.86	32.54	32.22	31.91	31.61	31.31	31.02	30.73	30.45
20	29.62	29.10	28.59	28.09	27.62	27.16	26.72	26.29	25.88	25.47	25.09	24.71	24.34	23.99	23.64
30	25.40	24.81	24.25	23.71	23.20	22.71	22.24	21.79	21.36	20.94	20.55	20.16	19.80	19.44	19.10
40	21.93	21.34	20.78	20.24	19.74	19.26	18.81	18.38	17.97	17.57	17.20	16.84	16.50	16.17	15.85
50	19.05	18.48	17.95	17.45	16.98	16.53	16.11	15.71	15.34	14.98	14.63	14.31	14.00	13.70	13.41
60	16.63	16.10	15.62	15.16	14.73	14.33	13.95	13.59	13.25	12.93	12.62	12.33	12.05	11.78	11.53
70	14.59	14.12	13.68	13.27	12.89	12.53	12.19	11.86	11.56	11.27	11.00	10.74	10.50	10.26	10.04
80	12.87	12.45	12.06	11.69	11.35	11.03	10.73	10.45	10.18	9.92	9.68	9.45	9.23	9.02	8.83
90	11.41	11.04	10.69	10.37	10.07	9.78	9.52	9.27	9.03	8.80	8.59	8.38	8.19	8.01	7.83
100	10.16	9.84	9.53	9.25	8.98	8.73	8.50	8.27	8.06	7.86	7.67	7.49	7.32	7.16	7.00
110	9.10	8.81	8.55	8.30	8.06	7.84	7.63	7.43	7.24	7.07	6.90	6.74	6.59	6.44	6.30
120	8.19	7.94	7.70	7.48	7.27	7.07	6.89	6.71	6.55	6.39	6.24	6.09	5.96	5.83	5.70
130	7.40	7.18	6.97	6.77	6.59	6.41	6.25	6.09	5.94	5.80	5.67	5.54	5.42	5.30	5.19
140	6.72	6.52	6.33	6.16	5.99	5.84	5.69	5.55	5.42	5.29	5.17	5.06	4.95	4.85	4.75
150	6.12	5.95	5.78	5.63	5.48	5.34	5.21	5.08	4.96	4.85	4.74	4.64	4.54	4.45	4.36
160	5.60	5.44	5.30	5.16	5.03	4.90	4.78	4.67	4.56	4.46	4.36	4.27	4.18	4.10	4.02
170	5.14	5.00	4.87	4.74	4.63	4.51	4.41	4.31	4.21	4.12	4.03	3.95	3.87	3.79	3.71
180	4.73	4.61	4.49	4.38	4.27	4.17	4.07	3.98	3.90	3.81	3.73	3.66	3.58	3.51	3.45
190	4.37	4.26	4.15	4.05	3.96	3.87	3.78	3.70	3.62	3.54	3.47	3.40	3.33	3.27	3.21
200	4.05	3.95	3.85	3.76	3.68	3.59	3.51	3.44	3.37	3.30	3.23	3.17	3.11	3.05	2.99

Table 8.1 (Continued)

Average Axial Stress, ksi, at Initial Yield in Beam Columns

$$f_y = 46 \text{ ksi}$$

Values of $\dfrac{k_1 c}{r}$

Slenderness Ratio, L/r	.01	.02	.03	.04	.05	.06	.07	.08	.09	.10	.11	.12	.13	.14	.15
10	45.42	44.86	44.31	43.78	43.25	42.74	42.25	41.76	41.29	40.82	40.37	39.92	39.49	39.07	38.65
20	44.80	43.67	42.60	41.58	40.61	39.69	38.81	37.97	37.17	36.40	35.66	34.96	34.28	33.63	33.01
30	44.07	42.32	40.73	39.26	37.90	36.65	35.48	34.40	33.38	32.42	31.52	30.68	29.88	29.12	28.41
40	43.14	40.70	38.58	36.71	35.04	33.55	32.19	30.95	29.82	28.78	27.81	26.91	26.08	25.30	24.56
50	41.84	38.64	36.05	33.87	32.01	30.38	28.94	27.65	26.49	25.44	24.47	23.59	22.77	22.02	21.32
60	39.91	36.00	33.09	30.77	28.85	27.21	25.78	24.53	23.41	22.41	21.50	20.67	19.91	19.21	18.57
70	37.01	32.75	29.80	27.53	25.69	24.14	22.82	21.66	20.63	19.71	18.89	18.14	17.45	16.82	16.24
80	33.06	29.08	26.38	24.33	22.67	21.29	20.11	19.07	18.16	17.35	16.62	15.95	15.34	14.79	14.27
90	28.63	25.37	23.09	21.34	19.92	18.72	17.69	16.80	16.00	15.29	14.65	14.07	13.54	13.05	12.60
100	24.46	21.95	20.12	18.67	17.48	16.46	15.59	14.82	14.14	13.52	12.97	12.47	12.00	11.58	11.19
110	20.88	18.98	17.52	16.34	15.36	14.51	13.77	13.12	12.53	12.00	11.53	11.09	10.69	10.32	9.98
120	17.92	16.47	15.32	14.36	13.54	12.83	12.21	11.65	11.15	10.70	10.29	9.91	9.56	9.24	8.94
130	15.50	14.37	13.45	12.67	11.99	11.40	10.87	10.40	9.97	9.58	9.23	8.90	8.60	8.32	8.06
140	13.51	12.62	11.87	11.23	10.67	10.17	9.72	9.32	8.95	8.62	8.31	8.02	7.76	7.52	7.29
150	11.87	11.16	10.54	10.01	9.54	9.11	8.73	8.39	8.07	7.78	7.51	7.27	7.04	6.82	6.62
160	10.50	9.92	9.41	8.97	8.57	8.21	7.88	7.58	7.31	7.06	6.82	6.61	6.40	6.21	6.04
170	9.35	8.87	8.45	8.07	7.73	7.42	7.14	6.88	6.65	6.42	6.22	6.03	5.85	5.68	5.53
180	8.38	7.98	7.62	7.30	7.01	6.74	6.50	6.27	6.06	5.87	5.69	5.52	5.36	5.22	5.08
190	7.55	7.21	6.91	6.63	6.38	6.15	5.93	5.74	5.56	5.38	5.23	5.08	4.94	4.80	4.68
200	6.83	6.55	6.29	6.05	5.83	5.63	5.44	5.27	5.11	4.95	4.81	4.68	4.55	4.44	4.32

	.16	.17	.18	.19	.20	.21	.22	.23	.24	.25	.26	.27	.28	.29	.30
10	38.24	37.85	37.46	37.08	36.70	36.34	35.98	35.63	35.28	34.94	34.61	34.28	33.97	33.65	33.34
20	32.41	31.83	31.27	30.73	30.21	29.71	29.22	28.75	28.30	27.86	27.44	27.02	26.62	26.24	25.86
30	27.73	27.08	26.47	25.88	25.32	24.79	24.27	23.78	23.31	22.86	22.43	22.01	21.61	21.22	20.85
40	23.88	23.23	22.62	22.04	21.49	20.97	20.48	20.01	19.56	19.14	18.73	18.34	17.96	17.61	17.26
50	20.66	20.05	19.47	18.93	18.43	17.95	17.49	17.06	16.65	16.26	15.89	15.54	15.20	14.88	14.57
60	17.97	17.41	16.89	16.40	15.94	15.50	15.09	14.71	14.34	14.00	13.67	13.35	13.05	12.77	12.50
70	15.70	15.20	14.74	14.30	13.89	13.51	13.14	12.80	12.48	12.17	11.88	11.60	11.34	11.09	10.85
80	13.80	13.36	12.94	12.56	12.20	11.86	11.54	11.24	10.95	10.68	10.42	10.18	9.95	9.73	9.52
90	12.19	11.80	11.44	11.10	10.78	10.48	10.20	9.94	9.69	9.45	9.22	9.01	8.80	8.61	8.42
100	10.82	10.48	10.17	9.87	9.59	9.33	9.08	8.85	8.63	8.42	8.22	8.03	7.85	7.68	7.51
110	9.66	9.36	9.09	8.83	8.58	8.35	8.13	7.93	7.73	7.55	7.37	7.21	7.05	6.89	6.75
120	8.67	8.41	8.16	7.94	7.72	7.52	7.32	7.14	6.97	6.81	6.65	6.50	6.36	6.23	6.10
130	7.81	7.58	7.37	7.17	6.98	6.80	6.63	6.47	6.32	6.17	6.03	5.90	5.77	5.65	5.54
140	7.07	6.87	6.68	6.51	6.34	6.18	6.03	5.88	5.75	5.62	5.49	5.38	5.26	5.16	5.05
150	6.43	6.25	6.09	5.93	5.78	5.64	5.50	5.38	5.25	5.14	5.03	4.92	4.82	4.72	4.63
160	5.87	5.71	5.56	5.42	5.29	5.16	5.04	4.93	4.82	4.72	4.62	4.52	4.43	4.34	4.26
170	5.38	5.24	5.11	4.98	4.86	4.75	4.64	4.54	4.44	4.35	4.26	4.17	4.09	4.01	3.93
180	4.94	4.82	4.70	4.59	4.48	4.38	4.28	4.19	4.10	4.02	3.94	3.86	3.78	3.71	3.64
190	4.56	4.45	4.34	4.24	4.14	4.05	3.97	3.88	3.80	3.73	3.65	3.58	3.51	3.45	3.39
200	4.22	4.12	4.02	3.93	3.84	3.76	3.68	3.61	3.53	3.46	3.40	3.33	3.27	3.21	3.15

Table 8.1 (Continued)

Average Axial Stress, ksi, at Initial Yield in Beam Columns

$$f_y = 50 \text{ ksi}$$

Values of $\dfrac{k_{lc}}{r}$

Slenderness Ratio, L/r	.01	.02	.03	.04	.05	.06	.07	.08	.09	.10	.11	.12	.13	.14	.15
10	49.37	48.76	48.16	47.58	47.01	46.46	45.92	45.39	44.87	44.36	43.87	43.39	42.92	42.46	42.00
20	48.69	47.45	46.28	45.17	44.11	43.11	42.15	41.23	40.36	39.52	38.72	37.96	37.22	36.51	35.83
30	47.88	45.95	44.20	42.59	41.11	39.74	38.47	37.29	36.18	35.14	34.16	33.24	32.38	31.56	30.78
40	46.81	44.11	41.77	39.72	37.90	36.27	34.80	33.45	32.22	31.09	30.05	29.07	28.17	27.33	26.54
50	45.27	41.71	38.86	36.49	34.46	32.70	31.14	29.75	28.50	27.37	26.33	25.38	24.51	23.70	22.95
60	42.90	38.60	35.44	32.94	30.87	29.12	27.60	26.26	25.07	24.00	23.03	22.15	21.34	20.60	19.91
70	39.30	34.74	31.62	29.23	27.29	25.67	24.27	23.05	21.97	21.01	20.14	19.35	18.62	17.96	17.35
80	34.53	30.48	27.73	25.62	23.91	22.48	21.26	20.19	19.24	18.39	17.63	16.94	16.30	15.72	15.18
90	29.49	26.32	24.06	22.30	20.87	19.65	18.60	17.69	16.87	16.14	15.48	14.88	14.33	13.83	13.36
100	24.97	22.59	20.81	19.39	18.20	17.19	16.31	15.53	14.84	14.21	13.65	13.13	12.66	12.22	11.82
110	21.20	19.43	18.03	16.89	15.92	15.08	14.34	13.69	13.10	12.57	12.09	11.64	11.24	10.86	10.51
120	18.14	16.79	15.69	14.77	13.98	13.28	12.67	12.12	11.62	11.17	10.75	10.37	10.02	9.70	9.39
130	15.65	14.61	13.74	12.99	12.34	11.76	11.24	10.78	10.36	9.97	9.61	9.29	8.98	8.70	8.44
140	13.62	12.80	12.10	11.49	10.95	10.46	10.03	9.63	9.27	8.94	8.64	8.35	8.09	7.84	7.62
150	11.95	11.29	10.72	10.22	9.76	9.36	8.99	8.65	8.34	8.06	7.79	7.55	7.32	7.10	6.90
160	10.57	10.03	9.56	9.14	8.75	8.41	8.10	7.81	7.54	7.29	7.06	6.85	6.65	6.46	6.28
170	9.40	8.96	8.57	8.21	7.89	7.59	7.32	7.07	6.84	6.63	6.43	6.24	6.06	5.90	5.74
180	8.42	8.05	7.72	7.42	7.14	6.89	6.65	6.44	6.23	6.05	5.87	5.71	5.55	5.40	5.27
190	7.58	7.27	6.99	6.73	6.49	6.27	6.07	5.88	5.70	5.54	5.38	5.24	5.10	4.97	4.85
200	6.86	6.60	6.35	6.13	5.93	5.73	5.56	5.39	5.23	5.09	4.95	4.82	4.70	4.58	4.47

	.16	.17	.18	.19	.20	.21	.22	.23	.24	.25	.26	.27	.28	.29	.30
10	41.56	41.13	40.71	40.29	39.88	39.49	39.10	38.71	38.34	37.97	37.61	37.26	36.91	36.57	36.23
20	35.18	34.55	33.94	33.36	32.79	32.25	31.72	31.21	30.72	30.24	29.78	29.33	28.90	28.48	28.07
30	30.04	29.34	28.67	28.04	27.43	26.85	26.30	25.76	25.25	24.77	24.30	23.85	23.41	22.99	22.59
40	25.79	25.09	24.43	23.81	23.22	22.66	22.13	21.62	21.14	20.68	20.24	19.82	19.42	19.03	18.66
50	22.24	21.59	20.97	20.39	19.85	19.33	18.84	18.38	17.94	17.53	17.13	16.75	16.39	16.05	15.71
60	19.27	18.67	18.12	17.60	17.11	16.65	16.21	15.80	15.41	15.04	14.69	14.35	14.03	13.73	13.44
70	16.78	16.25	15.76	15.30	14.86	14.46	14.07	13.71	13.37	13.04	12.73	12.44	12.16	11.89	11.64
80	14.69	14.22	13.79	13.39	13.01	12.65	12.32	12.00	11.70	11.41	11.14	10.89	10.64	10.41	10.18
90	12.93	12.52	12.15	11.80	11.47	11.15	10.86	10.58	10.32	10.07	9.83	9.61	9.39	9.19	8.99
100	11.44	11.09	10.77	10.46	10.17	9.90	9.64	9.40	9.17	8.95	8.74	8.54	8.36	8.18	8.00
110	10.18	9.88	9.59	9.33	9.07	8.84	8.61	8.40	8.20	8.01	7.82	7.65	7.48	7.32	7.17
120	9.11	8.85	8.60	8.36	8.14	7.93	7.74	7.55	7.37	7.20	7.04	6.89	6.74	6.60	6.47
130	8.19	7.96	7.74	7.54	7.34	7.16	6.99	6.82	6.67	6.52	6.37	6.24	6.11	5.98	5.86
140	7.40	7.20	7.01	6.83	6.66	6.49	6.34	6.19	6.05	5.92	5.80	5.67	5.56	5.45	5.34
150	6.71	6.54	6.37	6.21	6.06	5.91	5.78	5.65	5.52	5.41	5.29	5.18	5.08	4.98	4.89
160	6.12	5.96	5.81	5.67	5.54	5.41	5.29	5.17	5.06	4.95	4.85	4.76	4.66	4.57	4.49
170	5.59	5.45	5.32	5.20	5.08	4.96	4.86	4.75	4.65	4.56	4.47	4.38	4.30	4.22	4.14
180	5.13	5.01	4.89	4.78	4.67	4.57	4.47	4.38	4.29	4.21	4.13	4.05	3.97	3.90	3.83
190	4.73	4.62	4.51	4.41	4.32	4.22	4.14	4.05	3.97	3.90	3.82	3.75	3.68	3.62	3.55
200	4.37	4.27	4.17	4.08	4.00	3.92	3.84	3.76	3.69	3.62	3.55	3.49	3.42	3.36	3.31

Table 8.1 (Continued)

Average Axial Stress, ksi, at Initial Yield in Beam Columns

$$f_y = 60 \text{ ksi}$$

Values of $\dfrac{k_1 c}{r}$

Slenderness Ratio, L/r	.01	.02	.03	.04	.05	.06	.07	.08	.09	.10	.11	.12	.13	.14	.15
10	59.24	58.51	57.79	57.09	56.40	55.73	55.08	54.45	53.83	53.22	52.62	52.04	51.48	50.92	50.38
20	58.41	56.90	55.48	54.13	52.85	51.64	50.48	49.37	48.32	47.31	46.35	45.42	44.54	43.69	42.87
30	57.36	54.99	52.84	50.87	49.07	47.41	45.87	44.44	43.11	41.86	40.69	39.58	38.54	37.56	36.63
40	55.90	52.51	49.62	47.11	44.91	42.94	41.16	39.56	38.09	36.74	35.50	34.35	33.28	32.28	31.35
50	53.61	49.12	45.62	42.76	40.34	38.25	36.42	34.79	33.33	32.01	30.81	29.70	28.68	27.74	26.87
60	49.82	44.56	40.84	37.94	35.57	33.56	31.83	30.30	28.95	27.74	26.64	25.64	24.72	23.87	23.09
70	44.03	39.03	35.62	33.01	30.89	29.11	27.58	26.24	25.05	23.98	23.02	22.15	21.35	20.61	19.93
80	37.24	33.32	30.54	28.38	26.61	25.11	23.81	22.68	21.67	20.76	19.94	19.19	18.50	17.87	17.28
90	30.99	28.15	26.02	24.30	22.87	21.64	20.58	19.63	18.79	18.02	17.33	16.70	16.12	15.58	15.08
100	25.85	23.81	22.19	20.85	19.70	18.71	17.84	17.06	16.36	15.72	15.14	14.61	14.12	13.66	13.24
110	21.76	20.26	19.02	17.97	17.06	16.26	15.55	14.90	14.32	13.79	13.30	12.85	12.44	12.05	11.69
120	18.51	17.38	16.43	15.60	14.86	14.21	13.63	13.09	12.61	12.16	11.75	11.37	11.02	10.69	10.38
130	15.92	15.05	14.29	13.63	13.03	12.50	12.02	11.57	11.17	10.79	10.44	10.12	9.82	9.54	9.27
140	13.82	13.13	12.53	11.99	11.50	11.06	10.66	10.29	9.95	9.63	9.33	9.06	8.80	8.56	8.33
150	12.10	11.55	11.06	10.62	10.22	9.85	9.51	9.20	8.91	8.63	8.38	8.14	7.92	7.71	7.51
160	10.68	10.24	9.83	9.47	9.13	8.82	8.53	8.26	8.02	7.78	7.56	7.36	7.17	6.98	6.81
170	9.50	9.13	8.79	8.48	8.20	7.94	7.69	7.46	7.25	7.05	6.86	6.68	6.51	6.35	6.20
180	8.50	8.19	7.91	7.64	7.40	7.18	6.97	6.77	6.58	6.41	6.24	6.09	5.94	5.80	5.67
190	7.65	7.39	7.15	6.92	6.71	6.52	6.34	6.17	6.00	5.85	5.71	5.57	5.44	5.32	5.20
200	6.92	6.69	6.49	6.30	6.12	5.95	5.79	5.64	5.50	5.36	5.24	5.11	5.00	4.89	4.79

	.16	.17	.18	.19	.20	.21	.22	.23	.24	.25	.26	.27	.28	.29	.30
10	49.85	49.33	48.82	48.32	47.83	47.35	46.89	46.43	45.98	45.53	45.10	44.68	44.26	43.85	43.45
20	42.08	41.33	40.60	39.90	39.22	38.57	37.93	37.32	36.73	36.16	35.61	35.07	34.55	34.05	33.56
30	35.75	34.92	34.12	33.36	32.64	31.95	31.29	30.66	30.05	29.47	28.91	28.38	27.86	27.36	26.88
40	30.47	29.65	28.87	28.14	27.44	26.78	26.16	25.56	25.00	24.45	23.94	23.44	22.97	22.52	22.08
50	26.05	25.29	24.58	23.91	23.27	22.68	22.11	21.58	21.07	20.59	20.13	19.69	19.27	18.87	18.48
60	22.36	21.69	21.05	20.46	19.90	19.38	18.88	18.41	17.96	17.54	17.14	16.76	16.39	16.04	15.71
70	19.29	18.70	18.15	17.64	17.15	16.70	16.27	15.86	15.47	15.11	14.76	14.43	14.11	13.81	13.52
80	16.74	16.23	15.76	15.32	14.90	14.51	14.13	13.78	13.45	13.13	12.83	12.55	12.27	12.01	11.76
90	14.62	14.18	13.78	13.40	13.04	12.70	12.38	12.08	11.79	11.52	11.26	11.01	10.77	10.55	10.33
100	12.84	12.47	12.12	11.80	11.49	11.20	10.92	10.66	10.41	10.17	9.95	9.73	9.53	9.33	9.15
110	11.35	11.03	10.73	10.45	10.19	9.94	9.70	9.47	9.26	9.05	8.86	8.67	8.49	8.32	8.16
120	10.09	9.82	9.56	9.32	9.09	8.87	8.67	8.47	8.28	8.10	7.93	7.77	7.61	7.46	7.32
130	9.02	8.79	8.57	8.36	8.16	7.97	7.79	7.62	7.45	7.30	7.15	7.00	6.87	6.73	6.61
140	8.11	7.91	7.71	7.53	7.36	7.19	7.03	6.88	6.74	6.60	6.47	6.34	6.22	6.11	5.99
150	7.33	7.15	6.98	6.82	6.67	6.52	6.38	6.25	6.12	6.00	5.89	5.77	5.67	5.56	5.46
160	6.65	6.49	6.34	6.20	6.07	5.94	5.82	5.70	5.59	5.48	5.38	5.28	5.18	5.09	5.00
170	6.06	5.92	5.79	5.67	5.55	5.43	5.33	5.22	5.12	5.03	4.93	4.84	4.76	4.68	4.60
180	5.54	5.42	5.31	5.20	5.09	4.99	4.89	4.80	4.71	4.62	4.54	4.46	4.38	4.31	4.24
190	5.09	4.98	4.88	4.78	4.69	4.60	4.51	4.43	4.35	4.27	4.19	4.12	4.05	3.99	3.92
200	4.69	4.59	4.50	4.41	4.33	4.25	4.17	4.09	4.02	3.95	3.89	3.82	3.76	3.70	3.64

Table 8.1 (Continued)

Average Axial Stress, ksi, at Initial Yield in Beam Columns

$$f_y = 70 \text{ ksi}$$

Values of $\dfrac{k_1 c}{r}$

Slenderness Ratio, L/r	.01	.02	.03	.04	.05	.06	.07	.08	.09	.10	.11	.12	.13	.14	.15
10	69.11	68.25	67.41	66.59	65.79	65.01	64.25	63.50	62.78	62.07	61.37	60.69	60.03	59.38	58.75
20	68.11	66.33	64.66	63.07	61.56	60.13	58.77	57.47	56.24	55.06	53.93	52.85	51.81	50.82	49.86
30	66.81	63.96	61.39	59.06	56.93	54.97	53.16	51.49	49.92	48.47	47.10	45.82	44.61	43.47	42.39
40	64.86	60.72	57.26	54.28	51.68	49.38	47.32	45.45	43.76	42.20	40.77	39.45	38.22	37.07	36.00
50	61.55	56.07	51.94	48.62	45.84	43.46	41.37	39.52	37.87	36.38	35.02	33.77	32.63	31.57	30.58
60	55.74	49.73	45.58	42.37	39.76	37.55	35.65	33.98	32.49	31.15	29.95	28.84	27.83	26.90	26.04
70	47.43	42.39	38.89	36.17	33.95	32.08	30.46	29.03	27.77	26.63	25.60	24.66	23.80	23.00	22.27
80	38.97	35.38	32.71	30.58	28.80	27.29	25.96	24.79	23.75	22.80	21.95	21.16	20.44	19.77	19.15
90	31.92	29.43	27.47	25.84	24.46	23.25	22.19	21.24	20.39	19.62	18.91	18.26	17.66	17.10	16.58
100	26.40	24.64	23.19	21.95	20.87	19.92	19.07	18.30	17.61	16.98	16.39	15.85	15.36	14.89	14.46
110	22.11	20.83	19.73	18.78	17.93	17.18	16.50	15.88	15.31	14.79	14.31	13.86	13.44	13.05	12.69
120	18.76	17.79	16.95	16.20	15.53	14.93	14.37	13.87	13.40	12.97	12.57	12.20	11.85	11.52	11.21
130	16.09	15.35	14.69	14.10	13.56	13.06	12.61	12.20	11.81	11.45	11.12	10.80	10.51	10.23	9.97
140	13.95	13.37	12.84	12.36	11.92	11.52	11.14	10.80	10.47	10.17	9.89	9.62	9.37	9.14	8.91
150	12.20	11.74	11.31	10.92	10.55	10.22	9.91	9.62	9.35	9.09	8.85	8.62	8.41	8.21	8.01
160	10.76	10.38	10.03	9.71	9.40	9.12	8.86	8.62	8.38	8.17	7.96	7.77	7.58	7.41	7.24
170	9.56	9.25	8.95	8.68	8.43	8.19	7.97	7.76	7.56	7.37	7.20	7.03	6.87	6.72	6.57
180	8.55	8.29	8.04	7.81	7.60	7.39	7.20	7.02	6.85	6.69	6.54	6.39	6.25	6.12	5.99
190	7.69	7.47	7.26	7.06	6.88	6.70	6.54	6.38	6.23	6.09	5.96	5.83	5.71	5.59	5.48
200	6.95	6.76	6.58	6.42	6.26	6.11	5.96	5.83	5.70	5.57	5.46	5.34	5.24	5.13	5.03

	.16	.17	.18	.19	.20	.21	.22	.23	.24	.25	.26	.27	.28	.29	.30
10	58.13	57.52	56.92	56.34	55.77	55.21	54.67	54.13	53.60	53.09	52.58	52.09	51.60	51.12	50.65
20	48.94	48.06	47.21	46.39	45.60	44.84	44.10	43.39	42.71	42.04	41.39	40.77	40.17	39.58	39.01
30	41.37	40.40	39.47	38.60	37.76	36.96	36.20	35.46	34.76	34.09	33.45	32.83	32.23	31.66	31.11
40	35.00	34.06	33.17	32.33	31.53	30.78	30.06	29.38	28.73	28.12	27.53	26.96	26.42	25.90	25.41
50	29.67	28.81	28.01	27.25	26.54	25.87	25.23	24.63	24.05	23.51	22.99	22.50	22.02	21.57	21.14
60	25.24	24.49	23.79	23.13	22.51	21.93	21.38	20.86	20.37	19.90	19.45	19.02	18.62	18.23	17.86
70	21.58	20.94	20.35	19.79	19.26	18.76	18.29	17.85	17.42	17.02	16.64	16.28	15.93	15.60	15.28
80	18.57	18.04	17.53	17.06	16.61	16.19	15.79	15.41	15.05	14.71	14.38	14.07	13.78	13.49	13.22
90	16.10	15.64	15.22	14.82	14.44	14.08	13.74	13.42	13.11	12.82	12.54	12.28	12.03	11.78	11.55
100	14.05	13.67	13.31	12.97	12.65	12.34	12.05	11.78	11.52	11.27	11.03	10.80	10.59	10.38	10.18
110	12.35	12.02	11.72	11.43	11.16	10.90	10.65	10.42	10.19	9.98	9.77	9.58	9.39	9.21	9.04
120	10.92	10.65	10.39	10.14	9.91	9.69	9.47	9.27	9.08	8.89	8.72	8.55	8.38	8.23	8.08
130	9.72	9.49	9.26	9.05	8.85	8.66	8.48	8.30	8.13	7.97	7.82	7.67	7.53	7.39	7.26
140	8.70	8.50	8.31	8.13	7.95	7.79	7.63	7.48	7.33	7.19	7.05	6.93	6.80	6.68	6.57
150	7.83	7.66	7.49	7.33	7.18	7.04	6.90	6.76	6.64	6.51	6.40	6.28	6.17	6.07	5.97
160	7.08	6.93	6.79	6.65	6.52	6.39	6.27	6.15	6.04	5.93	5.83	5.73	5.63	5.54	5.44
170	6.43	6.30	6.17	6.05	5.94	5.83	5.72	5.62	5.52	5.42	5.33	5.24	5.15	5.07	4.99
180	5.87	5.75	5.64	5.53	5.43	5.33	5.24	5.15	5.06	4.97	4.89	4.81	4.74	4.66	4.59
190	5.37	5.27	5.17	5.08	4.99	4.90	4.82	4.73	4.66	4.58	4.51	4.44	4.37	4.30	4.24
200	4.94	4.85	4.76	4.68	4.60	4.52	4.44	4.37	4.30	4.23	4.16	4.10	4.04	3.98	3.92

Table 8.1 (Continued)

Average Axial Stress, ksi, at Initial Yield in Beam Columns

$$f_y = 80 \text{ ksi}$$

Values of $\dfrac{k_{tc}}{r}$

Slenderness Ratio, L/r	.01	.02	.03	.04	.05	.06	.07	.08	.09	.10	.11	.12	.13	.14	.15
10	78.98	77.99	77.03	76.09	75.17	74.28	73.40	72.55	71.72	70.91	70.11	69.33	68.58	67.83	67.11
20	77.81	75.75	73.81	71.97	70.24	68.59	67.02	65.53	64.11	62.76	61.46	60.23	59.04	57.90	56.81
30	76.22	72.87	69.87	67.15	64.69	62.43	60.35	58.42	56.63	54.96	53.40	51.94	50.56	49.26	48.04
40	73.67	68.72	64.66	61.21	58.22	55.59	53.24	51.13	49.21	47.46	45.85	44.36	42.98	41.69	40.49
50	68.97	62.52	57.80	54.06	50.95	48.30	45.99	43.95	42.12	40.48	38.98	37.61	36.35	35.18	34.10
60	60.55	54.11	49.68	46.26	43.47	41.12	39.08	37.30	35.70	34.27	32.97	31.79	30.70	29.70	28.77
70	49.79	44.99	41.53	38.80	36.54	34.62	32.95	31.48	30.16	28.98	27.90	26.91	26.01	25.17	24.39
80	40.11	36.89	34.39	32.34	30.60	29.10	27.78	26.60	25.54	24.58	23.70	22.90	22.15	21.46	20.82
90	32.54	30.36	28.56	27.04	25.72	24.56	23.53	22.59	21.75	20.97	20.26	19.61	19.00	18.43	17.90
100	26.77	25.24	23.93	22.79	21.78	20.88	20.07	19.33	18.65	18.03	17.45	16.92	16.42	15.95	15.51
110	22.36	21.24	20.26	19.40	18.61	17.91	17.26	16.67	16.12	15.62	15.15	14.71	14.30	13.91	13.55
120	18.93	18.09	17.34	16.66	16.05	15.49	14.97	14.49	14.05	13.63	13.25	12.88	12.54	12.22	11.92
130	16.22	15.57	14.99	14.45	13.96	13.51	13.09	12.70	12.33	11.99	11.67	11.36	11.08	10.81	10.55
140	14.04	13.54	13.07	12.64	12.24	11.87	11.53	11.20	10.90	10.61	10.34	10.09	9.85	9.62	9.40
150	12.28	11.87	11.49	11.14	10.81	10.51	10.22	9.95	9.70	9.46	9.23	9.01	8.81	8.61	8.43
160	10.82	10.49	10.18	9.89	9.62	9.36	9.12	8.89	8.68	8.47	8.28	8.10	7.92	7.75	7.59
170	9.61	9.33	9.08	8.83	8.60	8.39	8.19	7.99	7.81	7.64	7.47	7.31	7.16	7.02	6.88
180	8.59	8.36	8.14	7.94	7.74	7.56	7.39	7.22	7.06	6.91	6.77	6.63	6.50	6.38	6.25
190	7.72	7.53	7.34	7.17	7.00	6.85	6.70	6.55	6.42	6.29	6.16	6.04	5.93	5.82	5.71
200	6.98	6.81	6.66	6.51	6.36	6.23	6.10	5.97	5.85	5.74	5.63	5.53	5.43	5.33	5.24

	.16	.17	.18	.19	.20	.21	.22	.23	.24	.25	.26	.27	.28	.29	.30
10	66.40	65.70	65.02	64.35	63.70	63.06	62.44	61.82	61.22	60.63	60.05	59.49	58.93	58.38	57.85
20	55.76	54.75	53.78	52.84	51.94	51.07	50.23	49.42	48.63	47.87	47.14	46.43	45.74	45.07	44.42
30	46.88	45.77	44.73	43.73	42.78	41.88	41.01	40.19	39.39	38.63	37.90	37.20	36.53	35.88	35.25
40	39.37	38.31	37.32	36.38	35.49	34.64	33.84	33.08	32.36	31.67	31.01	30.37	29.77	29.19	28.63
50	33.09	32.14	31.26	30.43	29.64	28.90	28.20	27.53	26.90	26.30	25.73	25.18	24.66	24.16	23.68
60	27.90	27.09	26.34	25.63	24.96	24.32	23.73	23.16	22.62	22.11	21.63	21.16	20.72	20.30	19.89
70	23.67	22.99	22.35	21.76	21.19	20.66	20.16	19.68	19.23	18.80	18.39	18.00	17.63	17.27	16.93
80	20.22	19.65	19.13	18.63	18.16	17.71	17.29	16.89	16.51	16.15	15.81	15.48	15.16	14.86	14.57
90	17.41	16.94	16.50	16.08	15.69	15.32	14.97	14.63	14.31	14.01	13.72	13.44	13.17	12.91	12.67
100	15.10	14.71	14.35	14.00	13.67	13.36	13.06	12.78	12.51	12.25	12.00	11.77	11.54	11.32	11.11
110	13.21	12.88	12.57	12.28	12.01	11.74	11.49	11.25	11.02	10.80	10.59	10.39	10.19	10.01	9.83
120	11.63	11.36	11.10	10.85	10.62	10.39	10.18	9.97	9.78	9.59	9.41	9.23	9.07	8.91	8.75
130	10.31	10.08	9.86	9.65	9.45	9.26	9.07	8.90	8.73	8.57	8.41	8.26	8.12	7.98	7.84
140	9.20	9.00	8.81	8.63	8.46	8.30	8.14	7.99	7.84	7.70	7.56	7.43	7.31	7.19	7.07
150	8.25	8.08	7.92	7.77	7.62	7.47	7.34	7.20	7.08	6.96	6.84	6.72	6.61	6.51	6.41
160	7.44	7.30	7.16	7.02	6.89	6.77	6.65	6.53	6.42	6.31	6.21	6.11	6.01	5.92	5.83
170	6.74	6.62	6.49	6.38	6.26	6.16	6.05	5.95	5.85	5.76	5.67	5.58	5.49	5.41	5.33
180	6.14	6.03	5.92	5.82	5.72	5.62	5.53	5.44	5.35	5.27	5.19	5.11	5.04	4.96	4.89
190	5.61	5.51	5.42	5.33	5.24	5.16	5.07	4.99	4.92	4.84	4.77	4.70	4.63	4.57	4.50
200	5.15	5.06	4.98	4.90	4.82	4.74	4.67	4.60	4.53	4.47	4.40	4.34	4.28	4.22	4.16

Table 8.1 (Continued)

Average Axial Stress, ksi, at Initial Yield in Beam Columns

$$f_y = 90 \text{ ksi}$$

Values of $\dfrac{k_1 c}{r}$

Slenderness Ratio, L/r	.01	.02	.03	.04	.05	.06	.07	.08	.09	.10	.11	.12	.13	.14	.15
10	88.85	87.74	86.65	85.59	84.55	83.54	82.56	81.59	80.66	79.74	78.84	77.97	77.11	76.28	75.46
20	87.50	85.15	82.94	80.86	78.88	77.02	75.24	73.56	71.95	70.42	68.96	67.56	66.22	64.94	63.71
30	85.58	81.70	78.24	75.14	72.33	69.77	67.41	65.24	63.22	61.34	59.59	57.95	56.41	54.95	53.58
40	82.23	76.48	71.80	67.89	64.52	61.57	58.95	56.59	54.46	52.52	50.74	49.09	47.57	46.15	44.82
50	75.75	68.40	63.17	59.06	55.67	52.79	50.29	48.07	46.10	44.32	42.70	41.21	39.85	38.59	37.42
60	64.27	57.73	53.18	49.65	46.75	44.29	42.16	40.29	38.62	37.11	35.75	34.49	33.34	32.28	31.30
70	51.43	46.99	43.66	40.98	38.74	36.81	35.12	33.63	32.28	31.07	29.96	28.94	28.00	27.13	26.32
80	40.90	38.02	35.70	33.76	32.08	30.62	29.32	28.15	27.09	26.13	25.24	24.43	23.67	22.96	22.31
90	32.98	31.05	29.41	28.00	26.75	25.64	24.64	23.73	22.90	22.14	21.43	20.78	20.17	19.60	19.07
100	27.04	25.69	24.51	23.46	22.52	21.67	20.89	20.18	19.53	18.92	18.36	17.83	17.34	16.87	16.44
110	22.54	21.55	20.67	19.88	19.16	18.50	17.89	17.32	16.80	16.31	15.86	15.43	15.03	14.65	14.29
120	19.05	18.31	17.64	17.03	16.46	15.94	15.45	15.00	14.58	14.19	13.81	13.46	13.13	12.82	12.52
130	16.31	15.74	15.21	14.73	14.28	13.86	13.47	13.10	12.76	12.43	12.13	11.84	11.56	11.30	11.05
140	14.11	13.66	13.25	12.86	12.49	12.15	11.83	11.53	11.25	10.98	10.72	10.48	10.25	10.03	9.82
150	12.33	11.97	11.63	11.31	11.02	10.74	10.47	10.22	9.98	9.76	9.54	9.34	9.14	8.96	8.78
160	10.87	10.57	10.29	10.03	9.78	9.55	9.33	9.12	8.92	8.73	8.54	8.37	8.20	8.05	7.89
170	9.64	9.40	9.17	8.95	8.74	8.55	8.36	8.18	8.01	7.85	7.69	7.54	7.40	7.26	7.13
180	8.62	8.41	8.22	8.03	7.86	7.69	7.53	7.38	7.23	7.09	6.96	6.83	6.71	6.59	6.48
190	7.75	7.57	7.41	7.25	7.10	6.96	6.82	6.69	6.56	6.44	6.33	6.22	6.11	6.00	5.90
200	7.00	6.85	6.71	6.58	6.45	6.32	6.21	6.09	5.98	5.88	5.78	5.68	5.58	5.49	5.40

	.16	.17	.18	.19	.20	.21	.22	.23	.24	.25	.26	.27	.28	.29	.30
10	74.66	73.87	73.11	72.36	71.62	70.90	70.20	69.51	68.83	68.16	67.51	66.87	66.25	65.63	65.03
20	62.53	61.39	60.30	59.25	58.23	57.25	56.31	55.40	54.52	53.66	52.84	52.04	51.27	50.52	49.79
30	52.28	51.05	49.89	48.78	47.72	46.71	45.74	44.82	43.94	43.09	42.28	41.50	40.75	40.03	39.33
40	43.58	42.42	41.32	40.29	39.31	38.38	37.50	36.66	35.87	35.10	34.38	33.68	33.02	32.38	31.77
50	36.32	35.30	34.34	33.44	32.59	31.79	31.03	30.31	29.62	28.97	28.35	27.75	27.19	26.65	26.13
60	30.38	29.52	28.71	27.95	27.24	26.57	25.93	25.32	24.75	24.20	23.68	23.18	22.71	22.25	21.82
70	25.57	24.86	24.19	23.57	22.98	22.42	21.89	21.39	20.91	20.46	20.02	19.61	19.21	18.83	18.47
80	21.69	21.11	20.57	20.05	19.57	19.11	18.67	18.25	17.86	17.48	17.12	16.77	16.44	16.13	15.82
90	18.56	18.09	17.64	17.22	16.82	16.44	16.08	15.73	15.40	15.08	14.78	14.49	14.22	13.95	13.70
100	16.03	15.64	15.27	14.92	14.59	14.27	13.97	13.68	13.40	13.14	12.88	12.64	12.41	12.18	11.97
110	13.95	13.63	13.32	13.03	12.75	12.49	12.23	11.99	11.76	11.54	11.32	11.12	10.92	10.73	10.54
120	12.24	11.97	11.71	11.47	11.24	11.01	10.80	10.59	10.40	10.21	10.02	9.85	9.68	9.52	9.36
130	10.81	10.59	10.37	10.17	9.97	9.78	9.60	9.42	9.25	9.09	8.93	8.78	8.64	8.50	8.36
140	9.62	9.43	9.24	9.07	8.90	8.74	8.58	8.43	8.29	8.15	8.01	7.88	7.76	7.63	7.52
150	8.61	8.44	8.29	8.14	7.99	7.85	7.72	7.59	7.46	7.34	7.22	7.11	7.00	6.89	6.79
160	7.75	7.60	7.47	7.34	7.21	7.09	6.98	6.86	6.75	6.65	6.55	6.45	6.35	6.26	6.17
170	7.01	6.88	6.77	6.65	6.54	6.44	6.33	6.24	6.14	6.05	5.96	5.87	5.79	5.71	5.63
180	6.36	6.26	6.16	6.06	5.96	5.87	5.78	5.69	5.61	5.53	5.45	5.37	5.30	5.22	5.15
190	5.81	5.71	5.62	5.54	5.45	5.37	5.29	5.22	5.14	5.07	5.00	4.93	4.86	4.80	4.74
200	5.32	5.24	5.16	5.08	5.01	4.93	4.86	4.80	4.73	4.67	4.60	4.54	4.48	4.43	4.37

Table 8.1 (Continued)

Average Axial Stress, ksi, at Initial Yield in Beam Columns

$$f_y = 100 \text{ ksi}$$

Slenderness Ratio, L/r	Values of $\frac{k_1 c}{r}$														
	.01	.02	.03	.04	.05	.06	.07	.08	.09	.10	.11	.12	.13	.14	.15
10	98.72	97.47	96.26	95.08	93.92	92.80	91.70	90.63	89.59	88.57	87.57	86.59	85.64	84.71	83.80
20	97.18	94.53	92.05	89.71	87.50	85.40	83.42	81.54	79.74	78.04	76.41	74.85	73.36	71.93	70.56
30	94.89	90.44	86.53	83.02	79.86	76.99	74.36	71.93	69.69	67.61	65.67	63.85	62.14	60.54	59.02
40	90.67	83.97	78.67	74.29	70.55	67.29	64.41	61.83	59.50	57.38	55.44	53.64	51.98	50.44	49.00
50	81.76	73.69	68.03	63.63	60.01	56.93	54.27	51.91	49.81	47.91	46.18	44.60	43.15	41.80	40.55
60	67.07	60.69	56.15	52.57	49.62	47.11	44.92	42.99	41.26	39.70	38.28	36.98	35.78	34.67	33.63
70	52.60	48.54	45.39	42.80	40.60	38.70	37.01	35.51	34.16	32.93	31.80	30.76	29.80	28.91	28.08
80	41.47	38.89	36.75	34.91	33.32	31.90	30.63	29.48	28.44	27.48	26.60	25.78	25.02	24.31	23.64
90	33.30	31.57	30.08	28.77	27.59	26.54	25.58	24.70	23.89	23.14	22.45	21.80	21.20	20.63	20.10
100	27.25	26.04	24.96	24.00	23.12	22.32	21.58	20.90	20.27	19.68	19.13	18.62	18.14	17.68	17.25
110	22.67	21.79	21.00	20.27	19.60	18.98	18.41	17.87	17.37	16.90	16.46	16.05	15.66	15.29	14.94
120	19.15	18.49	17.88	17.32	16.80	16.31	15.86	15.43	15.03	14.65	14.30	13.96	13.64	13.33	13.04
130	16.38	15.87	15.40	14.95	14.54	14.15	13.79	13.44	13.12	12.81	12.52	12.24	11.97	11.72	11.48
140	14.17	13.77	13.39	13.03	12.70	12.38	12.09	11.80	11.54	11.28	11.04	10.81	10.59	10.38	10.18
150	12.37	12.05	11.74	11.46	11.18	10.92	10.68	10.44	10.22	10.01	9.81	9.61	9.43	9.25	9.08
160	10.90	10.63	10.38	10.14	9.92	9.70	9.50	9.30	9.12	8.94	8.77	8.60	8.44	8.29	8.15
170	9.67	9.45	9.24	9.05	8.86	8.67	8.50	8.34	8.18	8.03	7.88	7.74	7.60	7.47	7.35
180	8.64	8.46	8.28	8.11	7.95	7.80	7.65	7.51	7.38	7.25	7.12	7.00	6.88	6.77	6.66
190	7.77	7.61	7.46	7.32	7.18	7.05	6.92	6.80	6.69	6.57	6.46	6.36	6.26	6.16	6.07
200	7.02	6.88	6.76	6.63	6.52	6.40	6.29	6.19	6.09	5.99	5.89	5.80	5.71	5.63	5.55

	.16	.17	.18	.19	.20	.21	.22	.23	.24	.25	.26	.27	.28	.29	.30
10	82.91	82.04	81.19	80.35	79.53	78.73	77.95	77.18	76.43	75.69	74.96	74.25	73.56	72.87	72.20
20	69.25	67.99	66.77	65.60	64.48	63.39	62.35	61.33	60.36	59.41	58.50	57.61	56.75	55.92	55.12
30	57.59	56.23	54.95	53.72	52.56	51.45	50.39	49.37	48.40	47.47	46.58	45.72	44.89	44.10	43.34
40	47.65	46.38	45.19	44.07	43.00	42.00	41.04	40.13	39.26	38.44	37.65	36.89	36.17	35.48	34.81
50	39.38	38.29	37.27	36.31	35.40	34.54	33.72	32.95	32.22	31.52	30.85	30.22	29.61	29.02	28.47
60	32.67	31.77	30.93	30.13	29.38	28.67	28.00	27.36	26.75	26.17	25.62	25.09	24.59	24.11	23.65
70	27.30	26.57	25.88	25.24	24.62	24.04	23.49	22.97	22.47	22.00	21.54	21.11	20.70	20.30	19.92
80	23.02	22.43	21.87	21.35	20.85	20.38	19.98	19.50	19.09	18.70	18.33	17.97	17.63	17.30	16.98
90	19.59	19.12	18.67	18.24	17.83	17.45	17.08	16.73	16.39	16.07	15.76	15.46	15.18	14.90	14.64
100	16.84	16.45	16.08	15.73	15.40	15.08	14.78	14.49	14.21	13.94	13.68	13.43	13.20	12.97	12.75
110	14.60	14.28	13.98	13.69	13.42	13.15	12.90	12.65	12.42	12.20	11.98	11.77	11.57	11.38	11.19
120	12.77	12.50	12.25	12.01	11.78	11.56	11.35	11.14	10.95	10.76	10.57	10.40	10.23	10.06	9.91
130	11.25	11.03	10.82	10.62	10.42	10.23	10.05	9.88	9.71	9.55	9.40	9.25	9.10	8.96	8.83
140	9.98	9.80	9.62	9.45	9.28	9.12	8.97	8.82	8.68	8.54	8.41	8.28	8.15	8.03	7.91
150	8.91	8.76	8.60	8.46	8.32	8.18	8.05	7.92	7.80	7.68	7.56	7.45	7.34	7.24	7.14
160	8.00	7.87	7.74	7.61	7.49	7.37	7.26	7.15	7.04	6.94	6.84	6.74	6.65	6.56	6.47
170	7.23	7.11	7.00	6.89	6.78	6.68	6.58	6.49	6.39	6.30	6.21	6.13	6.05	5.97	5.89
180	6.56	6.45	6.36	6.26	6.17	6.08	5.99	5.91	5.83	5.75	5.67	5.60	5.52	5.45	5.38
190	5.97	5.89	5.80	5.72	5.63	5.56	5.48	5.41	5.33	5.26	5.20	5.13	5.07	5.00	4.94
200	5.47	5.39	5.31	5.24	5.17	5.10	5.03	4.96	4.90	4.84	4.78	4.72	4.66	4.61	4.55

Table 8.2

Summary of Simple-Support Membrane Analysis

Given: W_{oo} = midspan lateral initial deflection (before loading).*

$\quad\quad$ w_1 = longitudinal deflection.*

$\quad\quad\quad$ (movement of one edge toward the other).

$\quad\quad$ t = thickness of plate (or sheet).

$\quad\quad$ L = span length (short dimension of panel).

$\quad\quad$ q = uniform lateral loading per unit area.

1. $D = \dfrac{Et^3}{12(1-u^2)}$, where E = modulus of elasticity and u = Poisson's ratio.

2. $w_o = \left[\dfrac{5qL^4}{384D} + w_{oo} + \dfrac{2}{\pi}\sqrt{Lw_1}\right]$ = midspan deflection in absence of membrane tension.

3. α is obtained from the following equation:

$$[1 + \alpha]^2\left[\alpha + \dfrac{12L}{\pi^2 t^2}\left(w_1 + \dfrac{\pi^2 w_{oo}^2}{4L}\right)\right] = \dfrac{3w_o^2}{t^2}$$

4. $p = \sqrt{\dfrac{\pi^2 \alpha}{4}}$

5. Membrane tension per unit width, $T = \dfrac{4Dp^2}{L^2}$

6. Midspan bending moment $M_c = \dfrac{qL^2}{8}\left[\dfrac{1 - \text{sech } p}{p^2/2}\right]$

7. Axial unit stress $f_a = \dfrac{T}{t}$

8. Maximum bending unit stress $f_b = \pm\dfrac{6M_c}{t^2}$

9. Maximum combined unit stress $f_t = f_a + f_b$

10. Actual midspan deflection under load $\Delta = \left[\dfrac{w_o}{1 + \alpha}\right]$

* The initial deflection, w_{oo}, and longitudinal deflection, w_1, may be conservatively regarded as zero for stress calculations.

CHAPTER 9

Connections

9.1 Introduction

This chapter will consider bolted and riveted connections, welded connections, and bearing stresses such as those encountered at pinned connections, rollers, and rockers. Only the effects of static loads on connections are included in this chapter; the effects of repeated loads will be considered in Chapter 10.

9.2 Bolted and Riveted Connections

9.2.1 *Mechanical Properties and Installation*

The mechanical properties of bolts and rivets that are presently used for structural connections are listed in Table 9.1. Both tensile strength and proof load, as obtained from a direct-pull tension test, are specified for A325 and A490 high-strength bolts. The proof load is defined by ASTM A370 as the load that a bolt will withstand in a tension test without any permanent elongation.* The proof load and tensile load are indicated on the typical load-elongation curve for high-strength bolts shown in Figure 9.1.

In actual connections the tensile force in the bolt is induced by turning the nut, which results in elongation of the bolt. As shown in Figure 9.1, when tension is induced in the bolt by turning the nut the tensile strength and total elongation are somewhat less than in a direct-pull tension test because of the torsional stresses in the bolt caused by tightening.[1, 2] Specifications[3] generally require that all high-strength bolts be installed with a minimum tension equal to 0.70 times the specified minimum tensile load,

---

* An alternative 0.2 percent offset method is also allowed. Slightly higher proof loads are specified when the proof load is determined by the alternative method.

Table 9.2. A certain turn-of-the nut, usually a one-half turn from an initial "snug tight" position, is usually specified to assure the required tension. Greater amounts of turn are specified for long bolts or for bolts connecting two parts with slightly sloped surfaces.

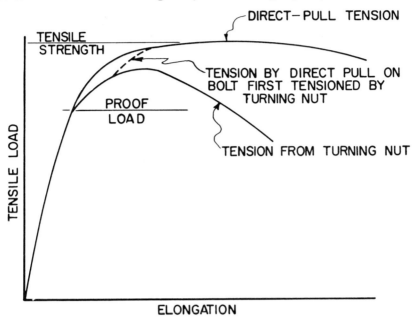

FIGURE 9.1 TYPICAL TENSILE LOAD-ELONGATION CURVE FOR HIGH-STRENGTH BOLT

The tensile strength of the A307 low-carbon steel bolt is only one-half to one-third that of the high-strength bolts. This bolt, which is sometimes referred to as an "unfinished bolt" or "common bolt," does not have a specified minimum proof load and should be used only where light loads are encountered.

As indicated in Table 9.1, the two grades of A502 structural rivets are manufactured to specified minimum hardness values. The expected minimum tensile strengths for the specified minimum hardness values are approximately 50,000 psi for Grade 1 and 68,000 psi for Grade 2. Structural rivets are usually driven while hot and, thus, develop a residual tension from cooling. However, the amount of tension developed is generally unpredictable.

In structural connections, bolts and rivets may be subjected to shear forces, tensile forces, or a combination of shear and tension.* Each of these types of loadings will be discussed below.

---

* Bending moments of structural joints generally cause shear and/or tension in the fasteners.

Connections

9.2.2 *Bolts and Rivets Subjected to Shear Forces*

Figure 9.2 illustrates several joints in which the fasteners are subjected to shear forces. The fasteners in the butt joint are in "double shear," since two shear planes intersect each fastener. The fasteners in the lap joint, as well as those in the bracket connections, are in "single shear," since they are intersected by only one shear plane. Generally, a rivet or bolt in double shear offers twice the resistance to shearing forces as a rivet or bolt in single shear.

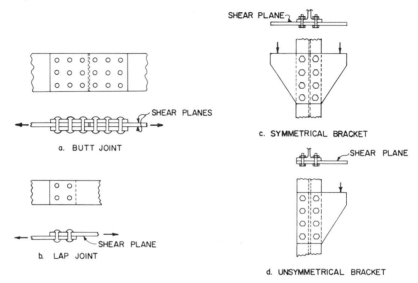

FIGURE 9.2   CONNECTIONS WITH BOLTS AND RIVETS SUBJECTED TO SHEAR FORCES

In designing the butt joint, lap joint, and symmetrical bracket connection, the total shear force is usually assumed to be equally divided among the fasteners. Actually, the end fasteners of a group are initially subjected to somewhat greater loads than the other fasteners, but, before ultimate load is reached, slight slip and deformation occurs, and the loads tend to equalize. However, in the unsymmetrical bracket, the initial loads on the fasteners vary greatly because of the different eccentricities of the fasteners with respect to the center of rotation of the bracket. This variation in load must be considered in design.

Connections—depending on the manner in which the shear force is resisted—may be classified as friction-type connections or bearing-type connections. Because a high tensile force in the fastener is required to develop a significant resisting friction force, only bolts that have a high tensile yield strength are used in friction-type connections. Thus, of the fasteners listed in Table 9.1, only the A325 and A490 bolts are used in friction-type connections. All the fasteners listed in the table may be used in bearing-type connections.

a. High-Strength Bolts in Friction-Type Connections

The forces acting in a friction-type connection are illustrated in Figure 9.3. Initially, if the bolt is adequately tightened and the surfaces meet the specified conditions, the frictional component of the clamping force developed between the connected plates is sufficient to resist the shear force. As the tensile load on the connection and shear force between the plates is increased, the resisting friction force will eventually be exceeded and the plates will slip. Before slip occurs, the bolts generally do not bear against the connected plates; hence, bearing stresses between the bolts and plates and shear stresses in the bolts do not develop. However, after slip occurs, the bearing and shear stresses do develop. Ultimate failure of the connection could result from a shear failure of the bolt, from excessive bearing stresses between the bolt shank and the hole, or from excessive yielding or a tensile failure through the net section of the connected material.* The mode of failure that occurs depends on the relative proportions or design of the joint.

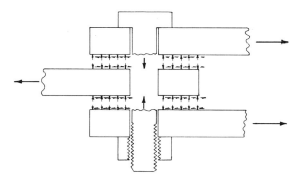

FIGURE 9.3   BOLT SUBJECTED TO SHEAR FORCES IN FRICTION-TYPE CONNECTION

Although the forces on a friction-type connection do not cause shear stresses in the bolts at design loads, such connections are usually designed for a fictitious allowable shear stress on the bolt that provides a safety factor of 1.40 to 1.55 against slip.[3] This convenient method is possible because the friction force necessary to prevent slip is proportional to the bolt clamping force, which in turn is proportional to the cross-sectional area of the bolt. Thus, the friction force can be expressed in terms of a fictitious bolt shear stress. Allowable stresses for A325 and A490 high-strength

---

* It is assumed that suitable minimum edge distances are provided to prevent premature failure of the connected plates.

bolts for friction-type connections are given for buildings in Table 9.3, and for bridges in Table 9.4. The number of bolts provided by this procedure is sufficient to prevent bolt shear failures before the yield strength of the net section of the connected material is reached, should an overload more than 1.4 times the design load be applied. Since the shank of the bolt does not bear against the sides of the hole at design loads, bearing stresses are not usually considered in the design of friction-type connections except those made in "light gage" material.[4]

b. **Bolts and Rivets in Bearing-Type Connections**

The forces acting in a bearing-type connection are illustrated in Figure 9.4. In bearing-type connections friction forces on the faying surfaces of connected plates are not depended upon for transferring the shear force. Under load, the shank of the fastener bears against the sides of the hole and causes "bearing stresses." The shear force across the joint is directly restricted by the shear strength of the fastener. Thus, the possible modes of ultimate failure are the same as those in friction-type joints.

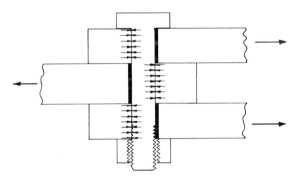

FIGURE 9.4   BOLT SUBJECTED TO SHEAR FORCES IN BEARING-TYPE CONNECTION

Both shear stresses and bearing stresses must be considered in the design of bearing-type connections. Allowable shear stresses for both rivets and bolts in bearing-type connections in buildings and bridges are included in Tables 9.3 and 9.4. The tabulated allowable stresses are for the nominal areas, that is, the unthreaded cross-sectional body area of bolts and the cross-sectional area of rivets before driving. For bolts, higher allowable shear stresses are specified when threads are excluded from the shear plane because of the greater shear area available. Since the area stressed in bearing is confined and since the stress rapidly decreases as the distance from the contact surface increases, relatively high allowable bearing stresses may be used. The allowable bearing stresses depends on the yield stress of the lowest-strength connected part and are tabulated in Table 9.5 for various steel yield points.

9.2.3 *Bolt and Rivet Subjected to Tensile Forces*

A tensile force applied to a fastener that has not been installed under an initial tension will cause a tensile stress in the fastener equal to the applied force divided by the cross-section area. However, if a tensile force is applied to a fastener that has been installed under a high initial tension, such as a properly installed high-strength bolt, the increase in the bolt tensile force is generally much smaller than the applied load. This is true because, as the tensile load is applied to a pretensioned joint, the bolt elongates and the compressed plates simultaneously expand as the contact pressure is reduced. Thus, the applied load is offset by both an increase in bolt tension and a decrease in contact pressure. The magnitude of the increase in bolt tension depends on the relative stiffness of the bolt and connected plates, but for high-strength bolts is likely to be less than 10 percent of the applied load.[5]

The tensile load applied to a fastener may sometimes be magnified by a prying action that can develop between the connected plates. As illustrated by the hanger brackets in Figure 9.5, when a tensile load is applied through a flexible flange, a pressure develops at the outer edge of the flange and tends to increase the tensile load applied to each fastener. Hence, hanger-bracket connections having two lines of fasteners in each flange are generally undesir-

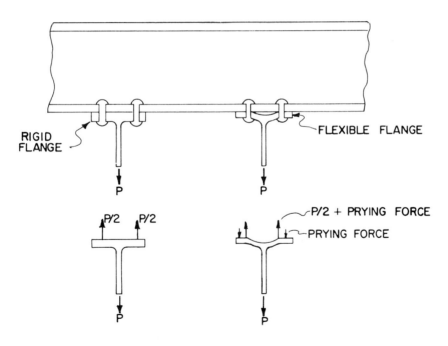

FIGURE 9.5 PRYING ACTION UNDER TENSILE LOAD

able because the inner line of fasteners tends to carry a substantially greater portion of the load than the outer line. Research to determine the magnitude of prying forces is not yet complete.

Allowable tensile stresses for bolts and rivets under pure tension in buildings and bridges are included in Tables 9.3 and 9.4. When these allowable stresses are used, the tensile stress due to the design loading should be computed on the nominal area of the fastener and should include the direct tension load and any tension caused by prying action, but should not include any initial tension. Since, for properly installed high-strength bolts the allowable stresses are less than the initial stress, such bolts would experience little actual change in tensile stress when the allowable tensile stress is reached.[3]

9.2.4 *Bolts and Rivets Under Combined Shear and Tensile Force*

Bolts and rivets, such as those in beam-to-column connections designed to transmit both shear force and bending moment, are often simultaneously subjected to shear and tensile forces. The effect of the combined forces differs in friction-type and in bearing-type connections. In a friction-type connection the applied tensile force, as previously explained, reduces the contact pressure between the connected plates and thus, the frictional resistance to shear forces is reduced. Since the reduction in frictional shear resistance is approximately proportional to the ratio of applied tensile force to installation tension, most specifications require that the allowable shear stress be reduced acordingly. For example, in friction-type connections under combined shear and tensile forces, the bolts can be designed for a reduced allowable shear stress, F'_v, equal to

$$F'_v = F_v \left(1 - \frac{F}{T}\right) \tag{9.1}$$

where F_v is the allowable shear stress when subjected to shear force only, F is the applied tensile force on the bolt, and T is the minimum tensile force after installation, Table 9.2. Specification [6, 7] provisions are similar to Equation 9.1.

In a bearing-type connection, the fastener yields under the combined shear and tensile stresses at a lower stress than if only shear or tension were present. Extensive research has shown that the ultimate strength of the fasteners can be closely represented by elliptical interaction curves.[8] Figures 9.6 and 9.7 give such curves in terms of allowable stress. Each of the curves shown is defined by the equation

$$(F'_v)^2 + \left(\frac{F_v}{F_t} F'_t\right)^2 = F_v^2 \tag{9.2}$$

where F'_v and F'_t are the allowable shear and tensile stresses under the combined loading, and F_v and F_t are the allowable shear and tensile stress when such stresses occur separately.

The AASHO specification[7] gives an equation similar to Equation 9.2 for allowable stresses in bearing-type connections, and the commentary to the AISC specification[6] notes that such an equation "should be allowed." However, for simplification of calculations, the AISC specification gives equations for allowable stresses that represent straight-line approximations to the elliptical interaction curves.

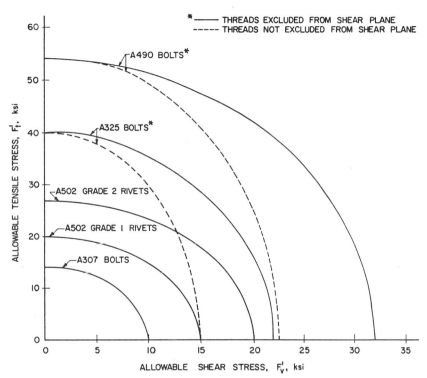

FIGURE 9.6   ALLOWABLE STRESSES FOR RIVETS AND BOLTS UNDER COMBINED TENSION AND SHEAR IN BEARING—TYPE CONNECTIONS IN BUILDINGS

9.3   Welded Connections

9.3.1   *Welding Processes and Weld Metal*

Structural welds are usually made by the submerged arc, gas metal-arc, or manual metal-arc process. In each process the heat of an electric arc simultaneously melts an electrode and the adjacent steel in the parts being joined. The joint results from the cooling and solidification of the fused material. Various coated stick electrodes for manual metal-arc welding and various wire electrodes and flux combinations for submerged arc or gas metal-arc welding may be selected to produce weld metals that, as indicated by Table 9.6, provide a wide range of specified minimum strength levels. Welding grades and electrode classes that are suitable for

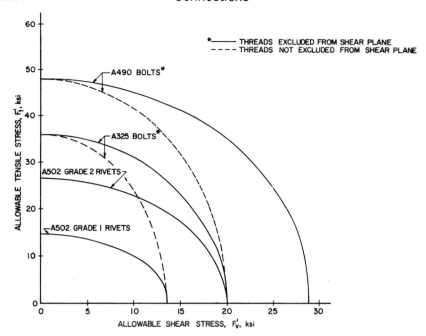

FIGURE 9.7   ALLOWABLE STRESSES FOR RIVETS AND BOLTS UNDER COMBINED
TENSION AND SHEAR IN BEARING-TYPE CONNECTIONS IN BRIDGES

welding particular steels for buildings and bridges are indicated in Tables 9.7 and 9.8.

As previously indicated, differential cooling that accompanies welding causes residual stresses in the weld and in the material joined. Although these stresses have an important effect on the strength of compression members, they do not usually have a significant effect on the strength of welded connections.

9.3.2 *Types of Structural Welds*

The principal types of structural welds are illustrated in Figure 9.8. In the groove welds shown, the loads are transferred directly across the weld by tensile or compressive stresses. For complete-penetration groove welds, the welding grade or electrode class is selected so that the resulting weld is as strong as the steel joined. Partial-penetration groove welds, in which only part of the metal thickness is welded, are sometimes used when stresses are low and there is no need to develop the complete strength of the material. The stress area of such a weld is the product of the length of the weld and an effective throat thickness. In single J- or U-type joints, the effective throat thickness is equal to the depth of the groove, but in bevel- or V-type joints it is equal to ¼ inch less than the depth of the groove because the weld at the bottom of the bevel is not always sound. Details of recommended types of joints are given in References 9 and 10.

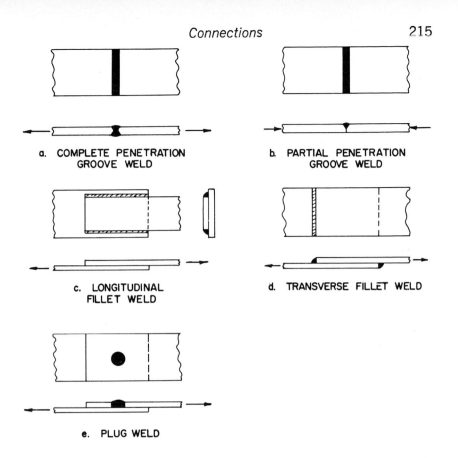

FIGURE 9.8 PRINCIPAL TYPES OF STRUCTURAL WELDS

In fillet welds the load is transferred between the connected plates by shear stresses in the fillet welds. The shear stress in a fillet weld is computed on an area equal to the product of the length of the weld times the effective throat thickness. The effective throat thickness is defined as the shortest distance from the root to the face of the weld, a flat face being assumed, and is 0.707 times the nominal size or leg of a fillet weld with equal legs. Actually, tests indicate that transverse fillet welds are stronger than longitudinal fillet welds of equal size, but this difference in strength is not usually considered in design.[11]

In fillet welds it is not generally necessary to provide weld metal that has a yield strength equal to that of the steel joined, since the required total strength can be obtained by varying the size of the weld. However, it is sometimes desirable to use a high-strength weld metal so that the required fillet weld size is not excessive. Thus, Tables 9.7 and 9.8 show more than one weld strength suitable for fillet welds that joint a particular steel.

Plug welds and slot welds are occasionally used to transfer shear stresses between plates. The shear area for the weld is the nominal cross-sectional area of the hole or slot. This type of connection should be avoided because of the difficulty in making a satisfactory weld and because of the severe stress concentration created.

9.3.3 *Allowable Stresses*

The basic allowable stresses for welds in buildings and bridges are shown in Tables 9.7 and 9.8. As indicated in the tables complete penetration groove welds in building or bridge construction, and certain other welds in building construction, have the same allowable stress as the steel joined. The allowable stresses shown for fillet welds provide a safety factor against ultimate weld shear failure of approximately 3.0 for building construction and 3.3 for bridge construction.

Table 9.9 gives minimum fillet-weld sizes for buildings and bridges that should be used in joints connected by fillet welds. Larger size welds must be used when required by the calculated stress. The minimum sizes are based on practical considerations; smaller size welds might crack because of rapid cooling or excessive restraint.

9.4 Bearing Stresses

High local stresses, referred to as bearing stresses, occur at the contact surfaces of pins, rollers, rockers, and bearing stiffeners. However, these local stresses reduce rapidly at increasing distances away from the surface. Although the actual stress conditions are complex and may involve local yielding, appropriate nominal allowable stresses have been established in various specifications that can be conveniently applied in design. Tables 9.10 and 9.11 give such allowable stresses for buildings and bridges, respectively.

9.5 Design Examples

Example 9.1

The angles shown carry a tensile load of 115 kips. The angles will be shop-riveted to the bracket, which will be bolted with a friction-type connection to the column flange. Determine the size and number of A502-Grade 2 rivets and A490 high-strength bolts in accordance with the AISC specification.

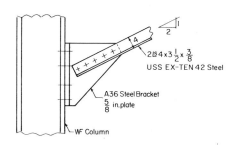

Solution:

The angles and bracket have been checked for strength. Allowable stresses for bolts and rivets are given in Tables 9.3 and 9.5.

Try ⅞-in.-diameter rivets.

Bearing value on ⅝-in. A36 plate = ⅞ × ⅝ × 48.6 = 26.6 kips/rivet.

Bearing value on ⅜-in. EX-TEN 42 angles = ⅞ × ⅜ × 56.7 × 2 = 37.2 kips/rivet.

Shear value of rivet in double shear = 2 × 0.601 × 20.0 = 24.0 kips/rivet.

Number required = 115/24.0 = 4.78.

Use 5 rivets, ⅞-in. diameter.

Try 8 bolts, ⅞-in. diameter.

Tensile force applied to each bolt is $\dfrac{2}{\sqrt{5}} \times \dfrac{115}{8} = 12.9$ kips

Shear force applied to each bolt is $\dfrac{1}{\sqrt{5}} \times \dfrac{115}{8} = 6.43$ kips

$F_t = 54.0$ ksi.

$T = 35.0$ kips   **(Table 9.2)**

$F'_v = F_v \left(1 - \dfrac{F}{T}\right) = 20.0 \left(1 - \dfrac{12.9}{35.0}\right) = 12.6$ ksi.   **(Equation 9.1)**

$f_t = 12.9/0.6013 = 21.5$ ksi < 54.0 ksi.

$f_v = 6.43/0.6013 = 10.7$ ksi < 12.6 ksi.

Use 8 bolts, ⅞-in. diameter.

Example 9.2

The beam-to-column connection must be designed to carry a shear force of 75 kips and a bending moment of 45 foot-kips. A502-Grade 2 shop rivets will be used for attaching the angles to the beam and A325 high-strength bolts will be used for a bearing-type connection to the column. Determine the size of connecting angles in accordance with AISC requirements.

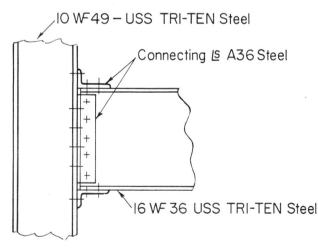

10 WF 49 – USS TRI-TEN Steel

Connecting ⌐ A36 Steel

16 WF 36 USS TRI-TEN Steel

Solution:

For this type of connection, the moment is usually assumed to be transmitted through the beam flange angles, and the shear force through the web angles. Allowable stresses are given in Tables 9.3 and 9.5.

1. Shear Force:

Try ¾-in.-diameter rivets to join web angle to beam.
Shear value of rivet in double shear $= 2 \times 0.442 \times 20.0 = 17.7$ kips/rivet.

Bearing value of rivet on beam web $= ¾ \times 0.299 \times 67.5 = 15.1$ kips/rivet.

Number required $= 75/15.1 = 4.97$.

Use 5 rivets, ¾-in. diameter (web angles to beam).

Try ¾-in.-diameter bolts, threads excluded from shear plane, to join web angle to column.

Shear value of bolt in single shear $= 0.442 \times 22.0 = 9.72$ kips/bolt.

Bearing on column flange will not govern.
Number required $= 75/9.72 = 7.72$.

Use 8 bolts, ¾-in. diameter (web angles to column).

Calculate required thickness for web angles.

For resistance to shear force, 11.5 in.-long angle, $2 \times 14.5 \times 11.5\ t = 75.0$, $t = 0.225$ in.

For bearing strength of rivet, $2 \times 48.6 \times ¾\ t = 15.1$, $t = 0.207$ in.

For bearing strength of bolt, $48.6 \times ¾\ t = 9.72$, $t = 0.272$ in.

Use 2 angles 4 $\times$ 3½ $\times$ ⁵⁄₁₆ $\times$ 11¾-in. long (web angles).

2. Bending Moment:

Depth of beam is 15.85 in. Moment may be resolved into a force couple assumed to act along outer surfaces of beam flange.

$F = M/d = 45 \times 12/15.85 = 34.1$ kips.

Try ¾-in.-diameter rivets to join flange angles to beam.

Shear value of rivet in single shear $= 0.442 \times 20.0 = 8.84$ kips/rivet.

Bearing on beam flange will not govern.

Number required $= 34.1/8.84 = 3.86$.

Use 4 rivets, ¾-in diameter (flange angles to beam).

Try ¾-in.-diameter bolts to join top and seat angles to column.

Tensile value of bolt $= 0.442 \times 40.0 = 17.7$ kips/bolt.

Number required $= 34.1/17.7 = 1.93$.

Use 2 bolts, ¾-in. diameter (flange angles to column).

Calculate required thickness for flange angles.

For bearing strength of rivet, $48.6 \times ¾\ t = 8.84$, $t = 0.243$ in.

An 8-in.-long angle with 4-in. vertical leg will be suitable. Consider bending of 4-in. leg. Try 1-in.- thick angle.

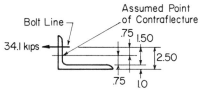

Moment in leg is $34.1 \times 0.75 = 25.6$ in. kips.

Section modulus of leg is $8 \times 1 \times 1/6 = 1.33$ in.³

$f = M/S = 25.6/1.33 = 19.2$ ksi < 22 ksi.

Use 8 $\times$ 4 $\times$ 1 $\times$ 8-in. long angle (flange angles).

Example 9.3

Select the number and size of A502 Grade 2 rivets required for the eccentric bracket connection in accordance with AISC requirements.

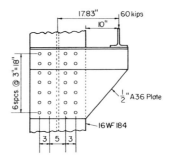

Solution:

1. Calculation of Shear Force

The shear forces on a fastener in an eccentrically loaded fastener group may be calculated from the expressions shown in the sketch. In the expression, x and y are the horizontal and vertical distances from the center of gravity of the fastener group to each fastener, e is the perpendicular distance from the vertical load P to the center of gravity, and N is the total number of fasteners. From the above expressions, which are based on ideal elastic behavior,

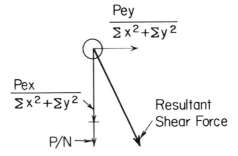

a corner fastener of the group is subjected to the greatest shear force, and other fasteners carry proportionately smaller loads. Tests have shown that it is not necessary to limit the shear force in the most highly stressed fastener to the usual allowable stress; some inelastic behavior of the most highly stressed fasteners at a load slightly above the design load may be tolerated to allow other fasteners in the group to be used more efficiently. Therefore, in the design of the fasteners, the distance, e, may be replaced by an effective eccentricity, e', given by the following empirical formulas:[6, 13]

$$e' = e - \left(\frac{1 + 2n}{4}\right) \text{ for a single gage line of fasteners.}$$

$$e' = e - \left(\frac{1 + n}{2}\right) \text{ for two or more gage lines of fasteners.}$$

In the equation, e and e' are in inches and n is the number of fasteners in one vertical gage line. The resultant shear force on the most highly stressed fastener calculated by using the equivalent eccentricity should be limited to the usual allowable values.

2. Determination of Required Number of Rivets

Assume 4 lines of rivets with 7 rivets per line on 3 inch centers. Calculate the resultant shear force on the upper right corner rivet.

$$\Sigma x^2 + \Sigma y^2 = 14[(2.5)^2 + (5.5)^2] + 8[(3)^2 + (6)^2 + (9)^2] = 1519 \text{ in.}^2$$

$$e' = e - \frac{1 + n}{2} = 17.83 - \frac{1 + 7}{2} = 13.83 \text{ in.}$$

$$\frac{Pe'y}{\Sigma x^2 + \Sigma y^2} = \frac{75 \times 13.83 \times 9.0}{1519} = 6.15$$

$$\frac{Pe'x}{\Sigma x^2 + \Sigma y^2} = \frac{75 \times 13.83 \times 5.5}{1519} = 3.76$$

$P/N = 75/28 = 2.68$

Total vertical component $= 3.76 + 2.68 = 6.44$

Resultant shear force $= \sqrt{(6.15)^2 + (6.44)^2} = 8.90$ kips.

Try ¾-in.-diameter rivets.

Allowable stresses are given in Tables 9.3 and 9.5

Shear values in single shear is $0.442 \times 20 = 8.84$ kips.

Bearing value on ½-in. plate is $\frac{1}{2} \times \frac{3}{4} \times 48.6 = 18.2$ kips.

Therefore, use **28 rivets, ¾-in. diameter.**

Example 9.4*

Determine the length of weld required to connect the angles to the bracket for the connection shown in Example 9.1.

Solution:

The allowable stresses are given in Table 9.7.

$1/16 \times 0.707 \times 13,600 = 600$ pounds/in./1/16 of weld.

Use E60xx electrodes and ¼-in. fillet weld.

Required length $= \dfrac{115,000}{600 \times 4} = 48$ in. total.

10 in. along each side of the 4-in. leg and 4 in. across end of the angle will give the required 24 in. of weld on each angle.

Example 9.5

Determine the fillet weld size required to connect the bracket shown in the sketch. Use the allowable stresses given in Table 9.7.

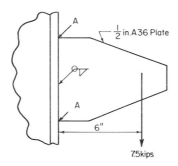

Solution:

The welds will be subjected to shear from bending and shear from the vertical load. The welds may be considered as line elements having a unit width.

---

* See Reference 11 for an extensive coverage of design examples for welded connections.

$$I = \frac{2 \times (6)^3}{12} + 2 \times \tfrac{1}{2} \times (3)^2 = 45$$

$$S = 45/3 = 15$$

Points A are the most highly stressed points.

$$\text{Weld shear at A from bending} = \frac{M}{S} = \frac{6 \times 7.5}{15} = 3.00 \text{ kips/in.}$$

$$\text{Vertical weld shear} = \frac{V}{A} = \frac{7.5}{6 + 6 + \tfrac{1}{2} + \tfrac{1}{2}} = 0.58 \text{ kips/in.}$$

$$\text{Resultant weld shear} = \sqrt{(3.00)^2 + (0.58)^2} = 3.06 \text{ kips/in.}$$

If E60XX electrodes are used, a 5/16-in. fillet will provide 600 × 5 or 3000 pounds/in. This is satisfactory—**use 5/16-in. weld.**

References (Chapter 9)

1. J. L. Rumpf and J. W. Fisher, "Calibration of A235 Bolts," **Journal of the Structural Division,** Proceedings ASCE, **89,** No. ST6, December 1963.

2. G. H. Sterling, **et al,** "Calibration Tests of A490 High Strength Bolts," **Journal of the Structural Division, Proceedings** ASCE, **91,** No. ST5, October 1965.

3. "Specifications for Structural Joints Using ASTM A325 or A490 Bolts," Research Council on Riveted and Bolted Structural Joints, 1966.

4. American Iron and Steel Institute, **Light Gage Cold-Formed Steel Design Manual,** 1962.

5. L. Tall, **et al, Structural Steel Design,** Ronald Press Company, New York City, 1964.

6. American Institute of Steel Construction, "Specification for the Design, Fabrication, and Erection of Structural Steel for Buildings," 1963.

7. American Association of State Highway Officials, "Standard Specifications for Highway Bridges," 1965.

8. E. Chesson, Jr., **et al,** "High-Strength Bolts Subjected to Tension and Shear," **Journal of the Structural Division, Proceedings** ASCE, **91,** No. ST5, October 1965.

9. American Welding Society, "Code for Welding in Building Construction," 1963, and "Addenda," March 1965.

10. American Welding Society, "Specifications for Welding Highway and Railway Bridges," 1963, and "Addenda," March 1965.

11. O. W. Blodgett and J. B. Scalzi, "Design of Welded Structural Connections," Lincoln Arc Welding Foundation, Cleveland, 1961.

12. American Welding Society, "Special Ruling by AWS Structural Welding Committee—Gas Metal-Arc Welding With Carbon Dioxide Shielding," 1965.

13. T. R. Higgins, "New Formulas for Fasteners Loaded Off Center," **Engineering News-Record,** May 21, 1964.

Table 9.1

Mechanical Properties of Structural Bolts and Rivets

Structural Bolts

ASTM Number	Description	Diameter, in.	Specified Minimum Proof Load* ÷ Stress Area, psi	Specified Minimum Ultimate Tensile Load ÷ Stress Area, psi
A307	Low-carbon steel bolt	¼ to 4, incl.		55,000
A325	High-strength carbon steel bolt	½, ⅝, ¾	85,000	120,000
		⅞, 1	78,000	115,000
		1⅛ to 1½, incl.	74,000	105,000
A490	Quenched and tempered alloy steel bolt	½ to 2½, incl.	120,000	150,000
		over 2½ to 4, incl.	105,000	140,000

Structural Rivets

ASTM Number	Description	Diameters, in.	Specified Minimum Hardness Rockwell B	Brinell 500kg—10mm
A502 Grade 1	Carbon steel rivet for general purposes	½ to 1½, incl.	55	103
A502 Grade 2	Carbon-manganese steel rivet for use with high-strength carbon and high-strength low-alloy structural steels	½ to 1½, incl.	76	137

* Based on length-measurement method. The stress area is defined by ASTM as $0.785\ (D - \frac{0.9743}{n})^2$ where D is the nominal bolt diameter and n is the number of threads per in.

Table 9.2

Minimum Tensile Force in High-Strength Bolts After Installation

Bolt Diameter, inches	Bolt Tension, kips	
	A325 Bolts	A490 Bolts
½	12	15
⅝	19	24
¾	28	35
⅞	39	49
1	51	64
1⅛	56	80
1¼	71	102
1⅜	85	121
1½	103	148
Over 1½	0.70 times specified minimum ultimate tensile load.	

Table 9.3

Allowable Stresses for Bolts and Rivets in Buildings

Type of Fastener	Tensile Stress, psi	Shear Stress, psi	
		Friction-Type Connections	Bearing Type Connections
A502—Grade 1 rivets, hot-driven	20,000	Not applicable	15,000
A502—Grade 2 rivets, hot-driven	27,000	Not applicable	20,000
A307 bolts and threaded parts of A7, A373, or A36 steel	14,000	Not applicable	10,000
Threaded parts of other steels	$0.40 f_y$	Not applicable	$0.30 f_y$
A325 bolts, threads **not** excluded from shear plane	40,000	15,000	15,000
A325 bolts, threads excluded from shear plane	40,000	15,000	22,000
A490 bolts, threads **not** excluded from shear plane	54,000	20,000	22,500
A490 bolts, threads excluded from shear plane	54,000	20,000	32,000

Notes:
1. Stresses are for nominal bolt and rivet areas and are based on References 3 and 6.
2. Allowable stresses for bolts and rivets under combined tension and shear in bearing-type connections are given in Figure 9.6.
3. Allowable stresses for high-strength bolts under combined tension and shear in friction-type connections are given by Equation 9.1.
4. Allowable bearing stresses in bearing-type connections are given in Table 9.5.

Table 9.4

Allowable Stresses for Bolts and Rivets in Bridges

Type of Fastener	Tensile Stress, psi	Shear Stress, psi	
		Friction-Type Connections	Connections Bearing-Type
A502-Grade 1 rivets, hot-driven	Not applicable	Not applicable	13,500
A502—Grade 2 rivets, hot-driven	Not applicable	Not applicable	20,000
A325 Bolts, threads **not** excluded from shear plane	36,000	13,500	13,500
A325 Bolts, threads excluded from shear plane	36,000	13,500	20,000
A490 Bolts, threads **not** excluded from shear plane	48,000	18,000	20,000
A490 Bolts, threads excluded from shear plane	48,000	18,000	29,000

Notes:
1. Stresses are for nominal bolt and rivet area and are based on References 3 and 7. Reference 7 specifies reduced shear stress values under certain conditions.
2. Allowable stresses for bolts and rivets under combined tension and shear in bearing-type connections are given in Figure 9.7.
3. Allowable stresses for high-strength bolts under combined tension and shear in friction type connections are given by Equation 9.1.
4. Allowable bearing stresses in bearing-type connections are given in Table 9.5.

Table 9.5
Allowable Bearing Stresses in Bearing-Type Connections in Buildings and Bridges

Specified Minimum Yield Stress of Connected Part, psi	Allowable Bearing Stress, psi	
	Bolts or Rivets in Building Connections	Bolts or Rivets in Bridge Connections**
	1.35 f_y	1.22 f_y
36,000	48,600	43,900
42,000	56,700	51,200
46,000	62,100	56,100
50,000	67,500	61,000
60,000	80,000*	73,200
70,000	90,500*	85,400
80,000	100,000*	97,600
90,000	105,500*	105,000*
100,000	115,000*	115,000*

* Reduced to the tensile strength of the connected part.[3]
** See Reference 7 for values limited by allowable bearing on the fastener.

Table 9.6
Specified Mechanical Properties of Deposited Weld Metal

Welding Grade or Electrode Class	Tensile Strength, psi	Yield Stress, psi	Elongation in 2 Inches, percent	Reduction of Area, percent
Submerged-Arc Process*				
SAW-1	62,000 to 80,000	45,000	25	40
SAW-2	70,000 to 90,000	50,000	22	40
SAW-3	90,000	77,000	17	40
SAW-4	110,000	97,000	15	40
Gas Metal-Arc Process*				
GMAW-1	67,000	55,000	22	Not specified
GMAW-2	70,000	60,000	20	Not specified
GMAW-3	90,000	77,000	17	Not specified
GMAW-4	110,000	97,000	15	Not specified
Manual Shielded Metal-Arc Process**				
E60XX	62,000 or 67,000	50,000 to 55,000	17, 22, or 25	Not specified
E70XX	72,000	60,000	17 or 22	Not specified
E70XX-X	70,000	57,000	22 or 25	Not specified
E80XX-X	80,000	67,000	16 or 19	Not specified
E90XX-X	90,000	77,000	14 or 17	Not specified
E100XX-X	100,000	87,000	13 or 16	Not specified
E110XX-X	110,000	97,000	15	Not specified
E120XX-X	120,000	107,000	14	Not specified

* Mechanical properties listed are specified minimum values except where a specified range of values (minimum to maximum) is given. Grades SAW-1, SAW-2, GMAW-1, and GMAW-2 are covered by AWS specifications.[10, 12] Grades SAW-3 and GMAW-3 are not presently included in AWS specifications but have specified mechanical properties similar to those of E90 electrodes. Grades SAW-4 and GMAW-4 are not presently included in AWS specifications but have specified mechanical properties similar to those of E110 electrodes.

** Mechanical properties listed are specified minimum values. Where more than one value is listed, different values are specified for different electrodes within the electrode class. Electrodes E60XX and E70XX are included in ASTM A233, and the other electrodes listed are included in ASTM A316.

Table 9.7

Basic Allowable Stresses on Welds in Building Construction

Type of Weld and Loading	Welding Grade or Electrode Class	Steel Joined*	Allowable Stress, psi
Shear stress in fillet, plug, and slot welds; tension stress transverse to the axis of partial penetration groove welds and shear in such welds.	SAW-1, GMAW-1, E60XX	A36, A242, A441, and all EX-TEN steels	13,600
	SAW-2, GMAW-2, E70XX	A36, A242, A441, and all EX-TEN steels	15,800
Shear stress in fillet welds; tension stress transverse to the axis of partial-penetration grove welds and shear in such welds.	SAW-2, GMAW-2, E70XX	A514	15,800
	SAW-3, GMAW-3, E90XXX	A514	19,700
	SAW-4, GMAW-4, E110XXX	A514	24,100
Complete-penetration groove welds stressed in tension, compression, bending and bearing; partial-penetration groove welds stressed in compression, in bending, or in tension parallel to the axis of the weld.	SAW-1, GMAW-1, SAW-2, GMAW-2, E60XX, E70XX	A36, EX-TEN42	Use allowable stresses for steel joined
	SAW-2, GMAW-2, E70XX	A441, A242, EX-TEN 50	
	SAW-3, GMAW-3, E80XXX	EX-TEN 60, EX-TEN 70	
	SAW-4, GMAW-4, E110XXX	A514	

* If two different steels are joined, electrodes or welding grades for the lower strength steel may be used. Low-hydrogen electrodes must be used for manual welding if either of the steels joined is listed in Note 2.

Notes: 1. The information given is based on requirements of AISC[6] and AWS. [9, 12] GMAW grades and SAW-3 and SAW-4 are not presently included in the AISC specification. See footnotes for Table 9.6.

2. Low-hydrogen electrodes must be used for manual welding of A242, A441, and A514 steels and are desirable for the USS EX-TEN steels.

3. E70XX or E90XX-X electrodes used for welding A514 steel must meet the moisture-content requirements of E110XX-X electrodes.

Table. 9.8

Basic Allowable Stresses on Welds in Bridge Construction

Type of Weld and Loading	Welding Grade or Electrode Class	Steel Joined*	Allowable Stress, psi
Shear stress in fillet welds.	SAW-1, GMAW-1, E60XX	A36, A441	12,400
	SAW-2, GMAW-2, E70XX	A36	12,400
	SAW-2, GMAW-2, E70XX	A441, A514	14,700
	SAW-3, GMAW-3, E90XX-X	A514	18,000
	SAW-4, GMAW-4, E110XX-X	A514	22,000
Shear stress in plug and slot welds.	E60XX, E70XX	A36, A441	12,400
Complete-penetration groove welds stressed in tension, compression bending, shear, and bearing.	SAW-1, GMAW-1, SAW-2, GMAW-2, E60XX, E70XX	A36	Use allowable stresses for steel joined
	SAW-2, GMAW-2, E70XX	A441	
	SAW-4, GMAW-4, E110XX-X	A514	

* If two different steels are joined, electrodes or welding grades for the lower strength steel may be used. Low-hydrogen electrodes must be used for manual welding if either of the steels joined is listed in Note 2.

Notes: 1. The information given is based on requirements of AASHO[7] and AWS.[10, 12] Grades SAW-3, SAW-4, GMAW-3 and GMAW-4 are not presently included in the AASHO specification. See footnotes for Table 9.6.

2. Low-hydrogen electrodes must be used for manual welding of A36 steel over 1 inch thick and for all thicknesses of A441 and A514 steels.

3. E70XX or E90XX-X electrodes used for welding A514 steel must meet the moisture-content requirements of E110XX-X electrodes.

Table 9.9

Minimum Fillet-Weld Sizes for Building and Bridge Connections

Material Thickness of Thicker Part Joined, inches	Minimum Size of Fillet Weld, inch
to ½ inclusive	3/16
over ½ to ¾	¼
over ¾ to 1½	5/16
over 1½ to 2¼	3/8
over 2¼ to 6	½
over 6	5/8

Notes: The table is from References 9 and 10. Use larger weld where required by stress calculations.

Table 9.10

Allowable Bearing Stresses and Loads for Structural Steels in Buildings*

Specified Minimum Yield Stress, psi	Allowable Bearing Stress on Contact Area for Milled Surfaces, Bearing Stiffeners, and Pins in Drilled or Bored Holes, psi $0.90\,f_y$	Allowable Load on Expansion Rollers and Rockers, lb/in.** $\left(\dfrac{f_y-13,000}{20,000}\right)660d$
36,000	32,400	760d
42,000	37,800	960d
46,000	41,400	1090d
50,000	45,000	1220d
60,000	54,000	1550d
70,000	63,000	1880d
80,000	72,000	2210d
90,000	81,000	2540d
100,000	90,000	2870d

* Values are based on the AISC specification.[6] Where steels with different yield stresses are in contact, the smaller yield stress should be used in design.

** d is the diameter of the roller or rocker in inches and f_y is the yield stress in psi.

Table 9.11

Allowable Bearing Stresses and Loads for Structural Steels in Bridges*

	Contact Stress on Bearing Area, psi.		Load on Expansion Rollers and Rockers, lb./in.**	
Specified Minimum Yield Stress, psi	Milled Stiffeners and Other Steel Parts in Contact, Pins Not Subject to Rotation, and Pins Subject to Rotation Due Only to Expansion or Deflection $0.80\,f_y$	Other Pins Subject to Rotation $0.40\,f_y$	Diameters Under 25 in. $\left(\dfrac{f_y-13,000}{20,000}\right)600d$	Diameters from 25 to 125 in. $\left(\dfrac{f_y-13,000}{20,000}\right)3000\sqrt{d}$
36,000	28,800	14,400	690d	$3,450\sqrt{d}$
42,000	33,600	16,800	870d	$4,350\sqrt{d}$
46,000	36,800	18,400	990d	$4,950\sqrt{d}$
50,000	40,000	20,000	1110d	$5,550\sqrt{d}$
60,000	48,000	24,000	1410d	$7,050\sqrt{d}$
70,000	56,000	28,000	1710d	$8,550\sqrt{d}$
80,000	64,000	32,000	2010d	$10,050\sqrt{d}$
90,000	72,000	36,000	2310d	$11,550\sqrt{d}$
100,000	80,000	40,000	2610d	$13,050\sqrt{d}$

* Values are based on the AASHO specifications,[7] although some values listed differ slightly from those given in the specificaton. Where steels with different yield stresses are in contact, the smaller yield stress should be used in design.

** d is the diameter of the roller or rocker in inches and f_y is the yield stress in psi.

CHAPTER 10

Design for Repeated Load

10.1 Introduction

This chapter will consider the design of structural members subjected to repeated loads. The design of welded, bolted, and riveted connections is included, but the design of welded connections is emphasized. The design of connections under static loads has been considered in Chapter 9, and the behavior of polished specimens under repeated load has been considered in Chapter 1.

10.2 Fatigue Strength of As-Received Material

Because of the rougher surface of as-received material, the fatigue strength of such material is generally lower than the fatigue strength of polished specimens of the same steel. Furthermore, the fatigue strength of as-received material cannot generally be predicted by applying a correction factor to polished specimen data. Hence, fatigue data must be obtained from tests on as-received specimens for use in design.

The fatigue strengths of as-received plates of A36, USS TRI-TEN, and USS "T-1" steel are shown on the fatigue charts given in Figures 10.1, 10.2, and 10.3, respectively.[1, 2] The average tensile strength and yield stress of the specimens tested are indicated on the charts. The data for A36 and TRI-TEN steel were obtained at U.S. Steel's Applied Research Laboratory, whereas the data for "T-1" steel were obtained at Lehigh University and the University of Illinois. Each fatigue chart was constructed from S-N curves drawn for the mean values of fatigue strength obtained from axial-load fatigue tests of ¾-inch-thick plates.

Because it has been shown[2] that the fatigue strength of different steels having the same tensile strength does not vary appreciably,

228

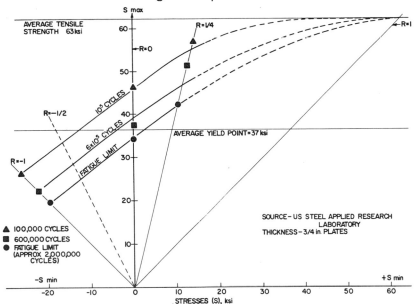

FIGURE 10.1 FATIGUE STRENGTH OF AS-RECEIVED A36 STRUCTURAL CARBON STEEL

the fatigue charts given may be used for other steels having a tensile strength about the same as that of the steel shown. Thus, the fatigue strength of A7 steel, which has a specified minimum tensile strength of 60,000 psi, is approximately the same as that of A36 steel, which has a specified minimum tensile strength of 58,000

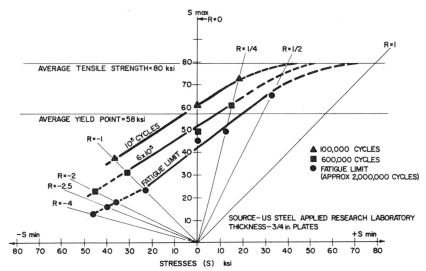

FIGURE 10.2 FATIGUE STRENGTH OF AS-RECEIVED USS TRI-TEN
HIGH-STRENGTH LOW-ALLOY STRUCTURAL STEEL

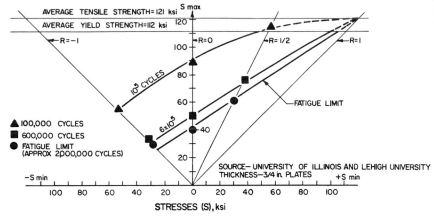

FIGURE 10.3   FATIGUE STRENGTH OF AS-RECEIVED USS "T–1" CONSTRUCTIONAL ALLOY STEEL

psi. Similarly, within certain thicknesses limitations, USS MAN-TEN, USS COR-TEN, and USS EX-TEN 50 steel have the same 70,000-psi tensile strength as TRI-TEN steel, and "T-1" type A and "T-1" type B steels have the same 115,000-psi minimum tensile strength as "T-1" steel.

The fatigue strengths of as-received plates of A36, TRI-TEN, and "T-1" steel are compared at a fatigue life of 100,000, 600,000, and 2,000,000 cycles in Figures 10.4, 10.5, and 10.6, respectively.[1, 2] The curves shown in these figures are taken from the previously presented fatigue charts. However, the slightly curved lifelines have been replaced with straight lines, and the portions of the curves above the yield stress are not shown.

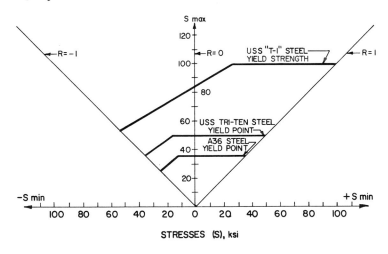

FIGURE 10.4   COMPARISON OF FATIGUE STRENGTH OF AS–RECEIVED
STRUCTURAL STEEL PLATES AT 100,000 STRESS CYCLES

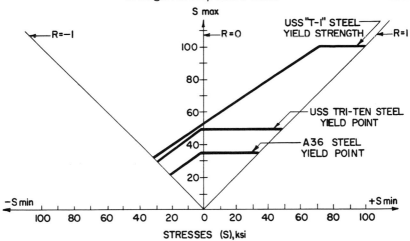

FIGURE 10.5   COMPARISON OF FATIGUE STRENGTH OF AS-RECEIVED STRUCTURAL STEEL PLATES AT 600,000 STRESS CYCLES

Figure 10.4 shows that for relatively short fatigue lives, 100,000 cycles, the higher strength steels have a higher fatigue strength than carbon steel at all stress ratios. Figure 10.5 and 10.6 show that the higher strength steels still have significantly higher fatigue strengths than carbon steel, particularly at positive stress ratios, for longer fatigue lives, 600,000 to 2,000,000 cycles.

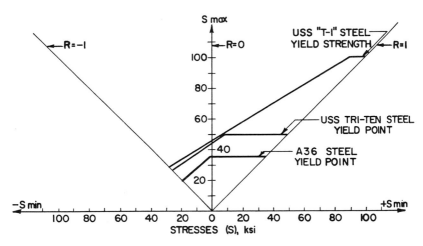

FIGURE 10.6   COMPARISON OF FATIGUE STRENGTH OF AS-RECEIVED STRUCTURAL STEEL PLATES AT 2,000,000 STRESS CYCLES

10.3   Fatigue Strength of Transversely Butt-Welded Plates

The fatigue strength of transversely butt-welded "T-1" steel plates, weld reinforcement in place, is shown in Figure 10.7. The chart was constructed from S-N curves drawn for the mean values of fatigue strength obtained from axial-load fatigue tests on ¾-inch-thick and ¼-inch-thick plates conducted at the University of Illinois and U.S. Steel's Applied Research Laboratory, respectively. In Figures 10.8, 10.9, and 10.10, this fatigue strength is compared with similar curves for butt-welded plates of A7 and TRI-TEN steels at fatigue lives of of 100,000, 600,000, and 2,000,000 cycles. Like as-received plates, transversely butt-welded plates of the higher strength steels have a higher fatigue strength than do carbon steel plates at all stress ratios.

Tests[1] on ¼-inch-thick plates of "T-1" steel at several stress ratios indicated that the fatigue strength for transversely butt-welded plates with the reinforcement properly removed by grinding to a surface finish in the range from 125 to 250 microinches are not significantly different from the fatigue strength of unwelded plates. A 24-grit grinding wheel was used to obtain the 125- to 250-microinch surface finish. Similar results would be expected for other steels.

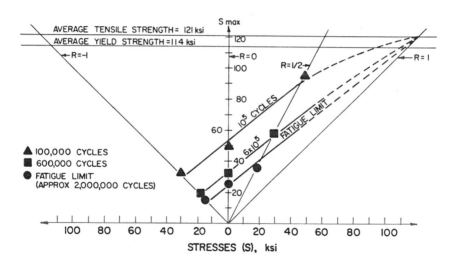

FIGURE 10.7 FATIGUE CHART OF TRANSVERSELY BUTT-WELDED USS "T-1" STEEL PLATES (WELD REINFORCEMENT IN PLACE)

10.4 Fatigue Strength of Fillet-Welded Connections

The fatigue strength of fillet welds depends on the type of connection in which the weld is used; for example, the fatigue strength of a fillet-welded lap joint is much lower than the fatigue strength of fillet-welded flange-to-web connections in fabricated beams. Hence, data must be obtained for specific types of fillet-welded connections rather than for fillet welds in general. Considerable data on the fatigue strength of various fillet-welded connections are

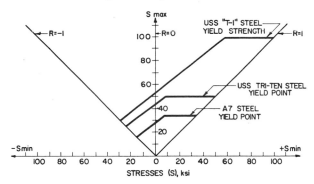

FIGURE 10.8   COMPARISON OF FATIGUE STRENGTH OF TRANSVERSELY BUTT-WELDED STRUCTURAL
STEEL PLATES (WELD REINFORCEMENT IN PLACE) AT 100,000 STRESS CYCLES

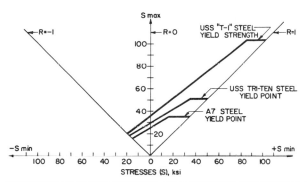

FIGURE 10.9   COMPARISON OF FATIGUE STRENGTH OF TRANSVERSELY BUTT-WELDED STRUCTURAL
STEEL PLATES (WELD REINFORCEMENT IN PLACE) AT 600,000 STRESS CYCLES

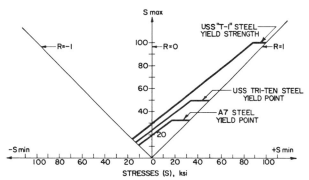

FIGURE 10.10   COMPARISON OF FATIGUE STRENGTH OF TRANVERSELY BUTT-WELDED STRUCTURAL
STEEL PLATES (WELD REINFORCEMENT IN PLACE) AT 2,000,000 STRESS CYCLES

given in Reference 3, and some of the more common types will be
considered below.[2] The data presented are for continuous rather
than for intermittent fillet welds because of their greater fatigue
strength.

The fatigue strength of fillet-welded flange-to-web connections in a fabricated member is less than the fatigue strength of the base metal from which the member is fabricated, and cannot be increased significantly by using larger fillet welds. Fatigue data presently available[4] from continuously fillet-welded tee specimens loaded axially at the centroid of the tee cross section so that axial stresses but no shear stresses are developed, indicate that such longitudinal flange-to-web fillet-welded connections have fatigue strength equal to, or greater than, transversely butt-welded joints with the weld reinforcement in place. This comparison is for welds made in the same steel subjected to equal fatigue lives. Therefore, it is conservative to design longitudinal fillet-welded joints subjected to repeated normal stresses only (axial or bending stresses without shear stresses) by the same formulas used to design transversely butt-welded joints with the weld reinforcement in place.

The available fatigue data on flange-to-web fillet welds under combined stresses[4] indicate that it is reasonable to design such welds subjected to combined bending and shear stress for the following equivalent stress, f_{eq}

$$f_{eq} = \sqrt{f_b^2 + 3f_s^2} \qquad (10.1)$$

where f_b and f_s are the bending and shear stress present, respectively (f_{eq} should be given the same algebraic sign as f_b).* The maximum and minimum values of f_b and f_s caused by a given loading may be used to compute the maximum and minimum values of f_{eq}, respectively. The maximum and minimum values of f_{eq}, in turn, may then be used to obtain the fatigue life from the appropriate fatigue chart for butt-welded plates. Conversely, Equation 10.1 can be used in conjunction with allowable stress formulas presented later to determine allowable weld sizes. In many practical applications the effect of shear on the fatigue strength of fabricated beams is small enough to be neglected.

When fillet welds are used to join attachments, such as stiffeners, to the web of a beam, or when they are used to make lap joints, the fatigue strength of such connections is usually considerably less than the fatigue strength of flange-to-web fillet-welded connections. Table 10.1 gives the experimentally determined percentage reduction in fatigue limits for joints of various types when compared with the fatigue limit for transverse butt welds in the same steel.[2] It is conservative to assume that the same percentage reductions in fatigue strengths apply at finite lives. Although most of the data was obtained for high-strength low-alloy steel, the same percentage reductions should be applicable to other steels. Hence, Table 10.1 can be used with the appropriate fatigue chart for butt-welded plates to predict the fatigue strength of various attachments.

---

* The use of this equivalent stress is somewhat more conservative than the assumption that the equivalent stress is equal to the maximum principal tensile stress due to combined bending and shear stresses.

10.5   Fatigue Strength of Riveted and Bolted Connections

Various tests have demonstrated that fatigue failures in both riveted and bolted connections generally occur in the connected material rather than in the fastener. Therefore, the fatigue strength of bolted or riveted butt (double lap) joints may be related to the stress ratio and maximum stress present on the net section of the connected plates, and may be shown on a fatigue chart similar to that used for welded joints.

Figure 10.11 shows a fatigue chart for such joints in A7 steel at 2,000,000 cycles.[5] The curves show that, because of their high clamping force, friction-type connections made with high-strength bolts provide much better fatigue strength than riveted connections. Also, a comparison of Figure 10.12 with Figures 10.6 and 10.10 shows that for A7 or A36 material, the fatigue strength of a friction-type connection with high-strength bolts (1) is about the same as that of as-received plates, and (2) is greater than that of butt-welded plates with the weld reinforcement in place.

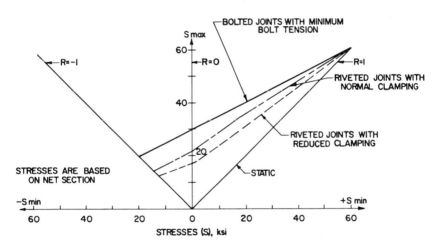

FIGURE 10.11   FATIGUE DIAGRAM FOR BOLTED AND RIVETED JOINTS IN A7 STEEL AT 2,000,000 CYCLES

10.6   Application of Fatigue Data to Design

To efficiently design a structure to resist fatigue, each individual detail should be checked for the stress conditions that exist at that detail. For example, in designing a rolled beam with a splice in the region of low stress, the fatigue life of the splice under the low stress would be checked, and the fatigue life of the beam itself would be checked at the location of maximum stress. The fatigue charts and other information presented earlier can be used to make this type of check.

To utilize the experimental fatigue charts presented earlier in the design of structures, however, it is usually necessary to apply a factor of safety to compensate for (1) scatter among the fatigue data, and (2) uncertainties in the loading. The choice of the magnitude and method of application of the factor of safety for a specific application can best be made by the designer. However, a smaller factor of safety is usually justified for fatigue stresses than for nonrepetitive stresses because of the minor effect of a few overloads on fatigue life, and the decreased likelihood of the number of stress cycles occurring at the design stress magnitude.

One convenient method of applying the factor of safety is to multiply either the maximum design stress or both the maximum and minimum design stresses by the factor and to use the resulting stresses in the mean-value fatigue charts to determine expected life. Another method is to derive allowable stress formulas by dividing the stresses in the fatigue charts by the factor of safety. Again, this latter method can be done in several different ways. Both the maximum and minimum stresses corresponding to any point on a life line of an experimental fatigue chart can be divided by the factor of safety to obtain a point on a life line of an allowable stress chart as shown in Figure 10.12. Alternatively, the experimental maximum stress and not the minimum stress can be divided by the factor of safety to obtain the allowable stress chart that might be appropriate for some applications in which the minimum stress results from a known dead load. For another alternative, the experimental stress range—the difference between the maximum and minimum stresses—can be divided by a factor of safety to obtain an allowable stress range.

The allowable design stresses shown in the illustrative fatigue chart, Figure 10.12, may be expressed as the smaller of the following equations:

$$f = \frac{S_o}{(1 - mR)\,(FSF)} \tag{10.2}$$

$$f = \frac{f_y}{FS} \tag{10.3}$$

In the equations, f is the allowable maximum stress, S_o is the experimental maximum stress at R = 0, m is the slope of the experimental fatigue curve, R is the stress ratio (algebraic ratio of minimum to maximum stress), FSF is the factor of safety for fatigue stresses, and FS is the factor of safety for static stresses.

In Tables 10.2, 10.3, and 10.4, Equations 10.2 and 10.3 have been written for the steels for which experimental fatigue charts were previously presented. These equations give allowable stresses in as-received material and transversely butt welded joints for the "T-1" steels, the high-strength and high-strength low-alloy steels, and the structural carbon steels. As mentioned earlier, the fatigue strength of butt welds with the reinforcement properly removed is about the same as that of as-received material. Allowable stresses for fillet welded joints of various types can be computed from the

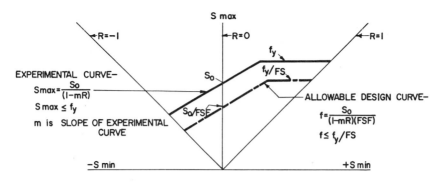

FIGURE 10.12   ILLUSTRATIVE FATIGUE CHART FOR DESIGN

formulas for allowable stresses for transverse butt welds by applying the suggested reduction factors given in Table 10.1 to the suggested allowable stress values given for transverse butt-welded
connections. For allowable stresses in longitudinally fillet-welded
flange-to-web connections subjected to fluctuating combined normal and shear stresses, Equation 10.1 can be used with the allowable formulas for transverse butt welds as previously explained.

10.7   Design Specifications

Members and connections subject to stress variations can be
safely and conveniently designed on the basis of the fatigue strength
of the worst detail that can reasonably be expected in any design.
Although fatigue specifications based on the worst expected detail
may be unduly conservative for many members, they are very simple
and, hence, are frequently applied in applications where fatigue is
rarely a problem, such as building design. The AISC specification[6]
gives fatigue provisions based on the worst expected detail that are
summarized in Table 10.5.*

The requirements of AASHO[7] for design for repeated load are
summarized in Table 10.6* Different allowable stress formulas are
given for the various types of details.

10.8   Design Examples

Example 10.1

A USS TRI-TEN steel hot-rolled beam is subjected to fluctuating bending
moments varying in magnitude from 600,000 in.-lb to − 100,000 in.-lb. (a) Select
a section to sustain 600,000 load cycles. (b) If the beam is spliced with a
transverse butt weld, determine the maximum bending moment that can be
allowed at the splice if the same stress ratio is maintained. The weld reinforcement at the splice is left as deposited. The factors of safety are 1.75 for
yielding and 1.50 for fatigue (applied to both maximum and minimum stresses).

---

*These design rules generally should not be applied to steels with a strength level
higher than those included in the referenced specification.

Solution:

(a) For this example, FSF = 1.50, FS = 1.75, and R = −100,000/600,000 = − 0.167. From Table 10.3, the maximum allowable stress in the rolled beam is

$$f_a = \frac{52,000}{(1 - 0.73R)\ FSF}$$

$$= \frac{34,667}{(1 + 0.122)} = 30,900\ \text{psi}$$

$$f_a \leq \frac{50,000}{1.75} = 28,570\ \text{psi}$$

Thus, the maximum allowable stress in the base metal is limited by yielding to 28,570 psi.

The required section modulus for the beam is

$$S = \frac{M_{max}}{f_a} = \frac{600,000}{28,570} = 21.0\ \text{in.}^3$$

Select a **12 B 19** hot-rolled section (S = 21.4 in.³).

(b) From Table 10.3, the maximum allowable stress in the transverse butt weld is

$$f_a = \frac{28,000}{(1 - 0.56R)\ FSF}$$

$$= \frac{18,667}{(1 + 0.094)} = 17,063\ \text{psi}$$

$$f_a \leq 28,570\ \text{psi}$$

The maximum allowable stress in the butt weld is limited by fatigue to 17,063 psi.

The bending moment allowed at the transversely butt-welded splice for a stress ratio of −0.167 should not exceed

$$M_{max} = f_a S = 17,063 \times 21.4 = \textbf{365,150 in.-lb}$$

Example 10.2

The fillet welds in a flange-to-web connection of a fabricated A36 steel beam are subjected to 2,000,000 cycles of fluctuating loads, which cause bending stresses in the weld metal at a section to vary from +20,000 to +12,000 psi and shearing stresses to vary from +4000 to +2400 psi. The required factor of safety is 1.35 for both yielding and fatigue. Determine if the connection meets the design requirements.

Solution:

The equivalent stress in the fillet welds is given by Equation 10.1.

$$f_{eq} = \sqrt{f_b^2 + 3f_s^2}$$

The maximum value of f_{eq} is

$$f_{eq} = \sqrt{20,000^2 + 3 \times 4,000^2} = +21,200\ \text{psi}$$

The minimum value of f_{eq} is

$$f_{eq} = \sqrt{12,000^2 + 3 \times 2,400^2} = +12,700\ \text{psi}$$

From Table 10.4, the maximum allowable stress in a transverse butt weld for 2,000,000 load cycles, when FSF = FS = 1.35 and R = 12,700/21,200 = +0.60 is

$$f_a = \frac{19,000}{(1 - 0.73R)\ FSF}$$

$$= \frac{14,100}{(1 - 0.44)} = 25,180\ psi$$

$$f_a \leq \frac{36,000}{1.35} = 26,700\ psi$$

Table 10.1 shows that no reduction in fatigue limit from that of a transverse butt weld is required. Therefore, the allowable stress in the connection is 25,180 psi. Since the maximum stress is only 21,200 psi, the connection meets the design requirements.

Example 10.3

Select a USS TRI-TEN steel hot-rolled beam with a nominal depth of 12 inches for the load conditions given in Example 10.1 if a 1-inch-square by 3-inch-long bar is fillet-welded to the web 2 inches above the bottom of the section. The length of the bar is parallel to the length of the beam. The bar is located along the beam in the region of maximum bending stresses.

Solution:

From Table 10.1, for a longitudinal attachment with one or both ends in high-stress regions, the fatigue limit is reduced from 41 to 25 percent for stress ratios of 0 to −1, respectively, compared with transversely butt-welded joints. By linear interpolation, the reduction for R = −0.167 is 27.7 percent.

From Example 10.1 the allowable design stress for transverse butt welds is 17,063 psi. Thus, the allowable design stress for the fillet-welded connection is

$$f_a = 17,063 \times (1.0 - 0.277) = 12,337\ psi$$

The maximum stress in the attachment fillet weld for a 12B19 shape is

$$f_b = \frac{M_{max}y}{I} = \frac{600,000 \times (6.125 - 2)}{96.2} = 25,728\ psi > 12,337\ psi$$

Because the maximum stress exceeds the allowable, a shape having a greater moment of inertia is required. Try I = (25,728 × 96.2)/12,337 = 200.6 in.⁴. This requirement is met by a 12 WF 27 TRI-TEN steel section (I = 204.1 in.⁴; d = 11.96 in.). The maximum stress in the fillet weld is

$$f_b = \frac{600,000 \times (5.98 - 2)}{204.1} = 11,700\ psi < 12,337$$

Therefore, select a **12 WF 27** TRI-TEN steel section.

Example 10.4

A USS "T-1" steel wide-flange beam is subjected to a maximum stress of 43,000 psi and a minimum stress of 21,500 psi. Determine the expected life if a safety factor of 1.4 is applied to both the maximum and minimum stress.

Solution:

$$43,000 \times 1.4 = 60,200\ psi$$

$$21,500 \times 1.4 = 30,000\ psi$$

From Figure 10.3, the beam will have a life of at least 2×10^6 cycles.

References (Chapter 10)

1. G. Haaijer, "Significant Research Data for Use in Steel Design," Design and Engineering Seminar, U. S. Steel Corporation, ADUSS 91-1008, June 1964.
2. C.A. Martin, "Fatigue in Constructional Steels," U. S. Steel Corporation, ADUSS 00-05099, February 1965.
3. W. H. Munse, **Fatigue of Welded Structures,** Welding Research Council, New York City, 1964.
4. H. S. Reemsnyder, "A Study of the Fatigue Resistance of Longitudinal Fillet Weldments in Steel," Ph.D. Dissertation, Lehigh University, 1963.
5. E. Chesson, Jr., and W. H. Munse, "Studies of the Behavior of High-Strength Bolts and Bolted Joints," University of Illinois, Engineering Experiment Station Bulletin 469, 1965.
6. American Institute of Steel Construction, "Specification for the Design, Fabrication, and Erection of Structural Steel for Buildings," 1963.
7. American Association of State Highway Officials, "Standard Specifications for Highway Bridges," 1965.

Table 10.1

Suggested Reductions in Fatigue Limit for Fillet-Welded Joints

(Continuous Welds Only)

Joint		Stress Ratio	Percentage Reduction in Fatigue Limit*
Longitudinal Flange-to-Web		0 −1	0 0
Longitudinal Attachment (both ends in low-stress regions)		0 −1	0 0
Transverse Attachment (full width, or one end in compressive stress region)		0 −1	3 8
Longitudinal Attachment (one or both ends in high stress regions)		0 −1	41 25
Transverse Tee Joint** (not complete penetration welds)		0 −1	51 50
Lap Joint***		0	59
Cover Plate on Tension Flange		0	57

* Compared with transversely butt-welded joints (weld reinforcement in place).
** The plate carrying the main stress is interrupted by a perpendicular plate in such a way that the main stress must be transferred through the joint.
*** Welded only on the sides of the plate parallel to the direction of the stress in the plates.

Table 10.2

Allowable Stress in As-Received Material and Butt-Welded Joints of USS "T-1", "T-1" Type A, and "T-1" Type B Constructional Alloy Steels

(100,000-psi Minimum Yield Strength)

No. of Repetitions of Loading That Produces Maximum stress in the Member	Maximum Allowable Stress in As-Received Material	Maximum Allowable Stress in Transverse Butt Welds (Weld Reinforcement in Place)
2,000,000	$f_a = \dfrac{45,000}{(1 - 0.61R)\,(FSF)}$ $f_a \leq \dfrac{100,000}{(FS)}$	$f_a = \dfrac{27,000}{(1 - 0.80R)\,(FSF)}$ $f_a \leq \dfrac{100,000}{(FS)}$
600,000	$f_a = \dfrac{54,000}{(1 - 0.64R)\,(FSF)}$ $f_a \leq \dfrac{100,000}{(FS)}$	$f_a = \dfrac{34,000}{(1 - 0.79R)\,(FSF)}$ $f_a \leq \dfrac{100,000}{(FS)}$
100,000	$f_a = \dfrac{85,000}{(1 - 0.60R)\,(FSF)}$ $f_a \leq \dfrac{100,000}{(FS)}$	$f_a = \dfrac{54,000}{(1 - 0.80R)\,(FSF)}$ $f_a \leq \dfrac{100,000}{(FS)}$

Note: f_a = allowable unit fatigue stress, psi.

    FSF = factor of safety for fatigue.

     FS = factor of safety for yielding.

      R = ratio of minimum to maximum stress taken algebraically. The maximum stress is defined as the largest positive (tension) stress. This ratio may be expressed in terms of ratio of minimum to maximum moment, torque, shear, or axial force. The formulas do not apply when both the maximum and minimum stresses are compressive.

Design for Repeated Load

Table 10.3

Allowable Stress in As-Received Material and Butt-Welded Joints of USS MAN-TEN, TRI-TEN, COR-TEN, and EX-TEN 50 High-Strength and High-Strength Low-Alloy Steels

(50,000-psi Minimum iYeld Point

No. of Repetitions of Loading That Produces Maximum Stress in The Member	Maximum Allowable Stress in As-Received Material	Maximum Allowable Stress in Transverse Butt Welds (Weld Reinforcement in Place)
2,000,000	$f_a = \dfrac{42,000}{(1 - 0.68R)\,(FSF)}$ $f_a \leq \dfrac{50,000}{(FS)}$	$f_a = \dfrac{23,000}{(1 - 0.77R)\,(FSF)}$ $f_a \leq \dfrac{50,000}{(FS)}$
600,000	$f_a = \dfrac{52,000}{(1 - 0.73R)\,(FSF)}$ $f_a \leq \dfrac{50,000}{(FS)}$	$f_a = \dfrac{28,000}{(1 - 0.56R)\,(FSF)}$ $f_a \leq \dfrac{50,000}{(FS)}$
100,000	$f_a = \dfrac{58,000}{(1 - 0.57R)\,(FSF)}$ $f_a \leq \dfrac{50,000}{(FS)}$	$f_a = \dfrac{43,000}{(1 - 0.72R)\,(FSF)}$ $f_a \leq \dfrac{50,000}{(FS)}$

Note: f_a = allowable unit fatigue stress, psi.

FSF = factor of safety for fatigue.

FS = factor of safety for yielding.

R = ratio of minimum to maximum stress taken algebraically. The maximum stress is defined as the largest positive (tension) stress. This ratio may be expressed in terms of ratio of minimum to maximum moment, torque, shear, or axial force. The formulas do not apply when both the maximum and minimum stresses are compressive.